Electricity

$$F = \frac{kq_1q_2}{r^2}$$

$$R = \frac{\rho L}{A}$$

$$I = \frac{V}{R}$$

Series Circuits

(a) $I = I_1 = I_2 = I_3 = \cdots$

(b) $R = R_1 + R_2 + R_3 + \cdots$

(c) $E = V_1 + V_2 + V_3 + \cdots$

Parallel Circuits

(a) $I = I_1 + I_2 + I_3 + \cdots$

(b) $\frac{1}{R} = \frac{1}{R_1} + \frac{1}{R_2} + \frac{1}{R_3} + \cdots$

(c) $E = V_1 = V_2 = V_3 = \cdots$

Cells in Series

(a) $I = I_1 = I_2 = I_3 = \cdots$

(b) $r = r_1 + r_2 + r_3 + \cdots$

(c) $E = E_1 + E_2 + E_3 + \cdots$

Cells in Parallel

(a) $I = I_1 + I_2 + I_3 + \cdots$

(b) $r = \frac{r \text{ of one cell}}{\text{number of like cells}}$

(c) $E = E_1 = E_2 = E_3 = \cdots$

$V = E - Ir$

$$P = VI = I^2R = \frac{V^2}{R}$$

Magnetism

$$B = \frac{\mu_0 I}{2\pi R}$$

$$B = \pi_0 In$$

Transformers

$$\frac{V_P}{V_S} = \frac{N_P}{N_S}$$

$$\frac{I_S}{I_P} = \frac{N_P}{N_S}$$

ac Circuits

$$X_L = 2\pi fL$$

$$I = \frac{E}{X_L}$$

$$I = \frac{E}{Z}$$

$$Z = \sqrt{R^2 + X_L^2}$$

$$\tan \phi = \frac{X_L}{R}$$

$$X_C = \frac{1}{2\pi fC}$$

$$Z = \sqrt{R^2 + X_C^2}$$

$$\tan \phi = \frac{X_C}{R}$$

$$Z = \sqrt{R^2 + (X_L - X_C)^2}$$

$$\tan \phi = \frac{X_L - X_C}{R}$$

$$f = \frac{1}{2\pi\sqrt{LC}}$$

Light

$$c = \lambda f$$

$$E = hf$$

$$E = \frac{I}{4\pi r^2}$$

$$\frac{1}{f} = \frac{1}{s_o} + \frac{1}{s_i}$$

$$M = \frac{h_i}{h_o} = \frac{-s_i}{s_o}$$

$$n = \frac{\sin i}{\sin r} = \frac{\text{speed of light in vacuum}}{\text{speed of light in substance}}$$

$$\sin i_c = \frac{1}{n}$$

Modern Physics

$$E = -\frac{kZ^2}{n^2}$$

$$E = \Delta mc^2$$

$$Q = (M_p - M_d - m_\alpha)c^2$$

$$N = N_0 e^{-\lambda t}$$

$$T_{1/2} = \frac{0.693}{\lambda}$$

$$A = \lambda N = \lambda N_0 e^{-\lambda t} = A_0 e^{-\lambda t}$$

APPLIED PHYSICS

DALE EWEN

NEILL SCHURTER

P. ERIK GUNDERSEN

NEW ENGLAND INSTITUTE OF TECHNOLOGY

New England Tech

CUSTOM EDITION FOR PHY 126

Taken From:

Applied Physics, Ninth Edition
by Dale Ewen, Neill Schurter, P. Erik Gundersen

Custom Publishing

New York   Boston   San Francisco
London   Toronto   Sydney   Tokyo   Singapore   Madrid
Mexico City   Munich   Paris   Cape Town   Hong Kong   Montreal

Cover Art: Boatbu1, by Barry Cronin

Taken from:

Applied Physics, Ninth Edition
by Dale Ewen, Neill Schurter, P. Erik Gundersen
Copyright © 2009, 2005, 2002, 1999, 1996, 1993, 1988, 1982, 1974 by Pearson Education, Inc.
Published by Prentice Hall
Upper Saddle River, New Jersey 07458

Printed in the United States of America

10 9 8 7 6 5 4 3 2 1

2008240008

WH

Pearson
Custom Publishing
is a division of

www.pearsonhighered.com   ISBN 10: 0-536-77931-7
                               ISBN 13: 978-0-536-77931-1

CONTENTS

4. Which of the following is not considered a branch of physics?
   (a) Thermodynamics   (b) Astronomy
   (c) Geophysics   (d) Atomic physics
5. Analyzing the braking distance of a sports car would most likely utilize which field of physics?
   (a) Molecular physics   (b) Quantum physics
   (c) Fluid dynamics   (d) Mechanics
6. Who is considered to be the first true physicist and what did he do to deserve this recognition in scientific history?
7. Explain the difference between science and technology. Are the two fields related?
8. Provide two examples of scientific knowledge and a technological development that relies on that scientific knowledge.
9. What is the difference between the scientific method and the problem-solving method?
10. Why is it important to study physics? Provide a few examples of what an understanding of the physical world can do for you today and in your future.

CHAPTER 1

THE PHYSICS TOOL KIT

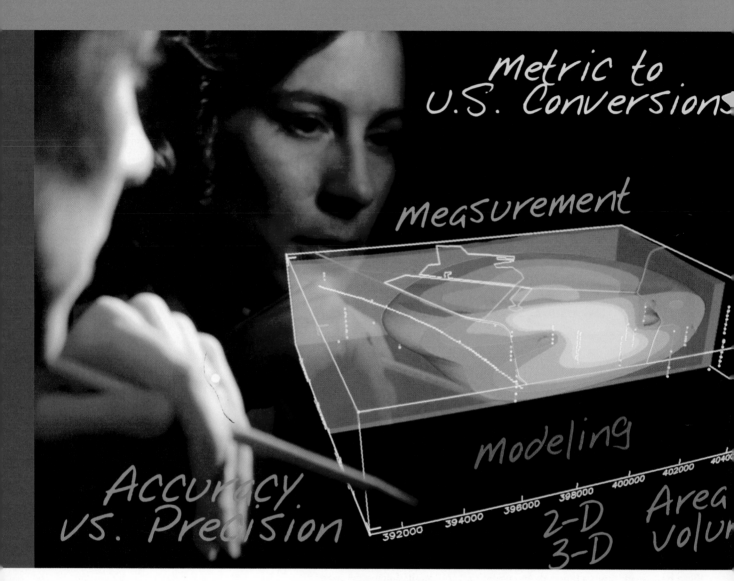

Metric to U.S. Conversions

Measurement

modeling

Accuracy vs. Precision

2-D
3-D

Area
Volume

A good mechanic needs not only the right tools for the job but also to be proficient in using those tools. The same applies to physics. Analyzing the problem, choosing the correct formula, and manipulating the equation will help you become a good physics student. In this chapter, we discuss mathematical techniques, significant digits, accuracy, precision, and the problem-solving method. These will be your basic tools for physics.

Objectives

The major goals of this chapter are to enable you to:

1. Explain the need for standardization of measurement.
2. Use the metric system of measurement.
3. Convert measurements from one system to another.
4. Solve problems involving length, area, and volume.
5. Distinguish between mass and weight.
6. Use significant digits to determine the accuracy of measurements.
7. Differentiate between accuracy and precision.
8. Solve problems with measurements and consistently express the results with the correct significant digits.
9. Use a systematic approach to solving physics problems.
10. Analyze problems using the problem-solving method.

1.1 Standards of Measure

When two people work together on the same job, they should both use the same standards of measure. If not, the result can be a problem (Fig. 1.1).

Figure 1.1   The trouble with inconsistent systems of measurement

Standards of measure are sets of units of measurement for length, weight, and other quantities defined in a way that is useful to a large number of people. Throughout history, there have been many standards by which measurements have been made:

◆ *Chain:* A measuring instrument of 100 links used in surveying. One chain has a length of 66 feet.
◆ *Rod:* A length determined by having each of 16 men put one foot behind the foot of the man before him in a straight line [Fig. 1.2(a)]. The rod is now standardized as $16\frac{1}{2}$ feet.
◆ *Yard:* The distance from the tip of the king's nose to the fingertips of his outstretched hand [Fig. 1.2(b)].
◆ *Foot:* The rod divided by 16; it was also common to use the length of one's own foot as the unit foot.
◆ *Inch:* The length of three barley corns, round and dry, taken from the center of the ear, and laid end to end [Fig. 1.2(c)].

The U.S. system of measure, which is derived from and sometimes called the English system, is a combination of makeshift units of Anglo-Saxon, Roman, and French-Norman weights and measures.

Figure 1.2   Definitions of some old units

(a) A rod used to be 16 "people feet." This distance divided by 16 equals one foot.

(b) The "old" yard

(c) At one time, three barley corns were used to define one inch.

After the standards based on parts of the human body and on other gimmicks, basic standards were accepted by world governments. They also agreed to construct and distribute accurate standard copies of all the standard units. During the 1790s, a decimal system based on our number system, the metric system, was developed in France. Its acceptance was gained mostly because it was easy to use and easy to remember. Many nations began adopting it as their official system of measurement. By 1900, most of Europe and South America were metric. In 1866, metric measurements for official use were legalized in the United States. In 1893, the Secretary of the Treasury, by administrative order, declared the new metric standards to be the nation's "fundamental standards" of mass and length. Thus, indirectly, the United States *officially* became a metric nation. Even today, the U.S. units are officially defined in terms of the standard metric units.

Throughout U.S. history, several attempts have been made to convert the nation to the metric system. By the 1970s, the United States found itself to be the only nonmetric industrialized country left in the world. However, government inaction to implement the metric system resulted in the United States regularly using a greater variety of confusing units than any other country. Industry and business, however, found their international markets drying up because metric products were preferred. Now many segments of American industry and business have independently gone metric because world trade is geared toward the metric system of measurement. The inherent simplicity of the metric system of measurement and standardization of weights and measures has led to major cost savings in industries that have converted to it.

Most major U.S. industries, such as the automotive, aviation, and farm implement industries, as well as the Department of Defense and other federal agencies have effectively converted to the metric system. In this text approximately 70% of our examples and exercises are metric in the sections where both U.S. and metric systems are still commonly used. In some industries, you—the student and worker—will need to know and use both systems.

TRY THIS ACTIVITY

Stepping Off

When a short distance needs to be measured and a tape measure is not available, some people measure the approximate length by using the length of their own foot as a unit. Measure the distance between two points approximately 15 to 25 ft apart by placing one foot in front of the other and counting the steps. Then, measure the same distance with a tape measure. How close to the standard foot is the length of your own foot? How much error did you generate?

For longer distances, some measure the approximate length by pacing off the distance using one stride as approximately 1 yd or 3 ft. Measure the distance between two points approximately 50 to 75 ft apart by pacing off the distance and counting the strides. Then, measure the same distance with a tape measure. How close to the standard yard is the length of your own stride? How much error did you generate?

PHYSICS CONNECTIONS

Lost in Space

Even professional engineers and scientists sometimes forget to include units or make mistakes when converting from one system of measurement to another. NASA's Mars Climate Orbiter (Fig. 1.3) was lost in space on September 23, 1999, after engineers from Lockheed Martin used U.S. measurements when calculating rocket thrusts and did not convert those measurements to the metric units used by NASA engineers. Such a simple mistake, common to students on physics exams, cost Lockheed Martin and NASA a $125 million space probe and a great deal of embarrassment.

According to officials, NASA assumed that the twice-daily rocket thrust calculations were based on metric units, whereas Lockheed Martin had neither converted the numbers to metric nor labeled them in U.S. units. As a result, the Mars Climate Orbiter, which was to orbit Mars, was inadvertently sent off course and lost. The orbiter was intended to collect atmospheric and surface data while also serving as a communications link for the Mars Lander.

Figure 1.3   NASA's Mars Climate Orbiter—artist's conception

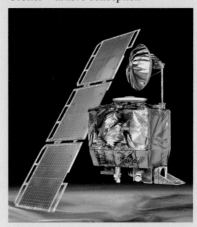

Photo courtesy of NASA Headquarters/Jet Propulsion Laboratory

1.2   Introduction to the Metric System

The modern metric system is identified in all languages by the abbreviation **SI** (for Système International d'Unités—the international system of units of measurement written in French). The SI metric system has seven *basic units* [Table 1.1(a)]. All other SI units are called *derived units*; that is, they can be defined in terms of these seven basic units (see Appendix C, Table 19). For example, the newton (N) is defined as 1 kg m/s^2 (kilogram metre per second per

> **Gabriel Mouton (1618–1694),**
>
> *a French vicar who spent much of his time studying mathematics and astronomy, is credited by many for originating the metric system. French scientists in the late 18th century are credited with replacing the chaotic collection of systems then in use with the metric system.*

Table 1.1   SI Units of Measure

(a) Basic Unit	SI Abbreviation	Used for Measuring
metre*	m	Length
kilogram	kg	Mass
second	s	Time
ampere	A	Electric current
kelvin	K	Temperature
candela	cd	Light intensity
mole	mol	Molecular substance

(b) Derived Unit	SI Abbreviation	Used for Measuring
litre*	L or ℓ	Volume
cubic metre	m^3	Volume
square metre	m^2	Area
newton	N	Force
metre per second	m/s	Speed
joule	J	Energy
watt	W	Power

*At present, there is some difference of opinion in the United States on the spelling of metre and litre. We have chosen the "re" spellings for two reasons. First, this is the internationally accepted spelling for all English-speaking countries. Second, the word "meter" already has many different meanings—parking meter, electric meter, odometer, and so on. Many feel that the metric units of length and volume should be distinctive and readily recognizable—thus the spellings "metre" and "litre."

Table 1.2   Prefixes for SI Units

Multiple or Submultiple[a] Decimal Form	Power of 10	Prefix[b]	Prefix Symbol	Pronunciation	Meaning
1,000,000,000,000	10^{12}	tera	T	tĕr'ă	One trillion times
1,000,000,000	10^{9}	giga	G	jĭg'ă	One billion times
1,000,000	10^{6}	mega	M	mĕg'ă	One million times
1,000	10^{3}	kilo	k	kĭl'ō	One thousand times
100	10^{2}	hecto	h	hĕk'tō	One hundred times
10	10^{1}	deka	da	dĕk'ă	Ten times
0.1	10^{-1}	deci	d	dĕs'ĭ	One tenth of
0.01	10^{-2}	centi	c	sĕnt'ĭ	One hundredth of
0.001	10^{-3}	milli	m	mĭl'ĭ	One thousandth of
0.000001	10^{-6}	micro	μ	mī'krō	One millionth of
0.000000001	10^{-9}	nano	n	năn'ō	One billionth of
0.000000000001	10^{-12}	pico	p	pē'kō	One trillionth of

[a]Factor by which the unit is multiplied.
[b]The same prefixes are used with all SI metric units.

second). Many derived units will be presented and discussed in this text. Some derived SI units are given in Table 1.1(b). **Gabriel Mouton** is often credited for originating the metric system.

Because the metric system is a decimal or base 10 system, it is very similar to our decimal number system and any decimal money system. It is an easy system to use because calculations are based on the number 10 and its multiples. Special prefixes are used to name these multiples and submultiples, which may be used with most all SI units. Because the same prefixes are used repeatedly, the memorization of many conversions has been significantly reduced. Table 1.2 shows these prefixes and the corresponding symbols.

EXAMPLE 1

Write the SI abbreviation for 36 centimetres.

The symbol for the prefix *centi* is c.
The symbol for the unit *metre* is m.

Thus, 36 cm is the SI abbreviation for 36 centimetres.

EXAMPLE 2

Write the SI metric unit for the abbreviation 45 kg.

The prefix for k is *kilo*; the unit for g is *gram*.

Thus, 45 kilograms is the SI metric unit for 45 kg.

PROBLEMS 1.2

Give the metric prefix for each value.

1. 1000   2. 0.01   3. 100   4. 0.1
5. 0.001   6. 10   7. 1,000,000   8. 0.000001

Give the metric symbol, or abbreviation, for each prefix.

9. hecto   10. kilo   11. milli   12. deci
13. mega   14. deka   15. centi   16. micro

Write the abbreviation for each quantity.

17. 135 millimetres   18. 83 dekagrams   19. 28 kilolitres
20. 52 centimetres   21. 49 centigrams   22. 85 milligrams
23. 75 hectometres   24. 15 decilitres

Write the SI unit for each abbreviation.

25.	24 m	26.	185 L	27.	59 g	28.	125 kg
29.	27 mm	30.	25 dL	31.	45 dam	32.	27 mg
33.	26 Mm	34.	275 μg				

35. The basic metric unit of length is _____.
36. The basic unit of mass is _____.
37. Two common metric units of volume are _____ and _____.
38. The basic unit for electric current is _____.
39. The basic metric unit for time is _____.
40. The common metric unit for power is _____.

1.3 Scientific Notation

Scientists and technicians often need to use very large or very small numbers. For example, the thickness of an oil film on water is about 0.0000001 m. **Scientific notation** is a useful method of expressing such very small (or very large) numbers. Expressed this way, the thickness of the film is 1×10^{-7} m or 10^{-7} m. For example:

$$0.1 = 1 \times 10^{-1} \quad \text{or} \quad 10^{-1}$$
$$10,000 = 1 \times 10^{4} \quad \text{or} \quad 10^{4}$$
$$0.001 = 1 \times 10^{-3} \quad \text{or} \quad 10^{-3}$$

A number in scientific notation is written as a product of a number between 1 and 10 and a power of 10. General form: $M \times 10^{n}$, where

M = a number between 1 and 10
n = the exponent or power of 10

The following numbers are written in scientific notation: **EXAMPLE 1**

(a) $325 = 3.25 \times 10^{2}$
(b) $100,000 = 1 \times 10^{5}$ or 10^{5}

· · · · · · · · · · · · · · · · ·

To write any decimal number in scientific notation:

1. Reading from left to right, place a decimal point after the first nonzero digit.
2. Place a caret (∧) at the position of the *original* decimal point.
3. If the newly added decimal point is to the *left* of the caret, the exponent of 10 is the number of places from the caret to the decimal point.
   Example: $83,662 = 8.3662_{\wedge} \times 10^{\underline{4}}$

4. If the newly added decimal point is to the *right* of the caret, the exponent of 10 is the negative of the number of places from the caret to the decimal point.
   Example: $0.00683 = {_{\wedge}}006.83 \times 10^{\underline{-3}}$

5. If the decimal point and the caret coincide, the exponent of 10 is zero.
   Example: $5.12 = 5.12 \times 10^{0}$

A number greater than 10 is expressed in scientific notation as a product of a decimal between 1 and 10 and a *positive* power of 10.

EXAMPLE 2

Write each number greater than 10 in scientific notation.

(a) $2580 = 2.58 \times 10^3$
(b) $54{,}600 = 5.46 \times 10^4$
(c) $42{,}000{,}000 = 4.2 \times 10^7$
(d) $715.8 = 7.158 \times 10^2$
(e) $34.775 = 3.4775 \times 10^1$

. . . .

A number between 0 and 1 is expressed in scientific notation as a product of a decimal between 1 and 10 and a *negative* power of 10.

EXAMPLE 3

Write each positive number less than 1 in scientific notation.

(a) $0.0815 = 8.15 \times 10^{-2}$
(b) $0.00065 = 6.5 \times 10^{-4}$
(c) $0.73 = 7.3 \times 10^{-1}$
(d) $0.0000008 = 8 \times 10^{-7}$

. . . .

A number between 1 and 10 is expressed in scientific notation as a product of a decimal between 1 and 10 and the *zero* power of 10.

EXAMPLE 4

Write each number between 1 and 10 in scientific notation.

(a) $7.33 = 7.33 \times 10^0$
(b) $1.06 = 1.06 \times 10^0$

. . . .

To change a number from scientific notation to decimal form:

1.   Multiply the decimal part by the power of 10 by moving the decimal point *to the right* the same number of decimal places as indicated by the power of 10 if it is *positive*.
2.   Multiply the decimal part by the power of 10 by moving the decimal point *to the left* the same number of decimal places as indicated by the power of 10 if it is *negative*.
3.   Supply zeros as needed.

EXAMPLE 5

Write 7.62×10^2 in decimal form.

$$7.62 \times 10^2 = 762 \qquad \text{Move the decimal point two places to the right.}$$

. . . .

EXAMPLE 6

Write 6.15×10^{-4} in decimal form.

$$6.15 \times 10^{-4} = 0.000615 \qquad \text{Move the decimal point four places to the left and insert three zeros.}$$

. . . .

EXAMPLE 7

Write each number in decimal form.

(a) $3.75 \times 10^2 = 375$
(b) $1.09 \times 10^5 = 109{,}000$
(c) $2.88 \times 10^{-2} = 0.0288$
(d) $9.4 \times 10^{-6} = 0.0000094$
(e) $6.7 \times 10^0 = 6.7$

. . . .

Since calculators used in science and technology accept numbers entered in scientific notation and give some results in scientific notation, it is essential that you fully understand this topic before going to the next section. See Appendix B, Section B.1, for using a calculator with numbers in scientific notation.

PHYSICS CONNECTIONS

Powers of Ten

The importance of scientific notation is illustrated by a famous short documentary film called *Powers of Ten*. The film begins with a 1-metre-wide overhead view of a man relaxing on a blanket while on a picnic. The camera then zooms out to a shot that covers a width of 10 metres (10^1 m) with the picnicking man still in the center of the image but now surrounded by green grass. Throughout the course of another 10 seconds, the camera continues to zoom out to 100 metres (10^2 m) wide. As the camera continues to zoom out, the viewer begins to grasp how enormous the changes in distance are when a number is raised by a power of 10. Eventually, the trip outward stops at 10^{24} m, and then the picture zooms back to 10^0 m before proceeding to enter the skin of the man by moving in by negative powers of 10. Although the majority of the images are artist's renditions of what scientists imagine these objects to look like, *Powers of Ten* is a powerful film that conceptualizes how large our universe is and how small atoms and subatomic particles are within our bodies. The series of photographs demonstrating the powers of ten can be found at http://www.powersof10.com.

Some of the views used in *Powers of Ten* include:

10^0 m or 1 metre: a view of a man on a blanket while on a picnic
10^7 m or 10 thousand kilometres: a view of the entire earth
10^{21} m or 100 thousand light-years: a view of our galaxy, the Milky Way
10^{-1} m or 10 centimetres: a view of a small section of skin on the man's hand
10^{-5} m or 10 microns: a view of a white blood cell inside a capillary in the man's hand
10^{-14} m or 10 fermis: the nucleus of a typical carbon-12 atom

PROBLEMS 1.3

Write each number in scientific notation.

1.	326	2.	798	3.	2650
4.	14,500	5.	826.4	6.	24.97
7.	0.00413	8.	0.00053	9.	6.43
10.	482,300	11.	0.000065	12.	0.00224
13.	540,000	14.	1,400,000	15.	0.0000075
16.	0.0000009	17.	0.00000005	18.	3,500,000,000
19.	732,000,000,000,000,000	20.	0.00000000000000618		

Write each number in decimal form.

21.	8.62×10^4	22.	8.67×10^2	23.	6.31×10^{-4}
24.	5.41×10^3	25.	7.68×10^{-1}	26.	9.94×10^1
27.	7.77×10^8	28.	4.19×10^{-6}	29.	6.93×10^1
30.	3.78×10^{-2}	31.	9.61×10^4	32.	7.33×10^3
33.	1.4×10^0	34.	9.6×10^{-5}	35.	8.4×10^{-6}
36.	9×10^8	37.	7×10^{11}	38.	4.05×10^0
39.	7.2×10^{-7}	40.	8×10^{-9}	41.	4.5×10^{12}
42.	1.5×10^{11}	43.	5.5×10^{-11}	44.	8.72×10^{-10}

1.4 Length

In most sections that introduce units of measure, we present the units in subsections as follows: metric units, U.S. units, and conversions between metric and U.S. units.

Metric Length

The basic SI unit of length is the **metre** (m) (Fig. 1.4). The first standard metre was chosen in the 1790s to be one ten-millionth of the distance from the earth's equator to either pole. Modern measurements of the earth's circumference show that the first length is off by about 0.02% from this initial standard. The current definition adopted in 1983 is based on the speed of light in a vacuum and reads "The metre is the length of path traveled by light in a vacuum during a time interval of 1/299,792,458 of a second." Long distances are measured in kilometres (km) (Fig. 1.5). We use the centimetre (cm) to measure short distances, such as the length of this book or the width of a board [Fig. 1.6(a)]. The millimetre (mm) is used to measure very small lengths, such as the thickness of this book or the depth of a tire tread [Fig. 1.6(b)]. A metric ruler is shown in Fig. 1.6(c).

Figure 1.4   One metre

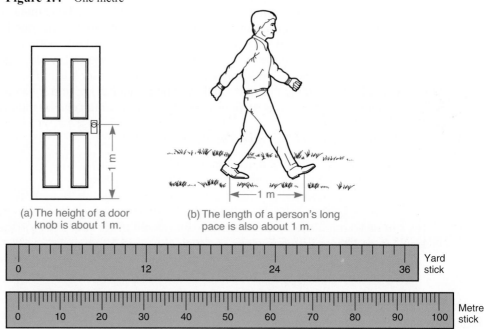

(a) The height of a door knob is about 1 m.

(b) The length of a person's long pace is also about 1 m.

(c) The length of 1 m is a little more than 1 yd.

Figure 1.5   The length of five city blocks is about 1 km.

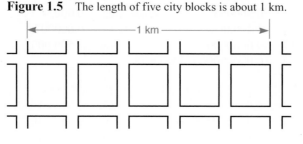

A **conversion factor** is an expression used to change from one unit or set of units to another. We know that we can multiply any number or quantity by 1 without changing the value of the original quantity. We also know that any fraction equals 1 when its numerator and denominator are equal. For example, $\frac{5}{5} = 1$, $\frac{12\ m}{12\ m} = 1$, and $\frac{6.5\ kg}{6.5\ kg} = 1$. In addition, since $1\ m = 100\ cm$, $\frac{1\ m}{100\ cm} = 1$. Similarly, $\frac{100\ cm}{1\ m} = 1$, because the numerator equals the denominator. We call such names for 1 *conversion factors*. The information necessary for forming a conversion factor is usually found in tables. As in the case $1\ m = 100\ cm$, there are two conversion factors for each set of data:

$$\frac{1\ m}{100\ cm} \quad \text{and} \quad \frac{100\ cm}{1\ m}$$

Figure 1.6   Small metric length units

(a) The width of your small fingernail is about 1 cm.   (b) The thickness of a dime is about 1 mm.

(c) The large numbered divisions are centimetres shown actual size.
Each centimetre is divided into 10 equal parts, called millimetres.

CONVERSION FACTORS

Choose a conversion factor in which the old units are in the numerator of the original expression and in the denominator of the conversion factor, or the old units are in the denominator of the original expression and in the numerator of the conversion factor. That is, we want the old units to cancel each other.

EXAMPLE 1

Change 215 cm to metres.
   As we saw before, the two possible conversion factors are

$$\frac{1 \text{ m}}{100 \text{ cm}} \quad \text{and} \quad \frac{100 \text{ cm}}{1 \text{ m}}$$

We choose the conversion factor with centimetres in the *denominator* so that the cm units cancel each other.

$$215 \text{ cm} \times \frac{1 \text{ m}}{100 \text{ cm}} = 2.15 \text{ m}$$

Note: Conversions *within* the metric system involve only moving the decimal point.

· · · · · · · · · · · · · · · · ·

EXAMPLE 2

Change 4 m to centimetres.

$$4 \text{ m} \times \frac{100 \text{ cm}}{1 \text{ m}} = 400 \text{ cm}$$

· · · · · · · · · · · · · · · · ·

EXAMPLE 3

Change 39.5 mm to centimetres.
   Choose the conversion factor with millimetres in the denominator so that the mm units cancel each other.

$$39.5 \text{ mm} \times \frac{1 \text{ cm}}{10 \text{ mm}} = 3.95 \text{ cm}$$

· · · · · · · · · · · · · · · · ·

EXAMPLE 4

Change 0.05 km to centimetres.

First, change to metres and then to centimetres.

$$0.05 \text{ km} \times \frac{1000 \text{ m}}{1 \text{ km}} = 50 \text{ m}$$

$$50 \text{ m} \times \frac{100 \text{ cm}}{1 \text{ m}} = 5000 \text{ cm}$$

Or,

$$0.05 \text{ km} \times \frac{1000 \text{ m}}{1 \text{ km}} \times \frac{100 \text{ cm}}{1 \text{ m}} = 5000 \text{ cm}$$

. . . .

U.S. Length

The basic units of the U.S. system are the foot, the pound, and the second. The foot is the basic unit of length and may be divided into 12 equal parts or inches. Common U.S. length conversions include

$$1 \text{ foot (ft)} = 12 \text{ inches (in.)}$$
$$1 \text{ yard (yd)} = 3 \text{ ft}$$
$$1 \text{ mile (mi)} = 5280 \text{ ft}$$

See Table 1 of Appendix C for U.S. weights and measures.

We also use a conversion factor to change from one U.S. length unit to another.

EXAMPLE 5

Change 84 in. to feet.

Choose the conversion factor with inches in the denominator and feet in the numerator.

$$84 \text{ in.} \times \frac{1 \text{ ft}}{12 \text{ in.}} = 7 \text{ ft}$$

. . . .

Metric–U.S. Conversions

To change from a U.S. unit to a metric unit or from a metric unit to a U.S. unit, again use a conversion factor, such as 1 in. = 2.54 cm.

EXAMPLE 6

Express 10 inches in centimetres.

$$1 \text{ in.} = 2.54 \text{ cm} \quad \text{so} \quad 10 \text{ in.} \times \frac{2.54 \text{ cm}}{1 \text{ in.}} = 25.4 \text{ cm}$$

. . . .

The conversion factors you will need are given in Appendix C. The following examples show you how to use these tables.

EXAMPLE 7

Change 15 miles to kilometres.

From Table 2 in Appendix C, we find 1 mile listed in the left-hand column. Moving over to the fourth column, under the heading "km," we see that 1 mile (mi) = 1.61 km. Then we have

$$15 \text{ mi} \times \frac{1.61 \text{ km}}{1 \text{ mi}} = 24.15 \text{ km}$$

. . . .

EXAMPLE 8

Change 220 centimetres to inches.

Find 1 centimetre in the left-hand column and move to the fifth column under the heading "in." We find that 1 centimetre = 0.394 in. Then

$$220 \text{ cm} \times \frac{0.394 \text{ in.}}{1 \text{ cm}} = 86.68 \text{ in.}$$

· · · · · · · · · · · · · · · ·

EXAMPLE 9

Change 3 yards to centimetres.

Since there is no direct conversion from yards to centimetres in the tables, we must first change yards to inches and then inches to centimetres:

$$3 \text{ yd} \times \frac{36 \text{ in.}}{1 \text{ yd}} \times \frac{2.54 \text{ cm}}{1 \text{ in.}} = 274.32 \text{ cm}$$

· · · · · · · · · · · · · · · ·

PROBLEMS 1.4

Which unit is longer?

1. 1 metre or 1 centimetre
2. 1 metre or 1 millimetre
3. 1 metre or 1 kilometre
4. 1 centimetre or 1 millimetre
5. 1 centimetre or 1 kilometre
6. 1 millimetre or 1 kilometre

Which metric unit (km, m, cm, or mm) would you use to measure the following?

7. Length of a wrench
8. Thickness of a saw blade
9. Height of a barn
10. Width of a table
11. Thickness of a hypodermic needle
12. Distance around an automobile racing track
13. Distance between New York and Miami
14. Length of a hurdle race
15. Thread size on a pipe
16. Width of a house lot

Fill in each blank with the most reasonable metric unit (km, m, cm, or mm).

17. Your car is about 6 _____ long.
18. Your pencil is about 20 _____ long.
19. The distance between New York and San Francisco is about 4200 _____.
20. Your pencil is about 7 _____ thick.
21. The ceiling in my bedroom is about 240 _____ high.
22. The length of a football field is about 90 _____.
23. A jet plane usually cruises at an altitude of 9 _____.
24. A standard film size for cameras is 35 _____.
25. The diameter of my car tire is about 60 _____.
26. The zipper on my jacket is about 70 _____ long.
27. Juan drives 9 _____ to school each day.
28. Jacob, our basketball center, is 203 _____ tall.
29. The width of your hand is about 80 _____.
30. A handsaw is about 70 _____ long.
31. A newborn baby is usually about 45 _____ long.
32. The standard metric piece of plywood is 120 _____ wide and 240 _____ long.

Fill in each blank.

33. 1 km = _____ m
34. 1 mm = _____ m
35. 1 m = _____ cm
36. 1 m = _____ hm
37. 1 dm = _____ m
38. 1 dam = _____ m
39. 1 m = _____ mm
40. 1 m = _____ dm

41. 1 hm = _____ m
42. 1 cm = _____ m
43. 1 m = _____ km
44. 1 m = _____ dam
45. 1 cm = _____ mm
46. Change 250 m to cm.
47. Change 250 m to km.
48. Change 546 mm to cm.
49. Change 178 km to m.
50. Change 35 dm to dam.
51. Change 830 cm to m.
52. Change 75 hm to km.
53. Change 375 cm to mm.
54. Change 7.5 mm to μm.
55. Change 4 m to μm.
56. State your height in centimetres and in metres.
57. The wheelbase of a certain automobile is 108 in. long. Find its length
    (a)   in feet.   (b)   in yards.
58. Change 43,296 ft
    (a)   to miles.   (b)   to yards.
59. Change 6.25 mi
    (a)   to yards.   (b)   to feet.
60. The length of a connecting rod is 7 in. What is its length in centimetres?
61. The distance between two cities is 256 mi. Find this distance in kilometres.
62. Change 5.94 m to feet.
63. Change 7.1 cm to inches.
64. Change 1.2 in. to centimetres.
65. The turning radius of an auto is 20 ft. What is this distance in metres?
66. Would a wrench with an opening of 25 mm be larger or smaller than a 1-in. wrench?
67. How many reamers, each 20 cm long, can be cut from a bar 6 ft long, allowing 3 mm for each saw cut?
68. If 214 pieces each 47 cm long are to be turned from $\frac{1}{4}$-in. round steel stock with $\frac{1}{8}$ in. of waste allowed on each piece, what length (in metres) of stock is required?

Figure 1.7   Actual sizes of 1 cm^2 and 1 in^2

One square centimetre (cm^2)

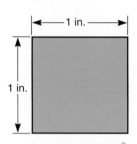

One square inch (in^2)

1.5 Area and Volume

Area

The **area** of a figure is the number of square units that it contains. To measure a surface area of an object, you must first decide on a standard unit of area. Standard units of area are based on the square and are called *square inches*, *square centimetres*, *square miles*, or some other square unit of measure. An area of 1 square centimetre (cm^2) is the amount of area found within a square 1 cm on each side. An area of 1 square inch (in^2) is the amount of area found within a square of 1 in. on each side (Fig. 1.7).

In general, when multiplying measurements of like units, multiply the numbers and then multiply the units as follows:

$$2 \text{ cm} \times 4 \text{ cm} = (2 \times 4)(\text{cm} \times \text{cm}) = 8 \text{ cm}^2$$
$$3 \text{ in.} \times 5 \text{ in.} = (3 \times 5)(\text{in.} \times \text{in.}) = 15 \text{ in}^2$$
$$1.4 \text{ m} \times 6.7 \text{ m} = (1.4 \times 6.7)(\text{m} \times \text{m}) = 9.38 \text{ m}^2$$

Figure 1.8

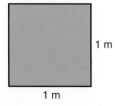

One square metre (m^2)

Metric Area

The basic unit of area in the metric system is the *square metre* (m^2), the area in a square whose sides are 1 m long (Fig. 1.8). The square centimetre (cm^2) and the square millimetre (mm^2) are smaller units of area. Larger units of area are the square kilometre (km^2) and the hectare (ha).

EXAMPLE 1

Find the area of a rectangle 5 m long and 3 m wide.

Each square in Fig. 1.9 represents 1 m^2. By simply counting the number of squares (square metres), we find that the area of the rectangle is 15 m^2. We can also find the area of the rectangle by using the formula

$$A = lw = (5 \text{ m})(3 \text{ m}) = 15 \text{ m}^2 \qquad (\textit{Note:} \quad \text{m} \times \text{m} = \text{m}^2)$$

Figure 1.9

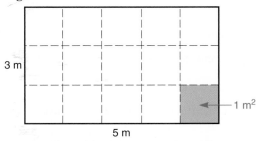

Find the area of the metal plate shown in Fig. 1.10.

EXAMPLE 2

Figure 1.10

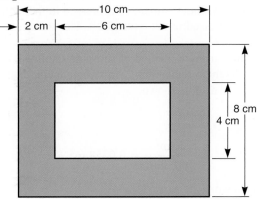

Find the area of the metal plate shown in Fig. 1.10.

To find the area of the metal plate, find the area of each of the two rectangles and then find the difference of their areas. The large rectangle is 10 cm long and 8 cm wide. The small rectangle is 6 cm long and 4 cm wide. Thus,

area of large rectangle: $A = lw = (10 \text{ cm})(8 \text{ cm}) = 80 \text{ cm}^2$

area of small rectangle: $A = lw = (6 \text{ cm})(4 \text{ cm}) = \underline{24 \text{ cm}^2}$

area of metal plate: 56 cm^2

The surface that would be seen by cutting a geometric solid with a thin plate parallel to one side of the solid represents the *cross-sectional area* of the solid.

Find the smallest cross-sectional area of the box shown in Fig. 1.11(a).

EXAMPLE 3

Figure 1.11

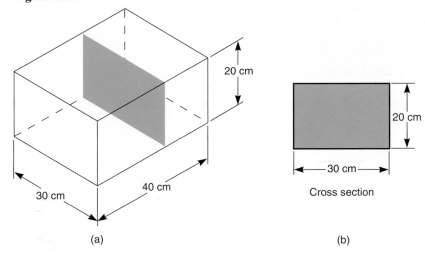

(a)   (b)

The indicated cross section of this box is a rectangle 30 cm long and 20 cm wide [Fig. 1.11(b)]. Thus

$$A = lw = (30 \text{ cm})(20 \text{ cm}) = 600 \text{ cm}^2$$

The area of this rectangle is 600 cm², which represents the cross-sectional area of the box.

· · · · · · · · · · · · · · · · ·

The formulas for finding the areas of other plane figures are found on the inside back cover.

The *hectare* is the fundamental SI unit for land area. An area of 1 hectare equals the area of a square 100 m on a side (Fig. 1.12). The hectare is used because it is more convenient to say and use than square hectometre. The metric prefixes are *not* used with the hectare unit. That is, instead of saying the prefix "kilo" with "hectare," we say "1000 hectares."

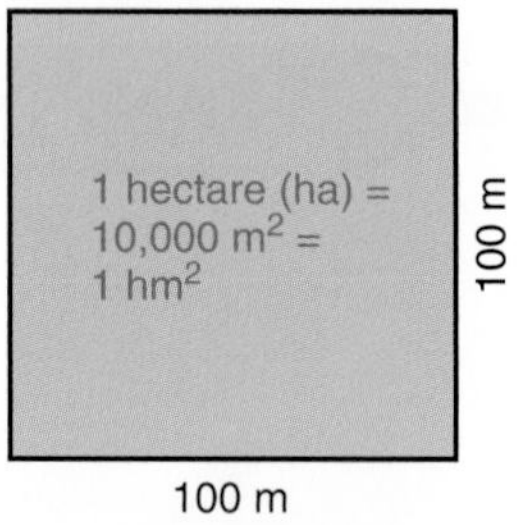

To convert area or square units, use a conversion factor. That is, the correct conversion factor will be in fractional form and equal to 1, with the numerator expressed in the units you wish to convert to and the denominator expressed in the units given. The conversion table for area is provided as Table 3 of Appendix C.

The conversion of area units will be shown using a method of squaring the linear or length conversion factor which you are most likely to remember. An alternate method emphasizing direct use of the conversion tables will also be shown.

Figure 1.12 One hectare

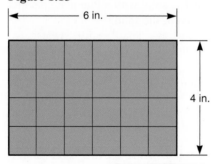

1 hectare (ha) = 10,000 m² = 1 hm²

100 m

100 m

EXAMPLE 4

Change 258 cm² to m².

$$258 \text{ cm}^2 \times \left(\frac{1 \text{ m}}{100 \text{ cm}} \right)^2 = 258 \text{ cm}^2 \times \frac{1^2 \text{ m}^2}{100^2 \text{ cm}^2} = 0.0258 \text{ m}^2$$

Note: The intermediate step is usually not shown.

Alternate Method:

$$258 \text{ cm}^2 \times \frac{1 \text{ m}^2}{10{,}000 \text{ cm}^2} = 0.0258 \text{ m}^2$$

· · · · · · · · · · · · · · · · ·

U.S. Area

EXAMPLE 5

Find the area of a rectangle that is 6 in. long and 4 in. wide (Fig. 1.13).

Figure 1.13

6 in.

4 in.

Each square is 1 in². To find the area of the rectangle, simply count the number of squares in the rectangle. Therefore, you find that the area = 24 in², or, by using the formula,

$$A = lw = (6 \text{ in.})(4 \text{ in.}) = 24 \text{ in}^2$$

· · · · · · · · · · · · · · · · ·

EXAMPLE 6

Change 324 in² to yd².

$$324 \text{ in}^2 \times \left(\frac{1 \text{ yd}}{36 \text{ in.}} \right)^2 = 0.25 \text{ yd}^2$$

Alternate Method:

$$324 \ \cancel{in^2} \times \frac{1 \ yd^2}{1296 \ \cancel{in^2}} = \frac{324}{1296} \ yd^2 = 0.25 \ yd^2$$

· · · · · · · · · · · · · · · · ·

Metric–U.S. Area Conversions

Change 25 cm² to in². ◄ ━━━━━━━━━━━━━━━━━━━━━━━━━━ **EXAMPLE 7**

$$25 \ cm^2 \times \left(\frac{1 \ in.}{2.54 \ cm} \right)^2 = 3.875 \ in^2$$

Alternate Method:

$$25 \ \cancel{cm^2} \times \frac{0.155 \ in^2}{1 \ \cancel{cm^2}} = 3.875 \ in^2$$

· · · · · · · · · · · · · · · · ·

Conversion factors found in tables are usually rounded. There are many rounding procedures in general use. We will use one of the simplest methods, stated as follows:

ROUNDING NUMBERS

To round a number to a particular place value:

1. If the digit in the next place to the right is less than 5, drop that digit and all other following digits. Replace any whole number places dropped with zeros.
2. If the digit in the next place to the right is 5 or greater, add 1 to the digit in the place to which you are rounding. Drop all other following digits. Replace any whole number places dropped with zeros.

Change 28.5 m² to in². ◄ ━━━━━━━━━━━━━━━━━━━━━━━━━━ **EXAMPLE 8**

$$28.5 \ m^2 \times \left(\frac{39.4 \ in.}{1 \ m} \right)^2 = 44,242.26 \ in^2$$

Alternate Method:

$$28.5 \ \cancel{m^2} \times \frac{1550 \ in^2}{1 \ \cancel{m^2}} = 44,175 \ in^2$$

Note: The choice of rounded conversion factors will often lead to results that differ slightly. When checking your answers, you must allow for such rounding differences.

· · · · · · · · · · · · · · · · ·

To convert between metric and U.S. land area units, use the relationship

$$1 \ hectare = 2.47 \ acres$$

Volume

The **volume** of a figure is the number of cubic units that it contains. Standard units of volume are based on the cube and are called *cubic centimetres, cubic inches, cubic yards,* or some other cubic unit of measure. A volume of 1 cubic centimetre (cm³) is the same as the amount of volume contained in a cube 1 cm on each side. One cubic inch (in³) is the volume contained in a cube 1 in. on each side (Fig. 1.14).

Note: When multiplying measurements of like units, multiply the numbers and then multiply the units as follows:

$$3 \ in. \times 5 \ in. \times 4 \ in. = (3 \times 5 \times 4)(in. \times in. \times in.) = 60 \ in^3$$
$$2 \ cm \times 4 \ cm \times 1 \ cm = (2 \times 4 \times 1)(cm \times cm \times cm) = 8 \ cm^3$$
$$1.5 \ ft \times 8.7 \ ft \times 6 \ ft = (1.5 \times 8.7 \times 6)(ft \times ft \times ft) = 78.3 \ ft^3$$

Figure 1.14

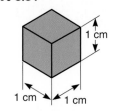

One cubic centimetre (cm³)

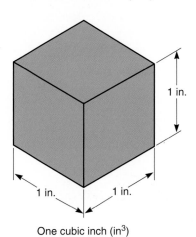

One cubic inch (in³)

EXAMPLE 9

Figure 1.15

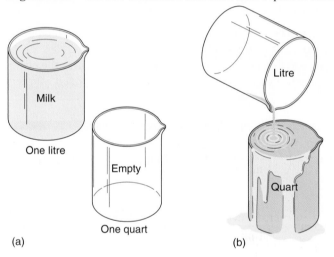

5 cm

4 cm

6 cm

Metric Volume

Find the volume of a rectangular prism 6 cm long, 4 cm wide, and 5 cm high.

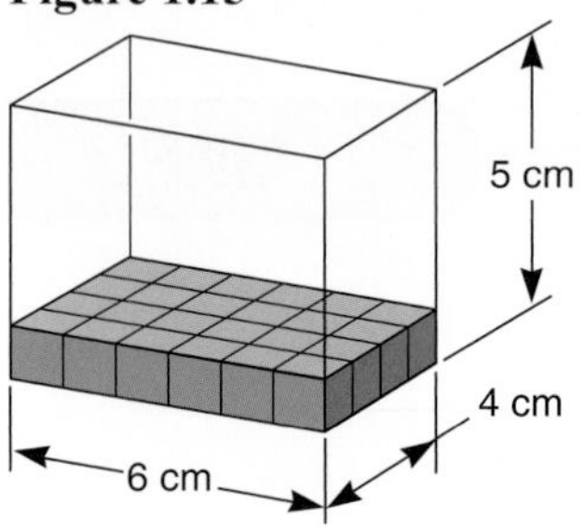

Each cube shown in Fig. 1.15 is 1 cm^3. To find the volume of the rectangular solid, count the number of cubes in the bottom layer of the rectangular solid and then multiply that number by the number of layers that the solid can hold. Therefore, there are 5 layers of 24 cubes, which is 120 cubes or 120 cubic centimetres.

Or, by formula, $V = Bh$, where B is the area of the base and h is the height. However, the area of the base is found by lw, where l is the length and w is the width of the rectangle. Therefore, the volume of a rectangular solid can be found by the formula

$$V = lwh = (6 \text{ cm})(4 \text{ cm})(5 \text{ cm}) = 120 \text{ cm}^3$$

Note: cm × cm × cm = cm^3.

. . . .

A common unit of volume in the metric system is the *litre* (L) (Fig. 1.16). The litre is commonly used for liquid volumes.

Figure 1.16   One litre of milk is a little more than 1 quart of milk.

Milk

One litre

Empty

One quart

(a)

Litre

Quart

(b)

The cubic metre (m^3) is used to measure large volumes. The cubic metre is the volume in a cube 1 m on an edge. For example, the usual teacher's desk could be boxed into 2 cubic metres side by side.

The relationship between the litre and the cubic centimetre deserves special mention. The litre is defined as the volume in 1 cubic decimetre (dm^3). That is, 1 litre of liquid fills a cube 1 dm (10 cm) on an edge (Fig. 1.17). The volume of this cube can be found by using the formula

$$V = lwh = (10 \text{ cm})(10 \text{ cm})(10 \text{ cm}) = 1000 \text{ cm}^3$$

That is,

$$1 \text{ L} = 1000 \text{ cm}^3$$

Then

$$\frac{1}{1000} \text{ L} = 1 \text{ cm}^3$$

Figure 1.17   One litre contains 1000 cm^3.

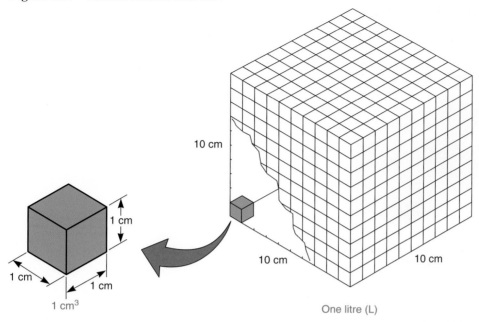

1 cm
1 cm
1 cm
1 cm^3

10 cm
10 cm
10 cm
One litre (L)

But

$$\frac{1}{1000}\, L = 1\ mL$$

Therefore,

$$1\ mL = 1\ cm^3$$

Milk, soda, and gasoline are usually sold by the litre in countries using the metric system. Liquid medicine, vanilla extract, and lighter fluid are usually sold by the millilitre. Many metric cooking recipes are given in millilitres. Very large quantities of oil are sold by the kilolitre (1000 L).

Change 0.75 L to millilitres.

EXAMPLE 10

$$0.75\ \cancel{L} \times \frac{1000\ mL}{1\ \cancel{L}} = 750\ mL$$

Similarly, the conversion of volume cubic units will be shown using a method of cubing the linear, or length, conversion factor that you are most likely to remember. An alternate method emphasizing direct use of the conversion tables will also be shown.

Change 0.65 cm^3 to cubic millimetres.

EXAMPLE 11

$$0.65\ cm^3 \times \left(\frac{10\ mm}{1\ cm}\right)^3 = 0.65\ \cancel{cm^3} \times \frac{10^3\ mm^3}{1^3\ \cancel{cm^3}} = 650\ mm^3$$

Note: The intermediate step is usually not shown.

Alternate Method:

$$0.65\ \cancel{cm^3} \times \frac{1000\ mm^3}{1\ \cancel{cm^3}} = 650\ mm^3$$

U.S. Volume

EXAMPLE 12

Find the volume of the prism shown in Fig. 1.18.

$$V = lwh = (8 \text{ in.})(4 \text{ in.})(5 \text{ in.}) = 160 \text{ in}^3$$

Figure 1.18

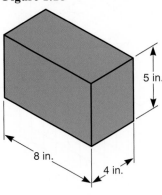

5 in.

8 in.

4 in.

EXAMPLE 13

Change 24 ft^3 to in^3.

$$24 \text{ ft}^3 \times \left(\frac{12 \text{ in.}}{1 \text{ ft}}\right)^3 = 41{,}472 \text{ in}^3$$

Alternate Method:

$$24 \text{ ft}^3 \times \frac{1728 \text{ in}^3}{1 \text{ ft}^3} = 41{,}472 \text{ in}^3$$

Metric–U.S. Volume Conversions

EXAMPLE 14

Change 56 in^3 to cm^3.

$$56 \text{ in}^3 \times \left(\frac{2.54 \text{ cm}}{1 \text{ in.}}\right)^3 = 917.68 \text{ cm}^3$$

Alternate Method:

$$56 \text{ in}^3 \times \frac{16.4 \text{ cm}^3}{1 \text{ in}^3} = 918.4 \text{ cm}^3$$

EXAMPLE 15

Change 28 m^3 to ft^3.

$$28 \text{ m}^3 \times \left(\frac{3.28 \text{ ft}}{1 \text{ m}}\right)^3 = 988.1 \text{ ft}^3$$

Alternate Method:

$$28 \text{ m}^3 \times \frac{35.3 \text{ ft}^3}{1 \text{ m}^3} = 988.4 \text{ ft}^3$$

Surface Area

The **lateral** (side) **surface area** of any geometric solid is the area of all the lateral faces. The **total surface area** of any geometric solid is the lateral surface area plus the area of the bases.

Find the lateral surface area of the prism shown in Fig. 1.19. ◄ **EXAMPLE 16**

$$\text{area of lateral face 1} = (6 \text{ in.})(5 \text{ in.}) = 30 \text{ in}^2$$
$$\text{area of lateral face 2} = (5 \text{ in.})(4 \text{ in.}) = 20 \text{ in}^2$$
$$\text{area of lateral face 3} = (6 \text{ in.})(5 \text{ in.}) = 30 \text{ in}^2$$
$$\text{area of lateral face 4} = (5 \text{ in.})(4 \text{ in.}) = \underline{20 \text{ in}^2}$$
$$\text{lateral surface area} = 100 \text{ in}^2$$

Figure 1.19

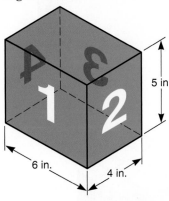

Find the total surface area of the prism shown in Fig. 1.19. ◄ **EXAMPLE 17**

$$\text{total surface area} = \text{lateral surface area} + \text{area of the bases}$$
$$\text{area of base} = (6 \text{ in.})(4 \text{ in.}) = 24 \text{ in}^2$$
$$\text{area of both bases} = 2(24 \text{ in}^2) = 48 \text{ in}^2$$
$$\text{total surface area} = 100 \text{ in}^2 + 48 \text{ in}^2 = 148 \text{ in}^2$$

Area formulas, volume formulas, and lateral surface area formulas are provided on the inside back cover.

PROBLEMS 1.5

Find the area of each figure.

1.
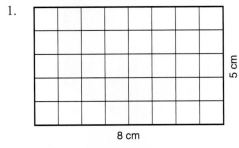

2.
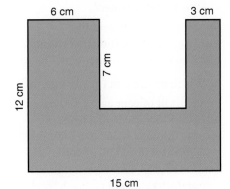

3.
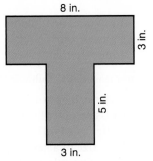

4.

5. Find the cross-sectional area of the I-beam.

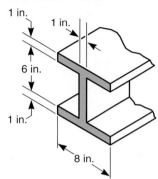

6. Find the largest cross-sectional area of the figure.

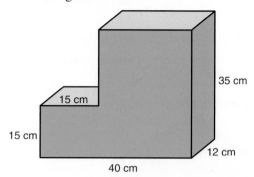

Find the volume in each figure.

7.

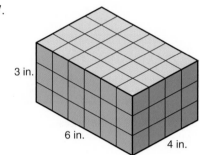

8.

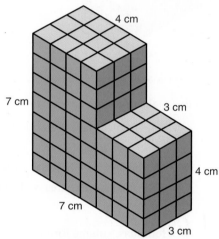

9.

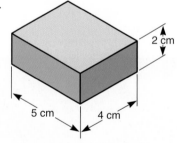

10.

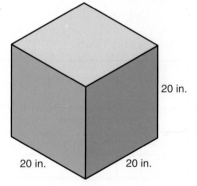

Which unit is larger?

11. 1 litre or 1 centilitre
12. 1 millilitre or 1 kilolitre
13. 1 cubic millimetre or 1 cubic centimetre
14. 1 cm^3 or 1 m^3
15. 1 square kilometre or 1 hectare
16. 1 mm^2 or 1 dm^2

Which metric unit (m^3, L, mL, m^2, cm^2, ha) would you use to measure the following?

17. Oil in your car's crankcase
18. Water in a bathtub
19. Floor space in a house
20. Cross section of a piston
21. Storage space in a miniwarehouse
22. Coffee in an office coffeepot
23. Size of a field of corn
24. Page size of a newspaper
25. A dose of cough syrup
26. Size of a cattle ranch

27. Cargo space in a truck
28. Gasoline in your car's gas tank
29. Piston displacement of an engine
30. Paint needed to paint a house
31. Dose of eye drops
32. Size of a plot of timber

Fill in the blank with the most reasonable metric unit (m^3, L, mL, m^2, cm^2, ha).

33. Go to the store and buy 4 _____ of root beer for the party.
34. I drank 200 _____ of orange juice for breakfast.
35. Craig bought a 30-_____ tarpaulin for his truck.
36. The cross section of a log is 3200 _____.
37. A farmer's gasoline storage tank holds 4000 _____.
38. Our city water tower holds 500 _____ of water.
39. Brian planted 60 _____ of soybeans this year.
40. David needs some copper tubing with a cross section of 3 _____.
41. Paula ordered 15 _____ of concrete for her new driveway.
42. Barbara heats 420 _____ of living space in her house.
43. Joyce's house has 210 _____ of floor space.
44. Kurt mows 5 _____ of grass each week.
45. Amy is told by her doctor to drink 2 _____ of water each day.
46. My favorite coffee cup holds 225 _____ of coffee.

Fill in each blank.

47. 1 L = _____ mL
48. 1 kL = _____ L
49. 1 L = _____ daL
50. 1 L = _____ kL
51. 1 L = _____ hL
52. 1 L = _____ dL
53. 1 daL = _____ L
54. 1 mL = _____ L
55. 1 mL = _____ cm^3
56. 1 L = _____ cm^3
57. 1 m^3 = _____ cm^3
58. 1 cm^3 = _____ mL
59. 1 cm^3 = _____ L
60. 1 dm^3 = _____ L
61. 1 m^2 = _____ cm^2
62. 1 km^2 = _____ m^2
63. 1 cm^2 = _____ mm^2
64. 1 mm^2 = _____ m^2
65. 1 dm^2 = _____ m^2
66. 1 ha = _____ m^2
67. 1 km^2 = _____ ha
68. 1 ha = _____ km^2
69. Change 7500 mL to L.
70. Change 0.85 L to mL.
71. Change 1.6 L to mL.
72. Change 9 mL to L.
73. Change 275 cm^3 to mm^3.
74. Change 5 m^3 to cm^3.
75. Change 4 m^3 to mm^3.
76. Change 520 mm^3 to cm^3.
77. Change 275 cm^3 to mL.
78. Change 125 cm^3 to L.
79. Change 1 m^3 to L.
80. Change 150 mm^3 to L.
81. Change 7.5 L to cm^3.
82. Change 450 L to m^3.
83. Change 5000 mm^2 to cm^2.
84. Change 1.75 km^2 to m^2.
85. Change 5 m^2 to cm^2.
86. Change 250 cm^2 to mm^2.
87. Change 4×10^8 m^2 to km^2.
88. Change 5×10^7 cm^2 to m^2.
89. Change 5 yd^2 to ft^2.
90. How many m^2 are in 225 ft^2?
91. Change 15 ft^2 to cm^2.
92. How many ft^2 are in a rectangle 15 m long and 12 m wide?
93. Change 108 in^2 to ft^2.
94. How many in^2 are in 51 cm^2?
95. How many in^2 are in a square 11 yd on a side?
96. How many m^2 are in a doorway whose area is 20 ft^2?
97. Change 19 yd^3 to ft^3.
98. How many in^3 are in 29 cm^3?
99. How many yd^3 are in 23 m^3?
100. How many cm^3 are in 88 in^3?
101. Change 8 ft^3 to in^3.
102. How many in^3 are in 12 m^3?
103. The volume of a casting is 38 in^3. What is its volume in cm^3?
104. How many castings of 14 cm^3 can be made from a 12-ft^3 block of steel?
105. Find the lateral surface area of the figure in Problem 9.
106. Find the lateral surface area of the figure in Problem 10.
107. Find the total surface area of the figure in Problem 9.
108. Find the total surface area of the figure in Problem 10.
109. How many mL of water would the figure in Problem 9 hold?
110. How many mL of water would the figure in Problem 8 hold?

1.6 Other Units

Mass and Weight

The **mass** of an object is the quantity of material making up the object. One unit of mass in the metric system is the *gram* (g) (Fig. 1.20). The gram is defined as the mass of 1 cubic centimetre (cm^3) of water at its maximum density. Since the gram is so small, the **kilogram** (kg) is the basic unit of mass in the metric system. One kilogram is defined as the mass of 1 cubic decimetre (dm^3) of water at its maximum density. The standard kilogram is a special platinum–iridium cylinder at the International Bureau of Weights and Measures near Paris, France. Since 1 dm^3 = 1 L, 1 litre of water has a mass of 1 kilogram.

Figure 1.20

(a) A common paper clip has a mass of about 1 g.

(b) Three aspirin have a mass of about 1 g.

For very, very small masses, such as medicine dosages, we use the *milligram* (mg). One grain of salt has a mass of about 1 mg. The *metric ton* (1000 kg) is used to measure the mass of very large quantities, such as the coal on a barge, a trainload of grain, or a shipload of ore.

EXAMPLE 1

Change 74 kg to grams.

Choose the conversion factor with kilograms in the denominator so that the kg units cancel each other.

$$74 \text{ kg} \times \frac{1000 \text{ g}}{1 \text{ kg}} = 74{,}000 \text{ g}$$

EXAMPLE 2

Change 600 mg to grams.

$$600 \text{ mg} \times \frac{1 \text{ g}}{1000 \text{ mg}} = 0.6 \text{ g}$$

Figure 1.21 Spring balance

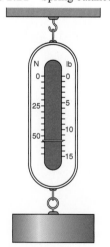

The **weight** of an object is a measure of the gravitational force or pull acting on it. The weight unit in the metric system is the *newton* (N). A small apple weighs about one newton.

The *pound* (lb), a unit of force, is one of the basic U.S. system units. It is defined as the pull of the earth on a cylinder of a platinum–iridium alloy that is stored in a vault at the U.S. Bureau of Standards. The *ounce* (oz) is another common unit of weight in the U.S. system. The relationship between pounds and ounces is

$$1 \text{ lb} = 16 \text{ oz}$$

The following relationships can be used for conversion between systems of units:

$$1 \text{ N} = 0.225 \text{ lb} \quad \text{or} \quad 1 \text{ lb} = 4.45 \text{ N}$$

The mass of an object remains constant, but its weight changes according to its distance from the earth or another planet. Mass and weight and their units of measure are discussed in more detail in Section 5.5.

A **spring balance** (Fig. 1.21) is an instrument containing a spring with a pointer attached to it. The spring stretches in proportion to the weight of the item being weighed. The weight is shown on a calibrated scale read directly in pounds or newtons. The common bathroom scale uses this principle to measure weight.

A **platform balance** (Fig. 1.22) consists of two platforms connected by a horizontal rod that balances on a knife edge. This device compares the pull of gravity on objects that are on the two platforms. The platforms are at the same height only when the unknown mass of the object on the left is equal to the known mass placed on the right. It is also possible to use one platform and a mass that slides along a calibrated scale. Variations of this basic design are found in some meat market and truck scales.

Figure 1.22 Platform balance

Photo courtesy of Dorling Kindersley

EXAMPLE 3

The weight of the intake valve of an auto engine is 0.18 lb. What is its weight in ounces and in newtons?

To find the weight in ounces, we simply use a conversion factor as follows:

$$0.18 \text{ lb} \times \frac{16 \text{ oz}}{1 \text{ lb}} = 2.88 \text{ oz}$$

To find the weight in newtons, we again use a conversion factor:

$$0.18 \text{ lb} \times \frac{4.45 \text{ N}}{1 \text{ lb}} = 0.801 \text{ N}$$

· · · · · · · · · · · · · · · ·

Time

Airlines and other transportation systems run on time schedules that would be meaningless if we did not have a common unit for time measurement. All the common units for time measurement are the same in both systems. These units are based on the motion of the earth (Fig. 1.23). The year is the amount of time required for one complete revolution of the earth about the sun. The month is the amount of time for one complete revolution of the moon about the earth. The day is the amount of time for one rotation of the earth about its axis.

Figure 1.23 Time units are based on the motion of the earth.

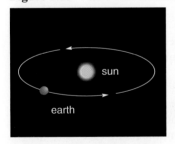

(a) One year is the amount of time it takes for the earth to revolve about the sun.

(b) One day is the amount of time it takes for the earth to rotate about its axis.

The basic time unit is the **second** (s). For many years, the second was defined as $\frac{1}{86,400}$ of a mean solar day. The standard second adopted in 1967 is defined more precisely in terms of the frequency of radiation emitted by cesium atoms when they pass between two particular states; this is the time required for 9,192,631,770 periods of this radiation. The second is not always convenient to use, so other units are necessary. The *minute* (min) is 60 seconds, the *hour* (h) is 60 minutes, and the *day* is 24 hours. The *year* is 365 days in length except for every fourth year, when it is 366 days long. This difference is necessary to keep the seasons at the same time each year, since one revolution of the earth about the sun takes approximately $365\frac{1}{4}$ days.

The Julian calendar introduced by Julius Caesar in 46 BC provided for an ordinary year of 365 days and a leap year of 366 days every fourth year. Astronomers have found that the length of a year has varied from 365.24253 days in 5000 BC to 365.24219 days in 2000 AD. The Gregorian calendar now used in most countries of the world was introduced by Pope Gregory XIII in 1582 to correct the Julian calendar discrepancies. The Gregorian calendar provides for an ordinary year of 365 days and a leap year of 366 days in years divisible by four except in century years not divisible by 400. Thus, years 1600 and 2000 are leap years but years 1700, 1800, 1900, and 2100 are not. In 1582, 10 days were omitted from the calendar to adjust for the accumulated difference of the Julian calendar since 46 BC. By decree, the day following October 4, 1582, became October 15, 1582. Now, small fractions-of-a-second adjustments are made in the calendar annually by international agreement to compensate for the variation of the earth's orbit around the sun.

Common devices for time measurement are the electric clock, the mechanical watch, and the quartz crystal watch. The accuracy of an electric clock depends on how accurately the 60-Hz (hertz = cycles per second) line voltage is controlled. In the United States this is controlled very accurately. Most mechanical watches have a balance wheel that oscillates near a given frequency, usually 18,000 to 36,000 vibrations per hour, and drives the hands of the watch (Fig. 1.24). The quartz crystal in a watch is excited by a small power cell and vibrates 32,768 times per second. The accuracy of the watch depends on how well the frequency of oscillation is controlled.

Figure 1.24   Oscillation of balance wheel

EXAMPLE 4

Change 2 h 15 min to seconds.
First,

$$2 \, \cancel{h} \times \frac{60 \text{ min}}{1 \, \cancel{h}} = 120 \text{ min}$$

Then

$$2 \text{ h } 15 \text{ min} = 120 \text{ min} + 15 \text{ min} = 135 \text{ min}$$

and

$$135 \, \cancel{\text{min}} \times \frac{60 \text{ s}}{1 \, \cancel{\text{min}}} = 8100 \text{ s}$$

· · · · · · · · · · · · · · · · · ·

Very short periods of time are measured in parts of a second, given with the appropriate metric prefix. Such units are commonly used in electronics.

EXAMPLE 5

What is the meaning of each unit?

(a)   1 ms = 1 millisecond $= 10^{-3}$ s and means one one-thousandth of a second.
(b)   1 μs = 1 microsecond $= 10^{-6}$ s and means one one-millionth of a second.
(c)   1 ns = 1 nanosecond $= 10^{-9}$ s and means one one-billionth of a second.
(d)   1 ps = 1 picosecond $= 10^{-12}$ s and means one one-trillionth of a second.

Note: The Greek letter μ is pronounced "myoo." However, 1 μs is stated or read as "one microsecond."

· · · · · · · · · · · · · · · · · ·

EXAMPLE 6

Change 45 ms to seconds.
Since 1 ms $= 10^{-3}$ s,

$$45 \, \cancel{\text{ms}} \times \frac{10^{-3} \text{ s}}{1 \, \cancel{\text{ms}}} = 45 \times 10^{-3} \text{ s} = 0.045 \text{ s}$$

· · · · · · · · · · · · · · · · · ·

EXAMPLE 7

Change 0.000000025 s to nanoseconds.
    Since 1 ns $= 10^{-9}$ s,

$$0.000000025 \; \text{s} \times \frac{1 \; \text{ns}}{10^{-9} \; \text{s}} = 25 \; \text{ns}$$

PROBLEMS 1.6

Which unit is larger?

1. 1 gram or 1 centigram
2. 1 gram or 1 milligram
3. 1 gram or 1 kilogram
4. 1 centigram or 1 milligram
5. 1 centigram or 1 kilogram
6. 1 milligram or 1 kilogram

Which metric unit (kg, g, mg, or metric ton) would you use to measure the following?

7. Your mass
8. An aspirin
9. A bag of lawn fertilizer
10. A bar of hand soap
11. A trainload of grain
12. A sewing needle
13. A small can of corn
14. A channel catfish
15. A vitamin capsule
16. A car

Fill in each blank with the most reasonable metric unit (kg, g, mg, or metric ton).

17. A newborn's mass is about 3 _____.
18. An elevator in a local department store has a load limit of 2000 _____.
19. Margie's diet calls for 250 _____ of meat.
20. A 200-car train carries 11,000 _____ of soybeans.
21. A truckload shipment of copper pipe has a mass of 900 _____.
22. A carrot has a mass of 75 _____.
23. A candy recipe calls for 175 _____ of chocolate.
24. My father has a mass of 70 _____.
25. A pencil has a mass of 10 _____.
26. Postage rates for letters would be based on the _____.
27. A heavyweight boxing champion has a mass of 93 _____.
28. A nickel has a mass of 5 _____.
29. My favorite spaghetti recipe calls for 1 _____ of ground beef.
30. My favorite spaghetti recipe calls for 150 _____ of tomato paste.
31. Our local grain elevator shipped 10,000 _____ of wheat last year.
32. A slice of bread has a mass of about 25 _____.
33. I bought a 5-_____ bag of potatoes at the store today.
34. My grandmother takes 250-_____ capsules for her arthritis.

Fill in each blank.

35. 1 kg = _____ g
36. 1 mg = _____ g
37. 1 g = _____ cg
38. 1 g = _____ hg
39. 1 dg = _____ g
40. 1 dag = _____ g
41. 1 g = _____ mg
42. 1 g = _____ dg
43. 1 hg = _____ g
44. 1 cg = _____ g
45. 1 g = _____ kg
46. 1 g = _____ dag
47. 1 g = _____ μg
48. 1 mg = _____ μg
49. Change 575 g to mg.
50. Change 575 g to kg.
51. Change 650 mg to g.
52. Change 375 kg to g.
53. Change 50 dg to g.
54. Change 485 dag to dg.
55. Change 30 kg to mg.
56. Change 4 metric tons to kg.
57. Change 25 hg to kg.
58. Change 58 μg to g.
59. Change 400 μg to mg.
60. Change 30,000 kg to metric tons.
61. What is the mass of 750 mL of water?
62. What is the mass of 1 m^3 of water?
63. The weight of a car is 3500 lb. Find its weight in newtons.

64.   A certain bridge is designed to support 150,000 lb. Find the maximum weight that it will support in newtons.
65.   Jose weighs 200 lb. What is his weight in newtons?
66.   Change 80 lb to newtons.   67.   Change 2000 N to pounds.
68.   Change 2000 lb to newtons.   69.   Change 120 oz to pounds.
70.   Change 3.5 lb to ounces.   71.   Change 10 N to ounces.
72.   Change 25 oz to newtons.
73.   Find the metric weight of a 94-lb bag of cement.
74.   What is the weight in newtons of 500 blocks if each weighs 3 lb?

Fill in each blank.

75.   The basic metric unit of time is _____. Its abbreviation is _____.
76.   The basic metric unit of mass is _____. Its abbreviation is _____.
77.   The common metric unit of weight is _____. Its abbreviation is _____.

Which is larger?

78.   1 second or 1 millisecond   79.   1 millisecond or 1 nanosecond
80.   1 ps or 1 μs   81.   1 ms or 1 μs

Write the abbreviation for each unit.

82.   8.6 microseconds   83.   45 nanoseconds   84.   75 picoseconds
85.   Change 345 μs to s.   86.   Change 1 h 25 min to min.
87.   Change 4 h 25 min 15 s to s.   88.   Change 7×10^6 s to h.
89.   Change 4 s to ns.   90.   Change 1 h to ps.

1.7 Measurement: Significant Digits and Accuracy

Up to this time in your studies, probably all numbers and all measurements have been treated as exact numbers. An **exact number** is a number that has been determined as a result of counting, such as 24 students are enrolled in this class, or by some definition, such as 1 h = 60 min or 1 in. = 2.54 cm, a conversion definition agreed to by the world governments' bureaus of standards. Generally, the treatment of the addition, subtraction, multiplication, and division of exact numbers is the emphasis or main content of elementary mathematics.

However, nearly all data of a technical nature involve **approximate numbers**; that is, numbers determined as a result of some measurement process—some direct, as with a ruler, and some indirect, as with a surveying transit or reading an electric meter. First, realize that no measurement can be found exactly. The length of the cover of this book can be found using many instruments. The better the measuring device used, the better is the measurement.

A measurement may be expressed in terms of its accuracy or its precision. The **accuracy** of a measurement refers to the number of digits, called **significant digits**, which indicates the number of units that we are reasonably sure of having counted when making a measurement. The greater the number of significant digits given in a measurement, the better is the accuracy and vice versa.

EXAMPLE 1

The average distance between the moon and the earth is 385,000 km. This measurement indicates measuring 385 thousands of kilometres; its accuracy is indicated by three significant digits.

· · · · · · · · · · · · · · · · · ·

EXAMPLE 2

A measurement of 0.025 cm indicates measuring 25 thousandths of a centimetre; its accuracy is indicated by two significant digits.

· · · · · · · · · · · · · · · · · ·

EXAMPLE 3

A measurement of 0.0500 s indicates measuring 50$\overline{0}$ ten-thousandths of a second; its accuracy is indicated by three significant digits.

. . . .

Notice that sometimes a zero is significant and sometimes it is not. To clarify this, we use the following rules for significant digits:

SIGNIFICANT DIGITS

1. All nonzero digits are significant: 156.4 m has four significant digits (this measurement indicates 1564 tenths of metres).
2. All zeros between significant digits are significant: 306.02 km has five significant digits (this measurement indicates 30,602 hundredths of kilometres).
3. In a number greater than 1, a zero that is specially tagged, such as by a bar above it, is significant: 23$\overline{0}$,000 km has three significant digits (this measurement indicates 23$\overline{0}$ thousands of kilometres).
4. All zeros to the right of a significant digit *and* a decimal point are significant: 86.10 cm has four significant digits (this measurement indicates 861$\overline{0}$ hundredths of centimetres).
5. In whole-number measurements, zeros at the right that are not tagged are *not* significant: 2500 m has two significant digits (25 hundreds of metres).
6. In measurements of less than 1, zeros at the left are *not* significant: 0.00752 m has three significant digits (752 hundred-thousandths of a metre).

When a number is written in scientific notation, the decimal part indicates the number of significant digits. For example, 20$\overline{0}$,000 m would be written in scientific notation as 2.00×10^5 m.

In summary:

To find the number of significant digits:

1. All nonzero digits are significant.
2. Zeros are significant when they
    (a) are between significant digits;
    (b) follow the decimal point and a significant digit; or
    (c) are in a whole number and a bar is placed over the zero.

EXAMPLE 4

Determine the accuracy (the number of significant digits) of each measurement.

Measurement	Accuracy (significant digits)
(a) 2642 ft	4
(b) 2005 m	4 (Both zeros are significant.)
(c) 2050 m	3 (Only the first zero is significant.)
(d) 2500 m	2 (No zero is significant.)
(e) 250$\overline{0}$ m	3 (Only the first zero is significant.)
(f) 250$\overline{0}$ m	4 (Both zeros are significant.)
(g) 34,000 mi	2 (No zeros are significant.)
(h) 15,670,000 lb	4 (No zeros are significant.)
(i) 203.05 km	5 (Both zeros are significant.)
(j) 0.000345 kg	3 (No zeros are significant.)

(continued)

Measurement	Accuracy (significant digits)
(k) 75 N	2
(l) 2.3 s	2
(m) 0.02700 g	4 (Only the right two zeros are significant.)
(n) 2.40 cm	3 (The zero is significant.)
(o) 4.050 μs	4 (All zeros are significant.)
(p) 100.050 km	6 (All zeros are significant.)
(q) 0.004 s	1 (No zeros are significant.)
(r) 2.03×10^4 m^2	3 (The zero is significant.)
(s) 1.0×10^{-3} N	2 (The zero is significant.)
(t) 5×10^6 kg	1
(u) 3.060×10^8 m^3	4 (Both zeros are significant.)

PROBLEMS 1.7

Determine the accuracy (the number of significant digits) of each measurement.

1. 536 ft	2. 307.3 mi	3. 5007 m
4. 5.00 cm	5. 0.0070 in.	6. 6.010 cm
7. $8\overline{4}00$ km	8. $30\overline{0}0$ ft	9. 187.40 m
10. $5\overline{0}0$ g	11. 0.00700 in.	12. 10.30 cm
13. 376.52 m	14. 3.05 mi	15. 4087 kg
16. 35.00 mm	17. 0.0160 in.	18. $37\overline{0}$ lb
19. $4\overline{0}00$ N	20. 5010 ft^3	21. 7 N
22. 32,000 tons	23. 70.00 m^2	24. 0.007 m
25. 2.4×10^3 kg	26. 1.20×10^{-5} ms	27. 3.00×10^{-4} kg
28. 4.0×10^6 ft	29. 5.106×10^7 kg	30. 1×10^{-9} m

1.8 Measurement: Precision

The **precision** of a measurement refers to the smallest unit with which a measurement is made, that is, the position of the last significant digit.

EXAMPLE 1

The precision of the measurement 385,000 km is 1000 km. (The position of the last significant digit is in the thousands place.)

EXAMPLE 2

The precision of the measurement 0.025 cm is 0.001 cm. (The position of the last significant digit is in the thousandths place.)

EXAMPLE 3

The precision of the measurement 0.0500 s is 0.0001 s. (The position of the last significant digit is in the ten-thousandths place.)

Unfortunately, the terms *accuracy* and *precision* have several different common meanings. Here we will use each term consistently as we have defined them. A measurement of

0.0004 cm has good precision and poor accuracy when compared with the measurement 378.0 cm.

Measurement	Precision	Accuracy
0.0004 cm	0.0001 cm	1 significant digit
378.0 cm	0.1 cm	4 significant digits

Determine the precision of each measurement given in Example 4 of Section 1.7.

EXAMPLE 4

Measurement	Precision	Accuracy (significant digits)
(a) 2642 ft	1 ft	4
(b) 2005 m	1 m	4
(c) 2050 m	10 m	3
(d) 2500 m	100 m	2
(e) 2500̄ m	10 m	3
(f) 250̄0̄ m	1 m	4
(g) 34,000 mi	1000 mi	2
(h) 15,670,000 lb	10,000 lb	4
(i) 203.05 km	0.01 km	5
(j) 0.000345 kg	0.000001 kg	3
(k) 75 N	1 N	2
(l) 2.3 s	0.1 s	2
(m) 0.02700 g	0.00001 g	4
(n) 2.40 cm	0.01 cm	3
(o) 4.050 μs	0.001 μs	4
(p) 100.050 km	0.001 km	6
(q) 0.004 s	0.001 s	1
(r) 2.03×10^4 m^2	0.01×10^4 m^2 or 100 m^2	3
(s) 1.0×10^{-3} N	0.1×10^{-3} N or 0.0001 N	2
(t) 5×10^6 kg	1×10^6 kg or 1,000,000 kg	1
(u) 3.060×10^8 m^3	0.001×10^8 m^3 or 1×10^5 m^3 or 100,000 m^3	4

PHYSICS CONNECTIONS

Precision and the New Clark Bridge

Bridges are usually not built from one end to the other. Construction typically begins in the middle of the bridge or on each end and meets in the middle. In doing so, it becomes extremely important that every section is in precise alignment so that the bridge will meet at the critical connection points.

For example, the New Clark Bridge crossing the Mississippi at Alton, Illinois, spans over 4600 ft and was designed to high precision so that each member of the bridge would be no more than $\frac{1}{8}$ in. out of alignment. As frames and towers were built in the flowing river, teams of surveyors used fixed points of reference and laser beams to survey the placement of each tower and pier. Ignoring the importance of accuracy and precision would have caused serious problems.

TRY THIS ACTIVITY

Accuracy and Precision

Measure the time it takes someone to run the 100-yard dash. Use a digital stopwatch and a regular wristwatch with a second hand. How accurate is each of the measurements? How precise is each of the measurements?

PROBLEMS 1.8

Determine the precision of each measurement.

1.	536 ft	2.	307.3 mi	3.	5007 m
4.	5.00 cm	5.	0.0070 in.	6.	6.010 cm
7.	84$\overline{0}$0 km	8.	30$\overline{0}$0 ft	9.	187.40 m
10.	5$\overline{0}$0 g	11.	0.00700 in.	12.	10.30 cm
13.	376.52 m	14.	3.05 mi	15.	4087 kg
16.	35.00 mm	17.	0.0160 in.	18.	37$\overline{0}$ lb
19.	4$\overline{0}$00 N	20.	5010 ft^3	21.	7 N
22.	32,000 tons	23.	70.00 m^2	24.	0.007 m
25.	2.4×10^3 kg	26.	1.20×10^{-5} ms	27.	3.00×10^{-4} kg
28.	4.0×10^6 ft	29.	5.106×10^7 kg	30.	1×10^{-9} m

In each set of the measurements, find the measurement that is (a) the most accurate and (b) the most precise.

31.	15.7 in.; 0.018 in.; 0.07 in.	32.	368 ft; 600 ft; 180 ft
33.	0.734 cm; 0.65 cm; 16.01 cm	34.	3.85 m; 8.90 m; 7.00 m
35.	0.0350 s; 0.025 s; 0.00040 s; 0.051 s	36.	125.00 g; 8.50 g; 9.000 g; 0.05 g
37.	27,0$\overline{0}$0 L; 350 L; 27.6 L; 4.75 L	38.	8.4 m; 15 m; 180 m; 0.40 m
39.	500 N; 10,000 N; 500,000 N; 50 N	40.	7.5 ms; 14.2 ms; 10.5 ms; 120.0 ms

In each set of measurements, find the measurement that is (a) the least accurate and (b) the least precise.

41.	16.4 in.; 0.075 in.; 0.05 in.	42.	475 ft; 300 ft; 360 ft
43.	27.5 m; 0.65 m; 12.02 m	44.	5.7 kg; 120 kg; 0.025 kg
45.	0.0250 g; 0.015 g; 0.00005 g; 0.75 g	46.	185.0 m; 6.75 m; 5.000 m; 0.09 m
47.	45,000 N; 250 N; 16.8 N; 0.25 N; 3 N	48.	2.50 kg; 42.0 kg; 15$\overline{0}$ kg; 0.500 kg
49.	20$\overline{0}$0 kg; 10,$\overline{0}$00 kg; 40$\overline{0}$,000 kg; 20 kg	50.	80 ft; 250 ft; 12,550 ft; 26$\overline{0}$0 ft

Figure 1.25 Micrometer with precision 0.01 mm

1.9 Calculations with Measurements

If one person measures the length of one of two parts of a shaft with a micrometer calibrated in 0.01 mm as 42.28 mm and another person measures the second part with a ruler calibrated in mm as 54 mm, would the total length be 96.28 mm? Note that the sum 96.28 mm indicates a precision of 0.01 mm. The precision of the ruler is 1 mm, which means that the measurement 54 mm with the ruler could actually be anywhere between 53.50 mm and 54.50 mm using the micrometer (which has a precision of 0.01 mm and is shown in Fig. 1.25). That is, using the ruler, any measurement between 53.50 mm and 54.50 mm can only be read as 54 mm. Of course, this means that the tenths and hundredths digits in the sum 96.28 mm are really meaningless. In other words, *the sum or difference of measurements can be no more precise than the least precise measurement.* That is,

To add or subtract measurements:

1. Make certain that all the measurements are expressed in the same unit. If they are not, convert them all to the same unit.
2. Add or subtract.
3. Round the results to the same precision as the least precise measurement.

Add the measurements 16.6 mi, 124 mi, 3.05 mi, and 0.837 mi.
EXAMPLE 1

All measurements are in the same unit, so add,

$$
\begin{array}{r}
16.6 \ \text{mi} \\
124 \ \text{mi} \\
3.05 \ \text{mi} \\
\underline{0.837 \ \text{mi}} \\
144.487 \ \text{mi} \rightarrow 144 \ \text{mi}
\end{array}
$$

Then, round this sum to the same precision as the least precise measurement, which is 124 mi. Thus, the sum is 144 mi.

Add the measurements 1370 cm, 1575 mm, 2.374 m, and 8.63 m.
EXAMPLE 2

First, convert all measurements to the same unit, say m.

$$
1370 \ \text{cm} = 13.7 \ \text{m}
$$
$$
1575 \ \text{mm} = 1.575 \ \text{m}
$$

Then add,

$$
\begin{array}{r}
13.7 \ \ \text{m} \\
1.575 \ \text{m} \\
2.374 \ \text{m} \\
\underline{8.63 \ \ \text{m}} \\
26.279 \ \text{m} \rightarrow 26.3 \ \text{m}
\end{array}
$$

Then, round this sum to the same precision as the least precise measurement, which is 13.7 m. Thus, the sum is 26.3 m.

Subtract the measurements 3457.8 g − 2.80 kg.
EXAMPLE 3

First, convert both measurements to the same unit, say g.

$$
2.80 \ \text{kg} = 28\overline{0}0 \ \text{g}
$$

Then subtract.

$$
\begin{array}{r}
3457.8 \ \text{g} \\
\underline{28\overline{0}0 \ \ \ \text{g}} \\
657.8 \ \text{g} \rightarrow 660 \ \text{g}
\end{array}
$$

Then, round this difference to the same precision as the least precise measurement, which is $28\overline{0}0$ g. Thus, the difference is 660 g.

Now suppose that you wish to find the area of the base of a rectangular building. You measure its length as 54.7 m and its width as 21.5 m. Its area is then

$$
A = lw
$$
$$
A = (54.7 \ \text{m})(21.5 \ \text{m})
$$
$$
= 1176.05 \ \text{m}^2
$$

Note that the result contains six significant digits, whereas each of the original measurements contains only three significant digits. To rectify this inconsistency, we say that the product or quotient of measurements can be no more accurate than the least accurate measurement. That is,

To multiply or divide measurements:

1. Multiply or divide the measurements as given.
2. Round the result to the same number of significant digits as the measurement with the least number of significant digits.

Using the preceding rules, we find that the area of the base of the rectangular building is 1180 m^2.

Note: We assume throughout that you are using a calculator to do all calculations.

EXAMPLE 4

Multiply the measurements (124 ft)(187 ft).

$$(124 \text{ ft})(187 \text{ ft}) = 23{,}188 \text{ ft}^2$$

Round this product to three significant digits, which is the accuracy of the least accurate measurement (and also the accuracy of each measurement in the example). That is,

$$(124 \text{ ft})(187 \text{ ft}) = 23{,}200 \text{ ft}^2$$

EXAMPLE 5

Multiply the measurements (2.75 m)(1.25 m)(0.75 m).

$$(2.75 \text{ m})(1.25 \text{ m})(0.75 \text{ m}) = 2.578125 \text{ m}^3$$

Round this product to two significant digits, which is the accuracy of the least accurate measurement (0.75 m). That is,

$$(2.75 \text{ m})(1.25 \text{ m})(0.75 \text{ m}) = 2.6 \text{ m}^3$$

EXAMPLE 6

Divide the measurements 144,000 ft^3 ÷ 108 ft.

$$144{,}000 \text{ ft}^3 \div 108 \text{ ft} = 1333.333\ldots \text{ ft}^2$$

Round this quotient to three significant digits, which is the accuracy of the least accurate measurement (the accuracy of both measurements in this example). That is,

$$144{,}000 \text{ ft}^3 \div 108 \text{ ft} = 1330 \text{ ft}^2$$

EXAMPLE 7

Find the value of $\dfrac{(68 \text{ ft})(10{,}\bar{0}00 \text{ lb})}{95.6 \text{ s}}$.

$$\frac{(68 \text{ ft})(10{,}\bar{0}00 \text{ lb})}{95.6 \text{ s}} = 7112.9707\ldots \frac{\text{ft lb}}{\text{s}}$$

Round this result to two significant digits, which is the accuracy of the least accurate measurement (68 ft). That is,

$$\frac{(68 \text{ ft})(10{,}\bar{0}00 \text{ lb})}{95.6 \text{ s}} = 7100 \text{ ft lb/s}$$

Find the value of $\dfrac{(58.0 \text{ kg})(2.40 \text{ m/s})^2}{5.40 \text{ m}}$.

EXAMPLE 8

$$\dfrac{(58.0 \text{ kg})(2.40 \text{ m/s})^2}{5.40 \text{ m}} = 61.8666\ldots \dfrac{\text{kg m}}{\text{s}^2}$$

Carefully simplify the units:

$$\dfrac{(\text{kg})(\text{m/s})^2}{\text{m}} = \dfrac{(\text{kg})(\overset{\text{m}}{\cancel{\text{m}}^2}/\text{s}^2)}{\cancel{\text{m}}} = \dfrac{\text{kg m}}{\text{s}^2}$$

Round this result to three significant digits, which is the accuracy of the least accurate measurement (the accuracy of all measurements in this example). That is,

$$\dfrac{(58.0 \text{ kg})(2.40 \text{ m/s})^2}{5.40 \text{ m}} = 61.9 \text{ kg m/s}^2$$

··················

Note: To multiply or divide measurements, the units do not need to be the same. The units must be the same to add or subtract measurements. Also, the units are multiplied and/or divided in the same manner as the corresponding numbers.

Any power or root of a measurement should be rounded to the same accuracy as the given measurement.

COMBINATIONS OF OPERATIONS WITH MEASUREMENTS

For combinations of additions, subtractions, multiplications, divisions, and powers involving measurements, follow the usual order of operations used in mathematics:

1. Perform all operations inside parentheses first.
2. Evaluate all powers.
3. Perform any multiplications or divisions, in order, from left to right; then express each product or quotient using its correct accuracy.
4. Perform any additions or subtractions, in order, from left to right; then express the final result using the correct precision.

Find the value of $(4.00 \text{ m})(12.65 \text{ m}) + (24.6 \text{ m})^2 + \dfrac{235.0 \text{ m}^3}{16.00 \text{ m}}$.

EXAMPLE 9

$$(4.00 \text{ m})(12.65 \text{ m}) + (24.6 \text{ m})^2 + \dfrac{235.0 \text{ m}^3}{16.00 \text{ m}} =$$

$$50.6 \text{ m}^2 + 605 \text{ m}^2 + 14.69 \text{ m}^2 = 67\overline{0} \text{ m}^2$$

··················

Obviously, such calculations with measurements should be done with a calculator. When no calculator is available, you may round the original measurements or any intermediate results to one more digit than the required accuracy or precision as required in the final result.

If both exact numbers and approximate numbers (measurements) occur in the same calculation, only the approximate numbers are used to determine the accuracy or precision of the result.

The procedures for operations with measurements shown here are based on methods followed and presented by the American Society for Testing and Materials. There are even more sophisticated methods for dealing with the calculations of measurements. The method one uses, and indeed whether one should even follow any given procedure, depends on the number of measurements and the sophistication needed for a particular situation.

In this book, we generally follow the customary practice of expressing measurements in terms of three significant digits, which is the accuracy used in most engineering and design work.

PROBLEMS 1.9

Use the rules for addition of measurements to add each set of measurements.

1.	3847 ft	2.	8,560 m	3.	42.8	cm	4.	0.456 g
	5800 ft		84,000 m		16.48	cm		0.93 g
	4520 ft		18,476 m		1.497	cm		0.402 g
			12,500 m		12.8	cm		0.079 g
					9.69	cm		0.964 g

5. 39,000 N; 19,600 N; 8470 N; 2500 N
6. 6800 ft; 2760 ft; 4000 ft; 2000 ft
7. 467 m; 970 cm; 1200 cm; 1352 cm; 300 m
8. 36.8 m; 147.5 cm; 1.967 m; 125.0 m; 98.3 cm
9. 12 s; 1.004 s; 0.040 s; 3.9 s; 0.87 s
10. 160,000 N; 84,200 N; 4300 N; 239,000 N; 17,450 N

Use the rules for subtraction of measurements to subtract each second measurement from the first.

11.	2876 kg	12.	14.73 m	13.	45.585 g	14.	34,500 kg
	2400 kg		9.378 m		4.6 g		9,500 kg

15. 4200 km − 975 km
16. 64.73 g − 9.4936 g
17. 1,600,000 kg − 685,000 kg
18. 170 mm − 10.2 cm
19. 3.00 m − 260 cm
20. 1.40 ms − 0.708 ms

Use the rules for multiplication of measurements to multiply each set of measurements.

21. (125 m)(39 m)
22. (470 ft)(1200 ft)
23. (1637 km)(857 km)
24. (9100 m)(600 m)
25. (18.70 m)(39.45 m)
26. (565 cm)(180 cm)
27. (14.5 cm)(18.7 cm)(20.5 cm)
28. (0.046 m)(0.0317 m)(0.0437 m)
29. (450 in.)(315 in.)(205 in.)
30. (18.7 kg)(217 m)

Use the rules for division of measurements to divide.

31. $360 \text{ ft}^3 \div 12 \text{ ft}^2$
32. $125 \text{ m}^2 \div 3.0 \text{ m}$
33. $275 \text{ cm}^2 \div 90.0 \text{ cm}$
34. $185 \text{ mi} \div 4.5 \text{ h}$
35. $\dfrac{347 \text{ km}}{4.6 \text{ h}}$
36. $\dfrac{2700 \text{ m}^3}{900 \text{ m}^2}$
37. $\dfrac{8800 \text{ mi}}{8.5 \text{ h}}$
38. $\dfrac{4960 \text{ ft}}{2.95 \text{ s}}$

Use the rules for multiplication and division of measurements to find the value of each of the following.

39. $\dfrac{(18 \text{ ft})(290 \text{ lb})}{4.6 \text{ s}}$

40. $\dfrac{(18.5 \text{ kg})(4.65 \text{ m})}{19.5 \text{ s}}$

41. $\dfrac{4500 \text{ mi}}{12.3 \text{ h}}$

42. $\dfrac{48.9 \text{ kg}}{(1.5 \text{ m})(3.25 \text{ m})}$

43. $\dfrac{(48.7 \text{ m})(68.5 \text{ m})(18.4 \text{ m})}{(35.5 \text{ m})(40.0 \text{ m})}$

44. $\frac{1}{2}(270 \text{ kg})(16.4 \text{ m/s})^2$

45. $\dfrac{(85.7 \text{ kg})(25.7 \text{ m/s})^2}{12.5 \text{ m}}$

46. $\dfrac{(45.2 \text{ kg})(13.7 \text{ m})}{(2.65 \text{ s})^2}$

47. $\frac{4}{3}\pi(13.5 \text{ m})^3$

48. $\dfrac{140 \text{ g}}{(3.4 \text{ cm})(2.8 \text{ cm})(5.6 \text{ cm})}$

49. (213 m)(65.3 m) − (175 m)(44.5 m)

50. $(4.5 \text{ ft})(7.2 \text{ ft})(12.4 \text{ ft}) + (5.42 \text{ ft})^3$

51. $\dfrac{(125 \text{ ft})(295 \text{ ft})}{44.7 \text{ ft}} + \dfrac{(215 \text{ ft})^3}{(68.8 \text{ ft})(12.4 \text{ ft})} + \dfrac{(454 \text{ ft})^3}{(75.5 \text{ ft})^2}$

52. $(12.5 \text{ m})(46.75 \text{ m}) + \dfrac{(6.76 \text{ m})^3}{4910 \text{ m}} - \dfrac{(41.5 \text{ m})(21 \text{ m})(28.8 \text{ m})}{31.7 \text{ m}}$

Glossary

Accuracy The number of digits, called significant digits, in a measurement, which indicates the number of units that we are reasonably sure of having counted. The greater the number of significant digits, the better is the accuracy. (p. 38)

Approximate Number A number that has been determined by some measurement or estimation process. (p. 38)

Area The number of square units contained in a figure. (p. 24)

Conversion Factor An expression used to convert from one set of units to another. Often expressed as a fraction whose numerator and denominator are equal to each other although in different units. (p. 20)

Exact Number A number that has been determined as a result of counting, such as 21 students enrolled in a class, or by some definition, such as 1 h = 60 min. (p. 38)

Kilogram The basic metric unit of mass. (p. 34)

Lateral Surface Area The area of all the lateral (side) faces of a geometric solid. (p. 30)

Mass A measure of the quantity of material making up an object. (p. 34)

Metre The basic metric unit of length. (p. 20)

Platform Balance An instrument consisting of two platforms connected by a horizontal rod that balances on a knife edge. The pull of gravity on objects placed on the two platforms is compared. (p. 35)

Precision Refers to the smallest unit with which a measurement is made, that is, the position of the last significant digit. (p. 40)

Scientific Notation A form in which a number can be written as a product of a number between 1 and 10 and a power of 10. The general form is $M \times 10^n$, where M is a number between 1 and 10 and n is the exponent or power of 10. (p. 17)

Second The basic unit of time. (p. 35)

SI (Système International d'Unités) The international modern metric system of units of measurement. (p. 15)

Significant Digits The number of digits in a measurement, which indicates the number of units we are reasonably sure of having counted. (p. 38)

Spring Balance An instrument containing a spring, which stretches in proportion to the force applied to it, and a pointer attached to the spring with a calibrated scale read directly in given units. (p. 34)

Standards of Measure A set of units of measurement for length, weight, and other quantities defined in such a way as to be useful to a large number of people. (p. 13)

Total Surface Area The total area of all the surfaces of a geometric solid; that is, the lateral surface area plus the area of the bases. (p. 30)

Volume The number of cubic units contained in a figure. (p. 27)

Weight A measure of the gravitational force or pull acting on an object. (p. 34)

Review Questions

1. What are the basic metric units for length, mass, and time?
   - (a) Foot, pound, hour
   - (b) Newton, litre, second
   - (c) Metre, kilogram, second
   - (d) Mile, ton, day
2. When a value is multiplied or divided by 1, the value is
   - (a) increased.
   - (b) unchanged.
   - (c) decreased.
   - (d) none of the above.
3. The lateral surface area of a solid is
   - (a) always equal to total surface area.
   - (b) never equal to total surface area.
   - (c) usually equal to total surface area.
   - (d) rarely equal to total surface area.
4. Accuracy is
   - (a) the same as precision.
   - (b) the smallest unit with which a measurement is made.

(c) the number of significant digits.

(d) all of the above.

5. When multiplying or dividing two or more measurements, the units
    (a) must be the same.   (b) must be different.   (c) can be different.

6. Cite three examples of problems that would arise in the construction of a home by workers using different systems of measurement.

7. Why is the metric system preferred worldwide to the U.S. system of measurement?

8. List a very large and a very small measurement that could be usefully written in scientific notation.

9. When using conversion factors, can units be treated like other algebraic quantities?

10. What is the meaning of cross-sectional area?

11. Can a brick have more than one cross-sectional area?

12. What is the fundamental metric unit for land area?

13. Which is larger, a litre or a quart?

14. List three things that might conveniently be measured in millilitres.

15. How do weight and mass differ?

16. What is the basic metric unit of weight?

17. A microsecond is one-_____ of a second.

18. Why must we concern ourselves with significant digits?

19. Can the sum or difference of two measurements ever be more precise than the least precise measurement?

20. When rounding the product or quotient of two measurements, is it necessary to consider significant digits?

Review Problems

Give the metric prefix for each value:

1. 1000   2. 0.001

Give the metric symbol, or abbreviation, for each prefix:

3. micro   4. mega

Write the abbreviation for each quantity:

5. 45 milligrams   6. 138 centimetres

Which is larger?

7. 1 L or 1 mL   8. 1 kg or 1 mg   9. 1 L or 1 m^3

Fill in each blank (round to three significant digits when necessary):

10. 250 m = _____ km   11. 850 mL = _____ L
12. 5.4 kg = _____ g   13. 0.55 s = _____ μs
14. 25 kg = _____ g   15. 75 μs = _____ ns
16. 275 cm^2 = _____ mm^2 17. 350 cm^2 = _____ m^2
18. 0.15 m^3 = _____ cm^3 19. 500 cm^3 = _____ mL
20. 150 lb = _____ kg   21. 36 ft = _____ m
22. 250 cm = _____ in.   23. 150 in^2 = _____ cm^2
24. 24 yd^2 = _____ ft^2 25. 6 m^3 = _____ ft^3
26. 16 lb = _____ N   27. 15,600 s = _____ h _____ min

Determine the accuracy (the number of significant digits) in each measurement:

28. 5.08 kg   29. 20,570 lb   30. 0.060 cm   31. 2.00×10^{-4} s

Determine the precision of each measurement:

32. 30.6 ft   33. 0.0500 s   34. 18,000 mi   35. 4×10^5 N

For each set of measurements, find the measurement that is

(a)   the most accurate.   (b)   the least accurate.
(c)   the most precise.   (d)   the least precise.

36.   12.00 m; 0.150 m; 2600 m; 0.008 m
37.   208 L; 18,050 L; 21.5 L; 0.75 L

Use the rules of measurements to add the following measurements:

38.   0.0250 s; 0.075 s; 0.00080 s; 0.024 s
39.   2100 N; 36,800 N; 24,000 N; 14.5 N; 470 N

Use the rules for multiplication and division of measurements to find the value of each of the following:

40.   (450 cm)(18.5 cm)(215 cm)   41. $\dfrac{1480 \text{ m}^3}{9.6 \text{ m}}$ 42. $\dfrac{(25.0 \text{ kg})(1.20 \text{ m/s})^2}{3.70 \text{ m}}$

43.   Find the area of a rectangle 4.50 m long and 2.20 m wide.
44.   Find the volume of a rectangular box 9.0 cm long, 6.0 cm wide, and 13 cm high.

CHAPTER 2

PROBLEM SOLVING

A formula is an equation, usually expressed in letters, called *variables,* and numbers. Much technical work includes the substitution of measured data into known formulas or relationships to find solutions to problems. A systematic approach to solving problems is a valuable tool.

The problem-solving method presented will assist you in processing data, analyzing the problems present, and finding the solution in an orderly manner.

Objectives

The major goals of this chapter are to enable you to:

1. Use formulas in problem solving.
2. Use a systematic approach to solving technical problems.
3. Analyze technical problems using a problem-solving method.

2.1 Formulas

A **formula** is an equation, usually expressed in letters (called *variables*) and numbers. A **variable** is a symbol, usually a letter, used to represent some unknown number or quantity.

The formula $s = vt$ states that the distance traveled, s, equals the product of the velocity, v, and the time, t.

◄ **EXAMPLE 1**

· · · · · · · · · · · · · · · ·

The formula $I = \dfrac{Q}{t}$ states that the current, I, equals the quotient of the charge, Q, and the time, t.

◄ **EXAMPLE 2**

· · · · · · · · · · · · · · · ·

To solve a formula for a given letter means to express the given letter or variable in terms of all the remaining letters. That is, by using the equation-solving principles, rewrite the formula so that the given letter appears on one side of the equation by itself and all the other letters appear on the other side.

Solve $s = vt$ for v. ◄

EXAMPLE 3

$$s = vt$$

$$\frac{s}{t} = \frac{vt}{t} \qquad \text{Divide both sides by } t.$$

$$\frac{s}{t} = v$$

· · · · · · · · · · · · · · · ·

Solve $I = Q/t$ ◄

EXAMPLE 4

(a) for Q.   (b) for t.

(a)

$$I = \frac{Q}{t}$$

$$(I)t = \left(\frac{Q}{t}\right)t \qquad \text{Multiply both sides by } t.$$

$$It = Q$$

(b)   Starting with $It = Q$, we obtain

$$\frac{It}{I} = \frac{Q}{I} \qquad \text{Divide both sides by } I.$$

$$t = \frac{Q}{I}$$

· · · · · · · · · · · · · · · · ·

EXAMPLE 5

Solve $V = E - Ir$ for r.

Method 1:

$$V = E - Ir$$

$$V - E = E - Ir - E \qquad \text{Subtract } E \text{ from both sides.}$$

$$V - E = -Ir$$

$$\frac{V - E}{-I} = \frac{-Ir}{-I} \qquad \text{Dvide both sides by } -I.$$

$$\frac{V - E}{-I} = r$$

Method 2:

$$V = E - Ir$$

$$V + Ir = E - Ir + Ir \qquad \text{Add } Ir \text{ to both sides.}$$

$$V + Ir = E$$

$$V + Ir - V = E - V \qquad \text{Subtract } V \text{ from both sides.}$$

$$Ir = E - V$$

$$\frac{Ir}{I} = \frac{E - V}{I} \qquad \text{Divide both sides by } I.$$

$$r = \frac{E - V}{I}$$

Note that the two results are equivalent. Take the first result and multiply both numerator and denominator by -1. That is,

$$\frac{V - E}{-I} = \left(\frac{V - E}{-I}\right)\left(\frac{-1}{-1}\right) = \frac{-V + E}{I} = \frac{E - V}{I}$$

which is the same as the second result.

· · · · · · · · · · · · · · · · ·

We often use the same quantity in more than one way in a formula. For example, we may wish to use a certain measurement of a quantity, such as velocity, at a given time, say at $t = 0$ s, then use the velocity at a later time, say at $t = 6$ s. To write these desired values of the velocity is rather awkward. We simplify this written statement by using *subscripts* (small letters or numbers printed a half space below the printed line and to the right of the variable) to shorten what we must write.

For the example given, v at time $t = 0$ s will be written as v_i (initial velocity); v at time $t = 6$ s will be written as v_f (final velocity). Mathematically, v_i and v_f are two different quantities, which in most cases are unequal. The sum of v_i and v_f is written as $v_i + v_f$. The product of v_i and v_f is written as $v_i v_f$. The subscript notation is used only to distinguish the general quantity, v, velocity, from the measure of that quantity at certain specified times.

Solve the formula $x = x_i + v_i t + \frac{1}{2}at^2$ for v_i.

EXAMPLE 6

Method 1:

$$x = x_i + v_i t + \tfrac{1}{2}at^2$$

$$x - v_i t = x_i + v_i t + \tfrac{1}{2}at^2 - v_i t \qquad \text{Subtract } v_i t \text{ from both sides.}$$

$$x - v_i t = x_i + \tfrac{1}{2}at^2$$

$$x - v_i t - x = x_i + \tfrac{1}{2}at^2 - x \qquad \text{Subtract } x \text{ from both sides.}$$

$$-v_i t = x_i + \tfrac{1}{2}at^2 - x$$

$$\frac{-v_i t}{-t} = \frac{x_i + \tfrac{1}{2}at^2 - x}{-t} \qquad \text{Divide both sides by } -t.$$

$$v_i = \frac{x_i + \tfrac{1}{2}at^2 - x}{-t}$$

Method 2:

$$x = x_i + v_i t + \tfrac{1}{2}at^2$$

$$x - x_i - \tfrac{1}{2}at^2 = x_i + v_i t + \tfrac{1}{2}at^2 - x_i - \tfrac{1}{2}at^2 \qquad \text{Subtract } x_i \text{ and } \tfrac{1}{2}at^2 \text{ from both sides.}$$

$$x - x_i - \tfrac{1}{2}at^2 = v_i t$$

$$\frac{x - x_i - \tfrac{1}{2}at^2}{t} = \frac{v_i t}{t} \qquad \text{Divide both sides by } t.$$

$$\frac{x - x_i - \tfrac{1}{2}at^2}{t} = v_i$$

· · · · · · · · · · · · · · · ·

Solve the formula $v_{avg} = \frac{1}{2}(v_f + v_i)$ for v_f (avg is used here as a subscript meaning average).

EXAMPLE 7

$$v_{avg} = \tfrac{1}{2}(v_f + v_i)$$

$$2v_{avg} = v_f + v_i \qquad \text{Multiply both sides by 2.}$$

$$2v_{avg} - v_i = v_f \qquad \text{Subtract } v_i \text{ from both sides.}$$

· · · · · · · · · · · · · · · ·

Solve $A = \dfrac{\pi d^2}{4}$ for d, where d is a diameter.

EXAMPLE 8

$$A = \frac{\pi d^2}{4}$$

$$4A = \left(\frac{\pi d^2}{4}\right)(4) \qquad \text{Multiply both sides by 4.}$$

$$4A = \pi d^2$$

$$\frac{4A}{\pi} = \frac{\pi d^2}{\pi} \qquad \text{Divide both sides by } \pi.$$

$$\frac{4A}{\pi} = d^2$$

$$\pm\sqrt{\frac{4A}{\pi}} = d \qquad \text{Take the square root of both sides.}$$

In this case, a negative diameter has no physical meaning, so the result is

$$d = \sqrt{\frac{4A}{\pi}}$$

PROBLEMS 2.1

Solve each formula for the quantity given.

1. $v = \dfrac{s}{t}$ for s

2. $a = \dfrac{v}{t}$ for v

3. $w = mg$ for m

4. $F = ma$ for a

5. $E = IR$ for R

6. $V = lwh$ for w

7. $PE = mgh$ for g

8. $PE = mgh$ for h

9. $v^2 = 2gh$ for h

10. $X_L = 2\pi f L$ for f

11. $P = \dfrac{W}{t}$ for W

12. $p = \dfrac{F}{A}$ for F

13. $P = \dfrac{W}{t}$ for t

14. $p = \dfrac{F}{A}$ for A

15. $KE = \frac{1}{2}mv^2$ for m

16. $KE = \frac{1}{2}mv^2$ for v^2

17. $W = Fs$ for s

18. $v_f = v_i + at$ for a

19. $V = E - Ir$ for I

20. $v_2 = v_1 + at$ for t

21. $R = \dfrac{\pi}{2P}$ for P

22. $R = \dfrac{kL}{d^2}$ for L

23. $F = \frac{9}{5}C + 32$ for C

24. $C = \frac{5}{9}(F - 32)$ for F

25. $X_C = \dfrac{1}{2\pi f C}$ for f

26. $R = \dfrac{\rho L}{A}$ for L

27. $R_T = R_1 + R_2 + R_3 + R_4$ for R_3

28. $Q_1 = P(Q_2 - Q_1)$ for Q_2

29. $\dfrac{I_S}{I_P} = \dfrac{N_P}{N_S}$ for I_P

30. $\dfrac{V_P}{V_S} = \dfrac{N_P}{N_S}$ for N_S

31. $v_{avg} = \frac{1}{2}(v_f + v_i)$ for v_i

32. $2a(s - s_i) = v^2 - v_i^2$ for a

33. $2a(s - s_i) = v^2 - v_i^2$ for s

34. $Ft = m(V_2 - V_1)$ for V_1

35. $Q = \dfrac{I^2 Rt}{J}$ for R

36. $x = x_i + v_i t + \frac{1}{2}at^2$ for x_i

37. $A = \pi r^2$ for r, where r is a radius

38. $V = \pi r^2 h$ for r, where r is a radius

39. $R = \dfrac{kL}{d^2}$ for d, where d is a diameter

40. $V = \frac{1}{3}\pi r^2 h$ for r, where r is a radius

41. $Q = \dfrac{I^2 Rt}{J}$ for I

42. $F = \dfrac{mv^2}{r}$ for v

2.2 Substituting Data into Formulas

An important part of problem solving is substituting the given data into the appropriate formula to find the value of the unknown quantity. Basically, there are two ways of substituting data into formulas to solve for the unknown quantity:

1. Solve the formula for the unknown quantity and then make the substitution of the data.
2. Substitute the data into the formula first and then solve for the unknown quantity.

When using a calculator, the first way is more useful. We will be using this way most of the time in this text.

Given the formula $A = bh$, $A = 120 \text{ m}^2$, and $b = 15$ m, find h.

First, solve for h:

$$A = bh$$

$$\frac{A}{b} = \frac{bh}{b} \qquad \text{Divide both sides by } b.$$

$$\frac{A}{b} = h$$

EXAMPLE 1

Then substitute the data:

$$h = \frac{A}{b} = \frac{120 \text{ m}^2}{15 \text{ m}} = 8.0 \text{ m}$$

(Remember to follow the rules of measurement discussed in Chapter 1. We use them consistently throughout.)

• • • • • • • • • • • • • • • • •

Given the formula $P = 2a + 2b$, $P = 824$ cm, and $a = 292$ cm, find b.

First, solve for b:

$$P = 2a + 2b$$

$$P - 2a = 2a + 2b - 2a \qquad \text{Subtract } 2a \text{ from both sides.}$$

$$P - 2a = 2b$$

$$\frac{P - 2a}{2} = \frac{2b}{2} \qquad \text{Divide both sides by 2.}$$

$$\frac{P - 2a}{2} = b \qquad \left(\text{or } b = \frac{P}{2} - a \right)$$

EXAMPLE 2

Then substitute the data:

$$b = \frac{P - 2a}{2} = \frac{824 \text{ cm} - 2(292 \text{ cm})}{2}$$

$$= \frac{824 \text{ cm} - 584 \text{ cm}}{2}$$

$$= \frac{24\overline{0} \text{ cm}}{2} = 12\overline{0} \text{ cm}$$

• • • • • • • • • • • • • • • • •

Given the formula $A = \left(\dfrac{a + b}{2} \right) h$, $A = 15\overline{0} \text{ m}^2$, $b = 18.0$ m, and $h = 10.0$ m, find a.

First, solve for a:

$$A = \left(\frac{a + b}{2} \right) h$$

$$2A = \left[\left(\frac{a + b}{2} \right) h \right] (2) \qquad \text{Multiply both sides by 2.}$$

$$2A = (a + b)h$$

$$2A = ah + bh \qquad \text{Remove the parentheses.}$$

$$2A - bh = ah + bh - bh \qquad \text{Subtract } bh \text{ from both sides.}$$

EXAMPLE 3

$$2A - bh = ah$$

$$\frac{2A - bh}{h} = \frac{ah}{h} \qquad \text{Divide both sides by } h.$$

$$\frac{2A - bh}{h} = a \qquad \left(\text{or } a = \frac{2A}{h} - b\right)$$

Then substitute the data:

$$a = \frac{2A - bh}{h}$$

$$= \frac{2(15\overline{0} \text{ m}^2) - (18.0 \text{ m})(10.0 \text{ m})}{10.0 \text{ m}}$$

$$= \frac{30\overline{0} \text{ m}^2 - 18\overline{0} \text{ m}^2}{10.0 \text{ m}}$$

$$= \frac{12\overline{0} \text{ m}^2}{10.0 \text{ m}} = 12.0 \text{ m}$$

EXAMPLE 4

Given the formula $V = \frac{1}{3}\pi r^2 h$, $V = 64{,}400 \text{ mm}^3$, and $h = 48.0 \text{ mm}$, find r, where r is a radius.

First, solve for r:

$$V = \frac{1}{3}\pi r^2 h$$

$$3V = \left(\frac{1}{3}\pi r^2 h\right)(3) \qquad \text{Multiply both sides by 3.}$$

$$3V = \pi r^2 h$$

$$\frac{3V}{\pi h} = \frac{\pi r^2 h}{\pi h} \qquad \text{Divide both sides by } \pi h.$$

$$\frac{3V}{\pi h} = r^2$$

$$\pm\sqrt{\frac{3V}{\pi h}} = r \qquad \text{Take the square root of both sides.}$$

In this case, a negative radius has no physical meaning, so the result is

$$r = \sqrt{\frac{3V}{\pi h}}$$

Then substitute the data:

$$r = \sqrt{\frac{3(64{,}400 \text{ mm}^3)}{\pi(48.0 \text{ mm})}}$$

$$= 35.8 \text{ mm}$$

PROBLEMS 2.2

For each formula, (a) solve for the indicated letter and then (b) substitute the given data to find the value of the indicated letter. Follow the rules of calculations with measurements.

Note: In Problems 14 and 16, r is a radius, and in Problem 15, b is the length of the side of a square.

Formula	Data	Find
1. $A = bh$	$b = 14.5$ cm, $h = 11.2$ cm	A
2. $V = lwh$	$l = 16.7$ m, $w = 10.5$ m, $h = 25.2$ m	V
3. $A = bh$	$A = 34.5$ cm^2, $h = 4.60$ cm	b
4. $P = 4b$	$P = 42\overline{0}$ in.	b
5. $P = a + b + c$	$P = 48.5$ cm, $a = 18.2$ cm, $b = 24.3$ cm	c
6. $C = \pi d$	$C = 495$ ft	d
7. $C = 2\pi r$	$C = 68.5$ yd	r
8. $A = \frac{1}{2}bh$	$A = 468$ m^2, $b = 36.0$ m	h
9. $P = 2(a + b)$	$P = 88.7$ km, $a = 11.2$ km	b
10. $V = \pi r^2 h$	$r = 61.0$ m, $h = 125.3$ m	V
11. $V = \pi r^2 h$	$V = 368$ m^3, $r = 4.38$ m	h
12. $A = 2\pi rh$	$A = 51\overline{0}$ cm^2, $r = 14.0$ cm	h
13. $V = Bh$	$V = 2185$ m^3, $h = 14.2$ m	B
14. $A = \pi r^2$	$A = 463.5$ m^2	r
15. $A = b^2$	$A = 465$ in^2	b
16. $V = \frac{1}{3}\pi r^2 h$	$V = 2680$ m^3, $h = 14.7$ m	r
17. $C = 2\pi r$	$r = 19.36$ m	C
18. $V = \frac{4}{3}\pi r^3$	$r = 25.65$ m	V
19. $V = \frac{1}{3}Bh$	$V = 19{,}850$ ft^3, $h = 486.5$ ft	B
20. $A = \left(\dfrac{a + b}{2}\right)h$	$A = 205.2$ m^2, $a = 16.50$ m, $b = 19.50$ m	h

2.3 Problem-Solving Method

Problem solving in technical fields is more than substituting numbers and units into formulas. You must develop skill in taking data, analyzing the problem, and finding the solution in an orderly manner. Understanding the principle involved in solving a problem is more important than blindly substituting into a formula. By following an orderly procedure for problem solving, we develop an approach to problem solving that you can use in your studies and on the job.

The following **problem-solving method** aids in understanding and solving problems and will be applied to all problems in this book where appropriate.

1. ***Read the problem carefully.*** This might appear obvious, but it is the most important step in solving a problem. As a matter of habit, you should read the problem at least twice.
   (a) The first time you should read the problem straight through from beginning to end. Do not stop to think about setting up an equation or formula. You are only trying to get a general overview of the problem during this first reading.
   (b) Read through a second time slowly and *completely*, beginning to think ahead to the following steps.
2. ***Make a sketch.*** Some problems may not lend themselves to a sketch. However, make a sketch whenever possible. Many times, seeing a sketch will show if you have forgotten important parts of the problem and may suggest the solution. This is a *very important* part of problem solving and is often overlooked.
3. ***Write all given information including units.*** This is necessary to have all essential facts in mind before looking for the solution. There are some common phrases that have understood physical meanings. For example, the term *from rest* means the initial velocity equals zero or $v_i = 0$; the term *smooth surface* means assume that no friction is present.
4. ***Write the unknown or quantity asked for in the problem.*** Many students have difficulty solving problems because they don't know what they are looking for and solve for the wrong quantity.

5. **Write the basic equation or formula that relates the known and unknown quantities.** Find the basic formula or equation to use by studying what is given and what you are asked to find. Then look for a formula or equation that relates these quantities. Sometimes, you may need to use more than one equation or formula in a problem.
6. **Find a working equation by solving the basic equation or formula for the unknown quantity.**
7. **Substitute the data in the working equation, including the appropriate units.** It is important that you *carry the units all the way through the problem* as a check that you have solved the problem correctly. For example, if you are asked to find the weight of an object in newtons and the units of your answer work out to be metres, you need to review your solution for the error. (When the unit analysis is not obvious, we will go through it step by step in a box nearby.)
8. **Perform the indicated operations and work out the solution.** Although this will be your final written step, you should always ask yourself, "Is my answer reasonable?" Here and on the job you will be dealing with practical problems. A quick estimate will often reveal an error in your calculations.
9. **Check your answer.** Ask yourself, "Did I answer the questions?"

To help you recall this procedure, with almost every problem set that follows, you will find Fig. 2.1 as shown here. This figure is not meant to be complete, and is only an outline to assist you in remembering and following the procedure for solving problems. *You should follow this outline in solving all problems in this course.*

This problem-solving method will now be demonstrated in terms of relationships and formulas with which you are probably familiar. The formulas for finding area and volume can be found on the inside back cover.

Figure 2.1

SKETCH

12 cm^2 w

4.0 cm

DATA

$A = 12 \text{ cm}^2$, $l = 4.0 \text{ cm}$, $w = ?$

BASIC EQUATION

$A = lw$

WORKING EQUATION

$w = \frac{A}{l}$

SUBSTITUTION

$w = \frac{12 \text{ cm}^2}{4.0 \text{ cm}} = 3.0 \text{ cm}$

EXAMPLE 1

Find the volume of concrete required to fill a rectangular bridge abutment whose dimensions are 6.00 m × 3.00 m × 15.0 m.

Sketch:

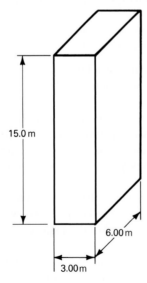

15.0 m

6.00 m

3.00 m

Data:

$l = 6.00 \text{ m}$
$w = 3.00 \text{ m}$ This is a listing of the information that is known.
$h = 15.0 \text{ m}$

$V = ?$ This identifies the unknown.

Basic Equation:

$$V = lwh$$

Working Equation: Same

Substitution:

$$V = (6.00 \text{ m})(3.00 \text{ m})(15.0 \text{ m})$$
$$= 27\overline{0} \text{ m}^3$$

Note: m × m × m = m³

· · · · · · · · · · · · · · · ·

A rectangular holding tank 24.0 m in length and 15.0 m in width is used to store water for short periods of time in an industrial plant. If 2880 m³ of water is pumped into the tank, what is the depth of the water?

EXAMPLE 2

Sketch:

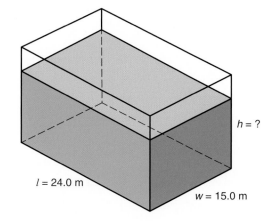

$h = ?$

$l = 24.0$ m

$w = 15.0$ m

Data:

$$V = 2880 \text{ m}^3$$
$$l = 24.0 \text{ m}$$
$$w = 15.0 \text{ m}$$
$$h = ?$$

Basic Equation:

$$V = lwh$$

Working Equation:

$$h = \frac{V}{lw}$$

Substitution:

$$h = \frac{2880 \text{ m}^3}{(24.0 \text{ m})(15.0 \text{ m})}$$
$$= 8.00 \text{ m}$$

$$\boxed{\frac{\text{m}^3}{\text{m} \times \text{m}} = \text{m}}$$

· · · · · · · · · · · · · · · ·

EXAMPLE 3

A storage bin in the shape of a cylinder contains 814 m³ of storage space. If its radius is 6.00 m, find its height.

Sketch:

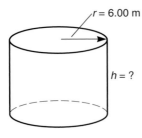

$r = 6.00$ m

$h = ?$

Data:

$$V = 814 \text{ m}^3$$
$$r = 6.00 \text{ m}$$
$$h = ?$$

Basic Equation:

$$V = \pi r^2 h$$

Working Equation:

$$h = \frac{V}{\pi r^2}$$

Substitution:

$$h = \frac{814 \text{ m}^3}{\pi (6.00 \text{ m})^2}$$

$$= 7.20 \text{ m}$$

$$\boxed{\frac{\text{m}^3}{\text{m}^2} = \text{m}}$$

. . . .

EXAMPLE 4

A rectangular piece of sheet metal measures 45.0 cm by 75.0 cm. A 10.0-cm square is then cut from each corner. The metal is then folded to form a box-like container without a top. Find the volume of the container.

Sketch:

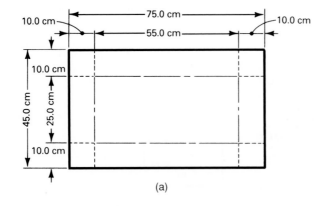

10.0 cm — 75.0 cm — 10.0 cm

55.0 cm

10.0 cm

45.0 cm   25.0 cm

10.0 cm

(a)

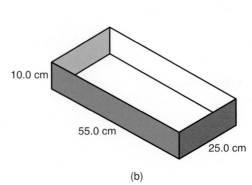

10.0 cm

55.0 cm

25.0 cm

(b)

Data:

$$l = 55.0 \text{ cm}$$
$$w = 25.0 \text{ cm}$$
$$h = 10.0 \text{ cm}$$
$$V = ?$$

Basic Equation:

$$V = lwh$$

Working Equation: Same

Substitution:

$$V = (55.0 \text{ cm})(25.0 \text{ cm})(10.0 \text{ cm})$$
$$= 13{,}800 \text{ cm}^3$$

$$\boxed{\text{cm} \times \text{cm} \times \text{cm} = \text{cm}^3}$$

. . . .

The cross-sectional area of a hole is 725 cm². Find its radius. ◄

EXAMPLE 5

Sketch:

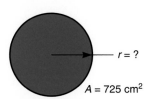

$r = ?$

$A = 725 \text{ cm}^2$

Data:

$$A = 725 \text{ cm}^2$$
$$r = ?$$

Basic Equation:

$$A = \pi r^2$$

Working Equation:

$$r = \sqrt{\frac{A}{\pi}}$$

Substitution:

$$r = \sqrt{\frac{725 \text{ cm}^2}{\pi}}$$
$$= 15.2 \text{ cm}$$

$$\boxed{\sqrt{\text{cm}^2} = \text{cm}}$$

. . . .

PHYSICS CONNECTIONS

Eratosthenes, a third-century Egyptian, used a problem-solving method to determine that the earth was not flat, but round, a fact that Columbus has been credited with discovering more than 1000 years later. Eratosthenes wondered why it was that at noon of the summer solstice, towers in Syene, Egypt (modern Aswan on the Nile), made no shadows, whereas documentation showed that towers in Alexandria, Egypt, did make distinct shadows. Eratosthenes decided to determine why towers in one city would cast shadows while towers in another city would not.

Eratosthenes sketched the problem, gathered data, and collected geometrical equations to solve this complex problem. He hired a person to pace the distance between the two cities (800 km) and used geometry to solve the problem (Fig. 2.2). After calculating the difference in the positions of the two cities to be approximately 7° out of a 360° sphere, he concluded that the earth's circumference was 40,000 km— remarkably accurate when compared to today's calculations. Eratosthenes had a problem to solve, so he, like all good scientists and problem solvers, followed several steps that included analyzing the problem, collecting data, selecting appropriate equations, and making the calculations.

Figure 2.2 Towers in Alexandria and Syene, the shadow cast by the tower in Alexandria, and the curvature of the earth with the angle and the distance between the two cities.

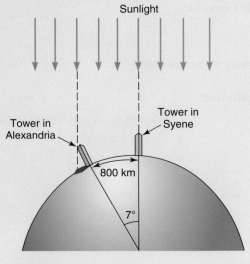

PROBLEMS 2.3

SKETCH

12 cm² | w

4.0 cm

DATA

A = 12 cm², l = 4.0 cm, w = ?

BASIC EQUATION

A = lw

WORKING EQUATION

w = $\frac{A}{l}$

SUBSTITUTION

w = $\frac{12 \text{ cm}^2}{4.0 \text{ cm}}$ = 3.0 cm

Use the problem-solving method to work each problem. (Here, as throughout the text, follow the rules for calculations with measurements.)

1.   Find the volume of the box in Fig. 2.3.
2.   Find the volume of a cylinder whose height is 7.50 in. and diameter is 4.20 in. (Fig. 2.4).
3.   Find the volume of a cone whose height is 9.30 cm if the radius of the base is 5.40 cm (Fig. 2.5).

Figure 2.3

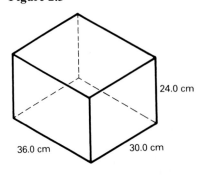

24.0 cm

36.0 cm   30.0 cm

Figure 2.4

4.20 in. diameter

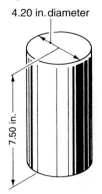

7.50 in.

Figure 2.5

9.30 cm

5.40 cm radius

The cylinder in an engine of a road grader as shown in Fig. 2.6 is 11.40 cm in diameter and 24.00 cm high. Use Fig. 2.6 for Problems 4 through 6.

4. Find the volume of the cylinder.
5. Find the cross-sectional area of the cylinder.
6. Find the lateral surface area of the cylinder.
7. Find the total volume of the building shown in Fig. 2.7.
8. Find the cross-sectional area of the concrete retaining wall shown in Fig. 2.8.

Figure 2.6

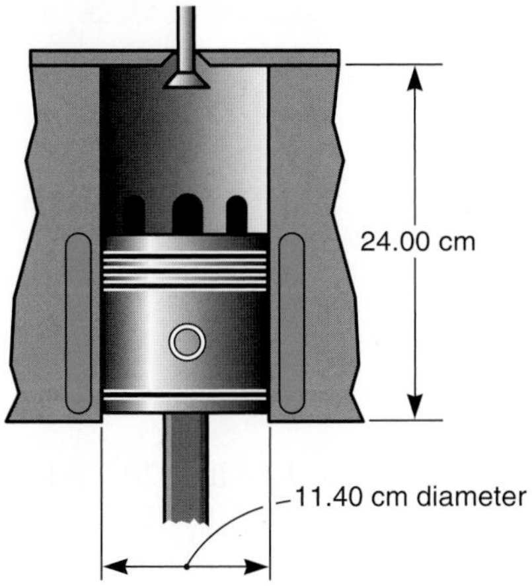

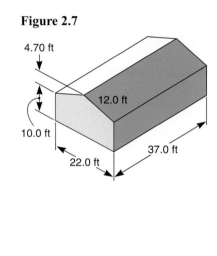

24.00 cm

—11.40 cm diameter

Figure 2.7

4.70 ft

12.0 ft

10.0 ft

22.0 ft

37.0 ft

Figure 2.8

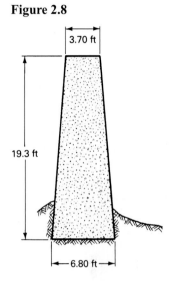

3.70 ft

19.3 ft

6.80 ft

9. Find the volume of a rectangular storage facility 9.00 ft by 12.0 ft by 8.00 ft.
10. Find the cross-sectional area of a piston head with a diameter of 3.25 cm.
11. Find the area of a right triangle that has legs of 4.00 cm and 6.00 cm.
12. Find the length of the hypotenuse of the right triangle in Problem 11.
13. Find the cross-sectional area of a pipe with outer diameter 3.50 cm and inner diameter 3.20 cm.
14. Find the volume of a spherical water tank with radius 8.00 m.
15. The area of a rectangular parking lot is $90\overline{0}$ m². If the length is 25.0 m, what is the width?
16. The volume of a rectangular crate is 192 ft³. If the length is 8.00 ft and the width is 4.00 ft, what is the height?
17. Find the volume of a brake cylinder whose diameter is 4.00 cm and whose length is 4.20 cm.
18. Find the volume of a tractor engine cylinder whose radius is 3.90 cm and whose length is 8.00 cm.
19. A cylindrical silo has a circumference of 29.5 m. Find its diameter.
20. If the silo in Problem 19 has a capacity of $100\overline{0}$ m³, what is its height?
21. A wheel 30.0 cm in diameter moving along level ground made 145 complete rotations. How many metres did the wheel travel?
22. The side of the silo in Problems 19 and 20 needs to be painted. If each litre of paint covers 5.0 m², how many litres of paint will be needed? (Round up to the nearest litre.)
23. You are asked to design a cylindrical water tank that holds $50\overline{0},000$ gal with radius 18.0 ft. Find its height. (1 ft³ = 7.50 gal)
24. If the height of the water tank in Problem 23 were 42.0 ft, what would be its radius?
25. A ceiling is 12.0 ft by 15.0 ft. How many suspension panels 1.00 ft by 3.00 ft are needed to cover the ceiling?
26. Find the cross-sectional area of the dovetail slide shown in Fig. 2.9.

Figure 2.9

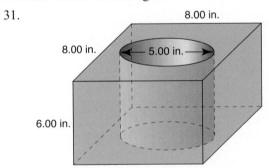

Cross section

Figure 2.10

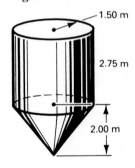

27. Find the volume of the storage bin shown in Fig. 2.10.

28. The maximum cross-sectional area of a spherical propane storage tank is 3.05 m^2. Will it fit into a 2.00-m-wide trailer?

29. How many cubic yards of concrete are needed to pour a patio 12.0 ft $\times$ 20.0 ft and 6.00 in. thick?

30. What length of sidewalk 4.00 in. thick and 4.00 ft wide could be poured with 2.00 yd^3 of concrete?

Find the volume of each figure.

31.

32.

Inside diameter: 20.0 cm
Outside diameter: 50.0 cm

Glossary

Formula An equation, usually expressed in letters (called *variables*) and numbers. (p. 51)
Problem-Solving Method An orderly procedure that aids in understanding and solving problems. (p. 57)
Variable A symbol, usually a letter, used to represent some unknown number or quantity. (p. 51)

Review Questions

1. A formula is
    (a) the amount of each value needed.
    (b) a solution for problems.
    (c) an equation usually expressed in letters and numbers.
2. Subscripts are
    (a) the same as exponents.
    (b) used to shorten what must be written.
    (c) used to make a problem look hard.
3. A working equation
    (a) is derived from the basic equation.
    (b) is totally different from the basic equation.
    (c) comes before the basic equation in the problem.
    (d) none of the above.
4. Cite two examples in industry in which formulas are used.
5. How are subscripts used in measurement?
6. Why is reading the problem carefully the most important step in problem solving?
7. How can making a sketch help in problem solving?
8. What do we call the relationship between data that are given and what we are asked to find?
9. How is a working equation different from a basic equation?
10. How can analysis of the units in a problem assist in solving the problem?
11. How can making an estimate of your answer assist in the correct solution of problems?

Review Problems

1. Solve $F = ma$ for (a) m and (b) a.
2. Solve $v = \sqrt{2gh}$ for h.
3. Solve $s = \frac{1}{2}(v_f + v_i)t$ for v_f.
4. Solve $KE = \frac{1}{2}mv^2$ for v.
5. Given $P = a + b + c$, with $P = 36$ ft, $a = 12$ ft, and $c = 6$ ft, find b.
6. Given $A = \left(\dfrac{a + b}{2}\right)h$, with $A = 21\overline{0}$ m^2, b = 16.0 m, and $h = 15.0$ m, find a.
7. Given $A = \pi r^2$, if $A = 15.0$ m^2, find r.
8. Given $A = \frac{1}{2}bh$, if b = 12.2 cm and h = 20.0 cm, what is A?
9. A cone has a volume of 314 cm^3 and radius of 5.00 cm. What is its height?
10. A right triangle has a side of 41.2 mm and a side of 9.80 mm. Find the length of the hypotenuse.
11. Given a cylinder with a radius of 7.20 cm and a height of 13.4 cm, find the lateral surface area.
12. A rectangle has a perimeter of 40.0 cm. One side has a length of 14.0 cm. What is the length of an adjacent side?

SKETCH

12 cm²   w

4.0 cm

DATA

A = 12 cm², l = 4.0 cm, w = ?

BASIC EQUATION

A = lw

WORKING EQUATION

$w = \frac{A}{l}$

SUBSTITUTION

$w = \frac{12 \text{ cm}^2}{4.0 \text{ cm}} = 3.0$ cm

PROBLEM SOLVING

13.   The formula for the volume of a cylinder is $V = \pi r^2 h$. If $V = 21\overline{0}0 \text{ m}^3$ and $h = 17.0 \text{ m}$, find r.

14.   The formula for the area of a triangle is $A = \frac{1}{2}bh$. If $b = 12.3 \text{ m}$ and $A = 88.6 \text{ m}^2$, find h.

15.   Find the volume of the lead sleeve with the cored hole in Fig. 2.11.

Figure 2.11

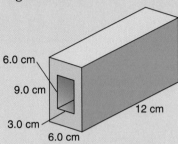

6.0 cm

9.0 cm

3.0 cm

6.0 cm

12 cm

16.   A rectangular plot of land measures 40.0 m by $12\overline{0}$ m with a parcel 10.0 m by 12.0 m out of one corner for an electrical transformer. What is the area of the remaining plot?

APPLIED   CONCEPTS

Use the problem-solving method outlined in Section 2.3 to solve each problem.

1. You run a landscaping business and know that you want to charge $50.00 to mow a person's lawn whose property is 10̄0 ft × 20̄0 ft. If the house dimensions take up a 35.0 ft × 80.0 ft area, how much are you charging per square yard?

2. A room that measures 10.0 ft wide, 32.0 ft long, and 8.00 ft high needs a certain amount of air pumped into it per minute to keep the air quality up to regulations. If the room needs completely new air every 20.0 minutes, what is the volume of air per second that is being pumped into the room?

3. Instead of using a solid iron beam, structural engineers and contractors use I-beams to save materials and money. How many I-beams can be molded from the same amount of iron contained in the solid iron beam as shown in Fig. 2.12?

Figure 2.12

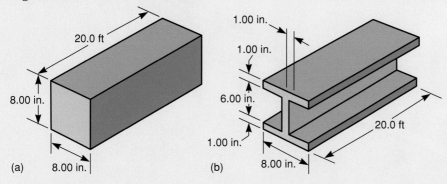

(a)

(b)

4. A shipping specialist at a craft store needs to pack Styrofoam balls of radius 4.00 in. into a 1.40 ft × 2.80 ft × 1.40 ft rectangular cardboard container. What is the maximum number of balls that can fit in the container? Hint: Spherical balls have spaces around them when packed in rectangular containers.

5. A crane needs to lift a spool of fine steel cable to the top of a bridge deck. The type of steel in the cable has a density of 7750 kg/m³. The maximum lifting mass of the crane is 43,400 kg. (a) Given the dimensions of the spool in Fig. 2.13, find the volume of the spool. (b) Can the crane safely lift the spool?

Figure 2.13

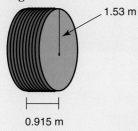

1.53 m

0.915 m

VECTORS

$\vec{V} = \vec{V}_x + \vec{V}_y$

$\vec{V}$

θ

$\vec{V}_x$

$\vec{V}_x = |\vec{V}| \cos\theta$

$\vec{V}_y = |\vec{V}| \sin\theta$

Some physical quantities, called *scalars,* may be described by and involve calculations with numerical quantities alone. Other physical quantities, called *vectors,* require both a numerical quantity and a direction to be completely described and often involve calculations using trigonometry. Vectors are developed in this chapter prior to their use in the following chapters.

Objectives

The major goals of this chapter are to enable you to:

1. Distinguish between a vector and a scalar quantity.
2. Add vectors graphically.
3. Find the components of a vector.
4. Work with vectors in standard position.
5. Apply the basic concepts of right-triangle trigonometry using displacement vectors.

3.1 Vectors and Scalars*

Every physical quantity can be classified as either a scalar or a vector quantity. A **scalar** is a quantity that can be completely described by a number (called its magnitude) and a unit. Examples of scalars are length, temperature, and volume. All these quantities can be expressed by a number with the appropriate units. For example, the length of a steel beam is expressed as 18 ft; the temperature at 11:00 A.M. is 15°C; and the volume of a room is 300 m³.

A **vector** is a quantity that requires both *magnitude* (size) and *direction* to be completely described. Examples of vectors are force, displacement, and velocity. To completely describe a force, you must give not only its magnitude (size or amount), but also its direction.

To describe the change of position of an object, such as an airplane flying from one city to another, we use the term *displacement.* **Displacement** is the net change in position of an object, or the direct distance and direction it moves. For example, to completely describe the flight of a plane between two cities requires both the *distance* between them and the *direction from* the first city *to* the second (Fig. 3.1). *The units of displacement are length units,* such as metres, kilometres, feet, or miles.

Suppose that a friend asks you how to reach your home from school. If you replied that he should walk four blocks, you would not have given him enough information [Fig. 3.2(a)].

Figure 3.1   Displacement

Figure 3.2   Displacement involves both a distance and a direction.

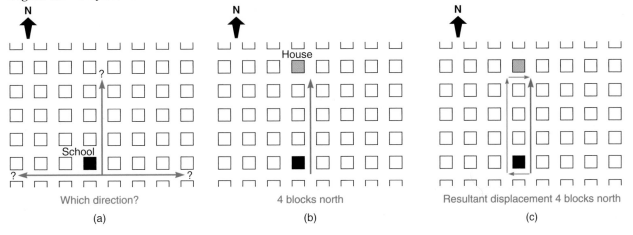

Which direction?	4 blocks north	Resultant displacement 4 blocks north
(a)	(b)	(c)

---

*Right-triangle trigonometry is developed in Appendix A.5, and instructions for using sin, cos, and tan keys on a scientific calculator are included in Appendix B.3 for those who have not studied this before or who need a review.

Figure 3.3

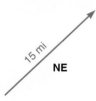

Obviously, you would need to tell him which direction to go. If you had replied, "Four blocks north," your friend could then find your home [Fig. 3.2(b)]. If your friend decides to walk one block west, four blocks north, and then one block east, he will still arrive at your house. This resultant displacement is the same as if he had walked four blocks north [Fig. 3.2(c)].

The magnitude of the displacement vector "15 miles NE" is 15 miles and its direction is northeast (Fig. 3.3).

To represent a vector in a diagram, we draw an arrow that points in the correct direction. The magnitude of the vector is indicated by the length of the arrow. We usually choose a scale, such as 1.0 cm = 25 mi, for this purpose (Fig. 3.4). Thus, a displacement of $10\bar{0}$ mi west is drawn as an arrow (pointing west) 4.0 cm long [Fig. 3.4(a)] since

$$10\bar{0} \text{ mi} \times \frac{1.0 \text{ cm}}{25 \text{ mi}} = 4.0 \text{ cm}$$

Displacements of $5\bar{0}$ mi north [Fig. 3.4(b)] and $5\bar{0}$ mi east [Fig. 3.4(c)] using the same scale are also shown.

Figure 3.4   Use a scale to draw the proper length of a given vector.

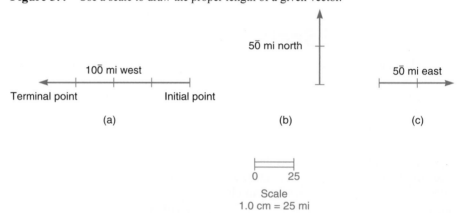

EXAMPLE 1

Using the scale 1.0 cm = $5\bar{0}$ km, draw the displacement vector 275 km at 45° north of west. First, find the length of the vector.

$$275 \text{ km} \times \frac{1.0 \text{ cm}}{5\bar{0} \text{ km}} = 5.5 \text{ cm}$$

Then draw the vector at an angle 45° north of west (Fig. 3.5).

Figure 3.5

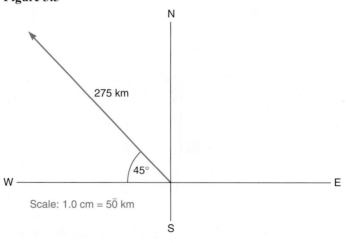

Using the scale $\frac{1}{4}$ in. $= 2\bar{0}$ mi, draw the displacement vector $15\bar{0}$ mi at 22° east of south.   **EXAMPLE 2**
First, find the length of the vector.

$$15\bar{0} \text{ mi} \times \frac{\frac{1}{4} \text{ in.}}{2\bar{0} \text{ mi}} = 1\frac{7}{8} \text{ in.}$$

Then draw the vector at 22° east of south (Fig. 3.6).

Figure 3.6

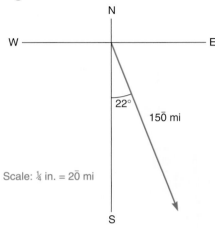

A vector may be denoted by a single letter with a small arrow above, such as $\vec{A}$, $\vec{v}$, or $\vec{R}$ [Fig. 3.7(a)]. This notation is especially useful when writing vectors on paper or on a chalkboard. In this book we use the traditional boldface type to denote vectors, such as **A**, **v**, or **R** [Fig. 3.7(b)]. The length of vector $\vec{A}$ is written $|\vec{A}|$; the length of vector **A** is written $|\mathbf{A}|$.

Figure 3.7

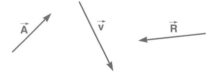

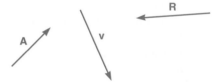

(a) Vector quantities $\vec{A}$, $\vec{v}$, and $\vec{R}$ usually have arrows when they are written on paper or on a chalkboard.

(b) Vector quantities **A**, **v**, and **R** usually are written in boldface type in textbooks.

TRY THIS ACTIVITY

New York Vectors

In 1811, a comprehensive plan was mapped out to create a rectangular grid of roadways on the island of Manhattan in New York City. As a result, giving directions in Manhattan can be done in a number of different ways while still achieving the same result. Assuming that the streets and avenues in the map in Fig. 3.8 are at right angles with one another and that the distance between streets is 0.05 mi and the distance between avenues in 0.20 mi, determine three different ways that someone could travel from Macy's at Herald Square to Times Square. What would be the distance traveled and the displacement for each of these paths?

Figure 3.8 A mid-town Manhattan map is a good way to demonstrate the usefulness of vectors.

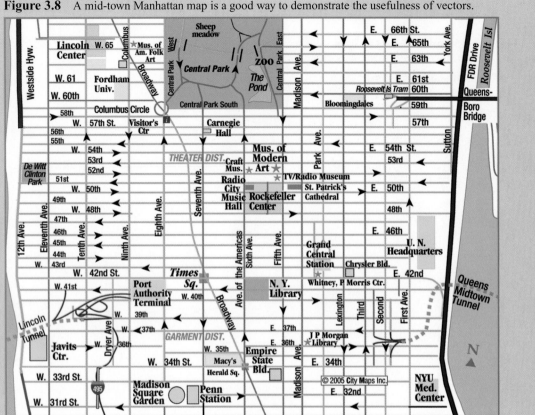

PROBLEMS 3.1

Using the scale 1.0 cm = $5\overline{0}$ km, find the length of the vector that represents each displacement.

1.	Displacement $10\overline{0}$ km east	length = _____ cm
2.	Displacement 125 km south	length = _____ cm
3.	Displacement $14\overline{0}$ km at 45° east of south	length = _____ cm
4.	Displacement $26\overline{0}$ km at $3\overline{0}°$ south of west	length = _____ cm
5.	Displacement 315 km at 65° north of east	length = _____ cm
6.	Displacement 187 km at 17° north of west	length = _____ cm

7–12. Draw the vectors in Problems 1 through 6 using the scale indicated.

Using the scale $\frac{1}{4}$ in. = $2\overline{0}$ mi, find the length of the vector that represents each displacement.

13.	Displacement $10\overline{0}$ mi west	length = _____ in.
14.	Displacement $17\overline{0}$ mi north	length = _____ in.
15.	Displacement $21\overline{0}$ mi at 45° south of west	length = _____ in.
16.	Displacement 145 mi at $6\overline{0}°$ north of east	length = _____ in.
17.	Displacement 75 mi at 25° west of north	length = _____ in.
18.	Displacement $16\overline{0}$ mi at 72° west of south	length = _____ in.

19–24. Draw the vectors in Problems 13 through 18 using the scale indicated.

3.2 Components of a Vector

Before we study vectors further, we need to discuss components of vectors and the number plane. The **number plane** (sometimes called the *Cartesian coordinate system,* after René Descartes) consists of a horizontal line called the *x*-axis and a vertical line called the *y*-axis intersecting at a right angle at a point called the *origin* as shown in Fig. 3.9. These two lines divide the number plane into four quadrants, which we label as quadrants I, II, III, and IV.

René Descartes (1596–1650), *mathematician and philosopher, was born in France. He founded analytic or coordinate geometry, often called Cartesian geometry, and made major contributions in optics.*

Figure 3.9 Number plane

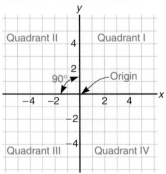

The *x*-axis contains positive numbers to the right of the origin and negative numbers to the left of the origin. The *y*-axis contains positive numbers above the origin and negative numbers below the origin.

Graphically, a vector is represented by a directed line segment. The length of the line segment indicates the magnitude of the quantity. An arrowhead indicates the direction. If *A* and *B* are the end points of a line segment as in Fig. 3.10, the symbol **AB** denotes the *vector from A to B*. Point *A* is called the *initial point.* Point *B* is called the *terminal point* or *end point* of the vector. Vector **BA** has the same length as vector **AB** but has the opposite direction. Vectors may also be denoted by a single letter, such as **u**, **v**, or **R**.

The sum of two or more vectors is called the **resultant vector**. When two or more vectors are added, each of these vectors is called a **component** of the resultant vector. The components of vector **R** in Fig. 3.11(a) are vectors **A**, **B**, and **C**. *Note:* A vector may have more than one set of component vectors. The components of vector **R** in Fig. 3.11(b) are vectors **E** and **F**.

Figure 3.10   Vector from *A* to *B*

Figure 3.11

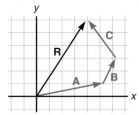 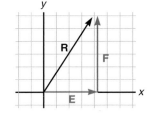

(a) Vectors **A**, **B**, and **C** are components of the resultant vector **R**.

(b) Vector **E** is a horizontal component and vector **F** is a vertical component of the resultant vector **R**.

We are often interested in the components of a vector that are perpendicular to each other and that are on or parallel to the *x*- and *y*-axes. In particular, we are interested in the type of component vectors shown in Fig. 3.11(b) (component vectors **E** and **F**). The horizontal component vector that lies on or is parallel to the *x*-axis is called the *x*-**component**. The vertical component vector that lies on or is parallel to the *y*-axis is called the *y*-**component**. Three examples are shown in Fig. 3.12.

Figure 3.12

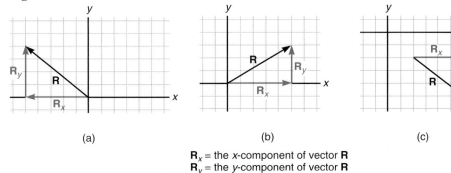

(a)   (b)   (c)

R_x = the *x*-component of vector **R**
R_y = the *y*-component of vector **R**

The *x*- and *y*-components of vectors can also be expressed as signed numbers. The absolute value of the signed number corresponds to the magnitude (length) of the component vector. The sign of the number corresponds to the direction of the component as follows:

x-component	*y*-component
+, if right	+, if up
−, if left	−, if down

EXAMPLE 1

Figure 3.13

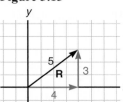

Find the x- and y-components of vector **R** in Fig. 3.13.

$$\mathbf{R}_x = x\text{-component of } \mathbf{R} = +4$$
$$\mathbf{R}_y = y\text{-component of } \mathbf{R} = +3$$

. . . .

EXAMPLE 2

Figure 3.14

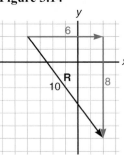

Find the x- and y-components of vector **R** in Fig. 3.14.

$$\mathbf{R}_x = x\text{-component of } \mathbf{R} = +6$$
$$\mathbf{R}_y = y\text{-component of } \mathbf{R} = -8$$

(The y-component points in a negative direction.)

. . . .

EXAMPLE 3

Figure 3.15

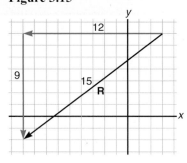

Find the x- and y-components of vector **R** in Fig. 3.15.

$$\mathbf{R}_x = -12$$
$$\mathbf{R}_y = -9$$

(Both x- and y-components point in a negative direction.)

. . . .

A vector may be placed in any position in the number plane as long as its magnitude and direction are not changed. The vectors in each set in Fig. 3.16 are equal because they have the same magnitude (length) and the same direction.

Figure 3.16

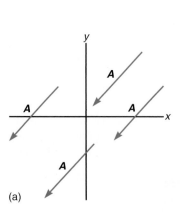

(a)

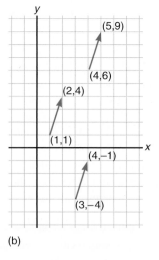

(b)

A vector is in **standard position** when its initial point is at the origin of the number plane. A vector in standard position is expressed in terms of its magnitude (length) and its angle θ, where θ *is measured counterclockwise from the positive x-axis to the vector.* The vectors shown in Fig. 3.17 are in standard position.

Figure 3.17   Vectors in standard position

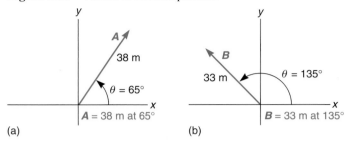

(a)

(b)

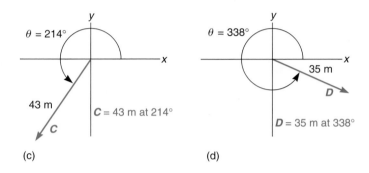

(c)

(d)

Finding the Components of a Vector

Find the *x*- and *y*-components of the vector **A** = 10.0 m at 60.0°.

EXAMPLE 4

First, draw the vector in standard position [Fig. 3.18(a)]. Then, draw a right triangle where the legs represent the *x*- and *y*-components [Fig. 3.18(b)]. The absolute value of the *x*-component of the vector is the length of the side adjacent to the 60.0° angle. Therefore, to find the *x*-component,

Figure 3.18

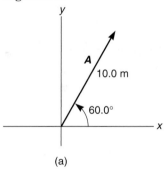

(a)

$$\cos 60.0° = \frac{\text{side adjacent to } 60.0°}{\text{hypotenuse}} = \frac{|\mathbf{A}_x|}{10.0 \text{ m}}$$

$$\cos 60.0° = \frac{|\mathbf{A}_x|}{10.0 \text{ m}}$$

$$(\cos 60.0°)(10.0 \text{ m}) = \left(\frac{|\mathbf{A}_x|}{10.0 \text{ m}}\right)(10.0 \text{ m}) \quad \text{Multiply both sides by 10.0 m.}$$

$$5.00 \text{ m} = |\mathbf{A}_x|$$

Since the *x*-component is pointing in the positive *x*-direction, $\mathbf{A}_x = +5.00$ m.

The absolute value of the *y*-component of the vector is the length of the side opposite the 60.0° angle. Therefore, to find the *y*-component,

$$\sin 60.0° = \frac{\text{side opposite } 60.0°}{\text{hypotenuse}} = \frac{|\mathbf{A}_y|}{10.0 \text{ m}}$$

$$\sin 60.0° = \frac{|\mathbf{A}_y|}{10.0 \text{ m}}$$

$$(\sin 60.0°)(10.0 \text{ m}) = \left(\frac{|\mathbf{A}_y|}{10.0 \text{ m}}\right)(10.0 \text{ m}) \quad \text{Multiply both sides by 10.0 m.}$$

$$8.66 \text{ m} = |\mathbf{A}_y|$$

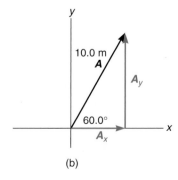

(b)

Since the *y*-component is pointing in the positive *y*-direction, $\mathbf{A}_y = +8.66$ m.

EXAMPLE 5

Find the x- and y-components of the vector $\mathbf{B} = 13.0$ km at $220.0°$.

First, draw the vector in standard position [Fig. 3.19(a)]. Then, complete a right triangle with the x- and y-components being the two legs [Fig. 3.19(b)].

We will let angle α (Greek letter alpha) be the acute angle (an angle whose measure is less than $90°$) between the vector in standard position and the x-axis.

Find angle α as follows:

$$180° + \alpha = 220.0°$$
$$\alpha = 40.0°$$

Figure 3.19

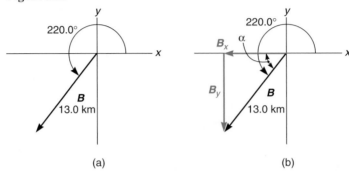

(a)   (b)

The absolute value of the x-component is the length of the side adjacent to angle α. Therefore, to find the x-component,

$$\cos \alpha = \frac{\text{side adjacent to } \alpha}{\text{hypotenuse}}$$

$$\cos 40.0° = \frac{|\mathbf{B}_x|}{13.0 \text{ km}}$$

$$(\cos 40.0°)(13.0 \text{ km}) = \left(\frac{|\mathbf{B}_x|}{13.0 \text{ km}}\right)(13.0 \text{ km}) \qquad \text{Multiply both sides by 13.0 km.}$$

$$9.96 \text{ km} = |\mathbf{B}_x|$$

Since the x-component is pointing in the negative x-direction, $\mathbf{B}_x = -9.96$ km.

The absolute value of the y-component of the vector is the length of the side opposite angle α. Therefore, to find the y-component,

$$\sin \alpha = \frac{\text{side opposite } \alpha}{\text{hypotenuse}}$$

$$\sin 40.0° = \frac{|\mathbf{B}_y|}{13.0 \text{ km}}$$

$$(\sin 40.0°)(13.0 \text{ km}) = \left(\frac{|\mathbf{B}_y|}{13.0 \text{ km}}\right)(13.0 \text{ km}) \qquad \text{Multiply both sides by 13.0 km.}$$

$$8.36 \text{ km} = |\mathbf{B}_y|$$

Since the y-component is pointing in the negative y-direction, $\mathbf{B}_y = -8.36$ km.

· · · · · · · · · · · · · · · · · ·

Figure 3.20

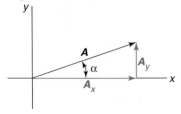

Vector **v** in standard position with its horizontal component $\mathbf{v}_x$ and its vertical component $\mathbf{v}_y$

In general, find the x- and y-components of a vector as follows. First, draw any vector **A** in standard position; then, draw its x- and y-components as shown in Fig. 3.20. Use the right triangle to find the x-component as follows:

$$\cos \alpha = \frac{\text{side adjacent to } \alpha}{\text{hypotenuse}}$$

$$\cos \alpha = \frac{|\mathbf{A}_x|}{|\mathbf{A}|}$$

$$|\mathbf{A}|(\cos \alpha) = \left(\frac{|\mathbf{A}_x|}{|\mathbf{A}|} \right) |\mathbf{A}| \qquad \text{Multiply both sides by } |\mathbf{A}|.$$

$$|\mathbf{A}|(\cos \alpha) = |\mathbf{A}_x|$$

Similarly, we use the right triangle to find the y-component as follows:

$$\sin \alpha = \frac{\text{side opposite } \alpha}{\text{hypotenuse}}$$

$$\sin \alpha = \frac{|\mathbf{A}_y|}{|\mathbf{A}|}$$

$$|\mathbf{A}|(\sin \alpha) = \left(\frac{|\mathbf{A}_y|}{|\mathbf{A}|} \right) |\mathbf{A}| \qquad \text{Multiply both sides by } |\mathbf{A}|.$$

$$|\mathbf{A}|(\sin \alpha) = |\mathbf{A}_y|$$

The signs of the x- and y-components are determined by the quadrants in which the vector in standard position lies.

In general:

To find the x- and y-components of a vector $\mathbf{A}$ given in standard position:

1. Complete the right triangle with the legs being the x- and y-components of the vector.
2. Find the lengths of the legs of the right triangle as follows:

$$|\mathbf{A}_x| = |\mathbf{A}|(\cos \alpha)$$
$$|\mathbf{A}_y| = |\mathbf{A}|(\sin \alpha)$$

where angle α is the acute angle between vector $\mathbf{A}$ in standard position and the x-axis.
3. Determine the signs of the x- and y-components.

Find the x- and y-components of the vector $\mathbf{C} = 27.0$ ft at $125.0°$.

EXAMPLE 6

First, draw the vector in standard position [Fig. 3.21(a)]. Then, complete a right triangle with the x- and y-components being the two legs [Fig. 3.21(b)]. Find angle α as follows:

$$\alpha + 125.0° = 180°$$
$$\alpha = 55.0°$$

Figure 3.21

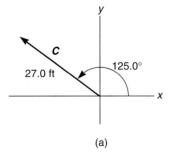

(a)

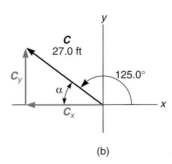

(b)

Next, find the x-component as follows:

$$|\mathbf{C}_x| = |\mathbf{C}|(\cos \alpha)$$
$$|\mathbf{C}_x| = (27.0 \text{ ft})(\cos 55.0°)$$
$$= 15.5 \text{ ft}$$

Since the x-component is pointing in the negative x-direction,

$$\mathbf{C}_x = -15.5 \text{ ft}$$

Then, find the y-component as follows:

$$|\mathbf{C}_y| = |\mathbf{C}|(\sin \alpha)$$
$$|\mathbf{C}_y| = (27.0 \text{ ft})(\sin 55.0°)$$
$$= 22.1 \text{ ft}$$

Since the y-component is pointing in the positive y-direction,

$$\mathbf{C}_y = +22.1 \text{ ft}$$

PROBLEMS 3.2

Find the x- and y-components of each vector in the following diagram. (Express them as signed numbers and then graph them as vectors.)

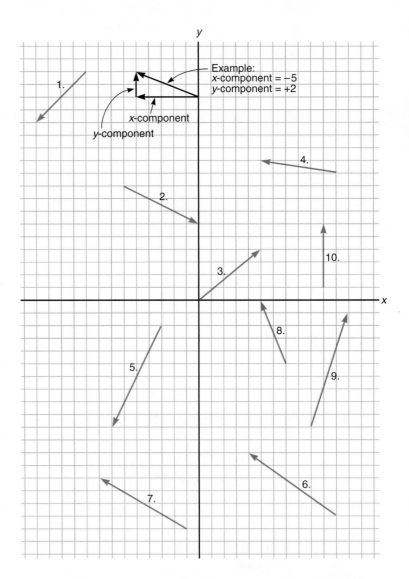

Make a sketch of each vector in standard position. Use the scale 1.0 cm = $1\overline{0}$ m.

11. **A** = $2\overline{0}$ m at 25°   12. **B** = 25 m at 125°
13. **C** = 25 m at 245°   14. **D** = $2\overline{0}$ m at 345°
15. **E** = 15 m at 105°   16. **F** = 35 m at 291°
17. **G** = $3\overline{0}$ m at 405°   18. **H** = 25 m at 525°

Find the *x*- and *y*-components of each vector.

19.
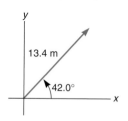

20.
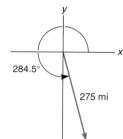

21.
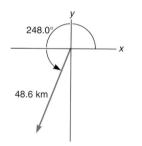

22.
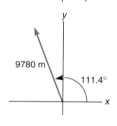

23.
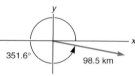

24.
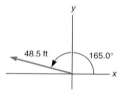

Find the *x*- and *y*-components of each vector given in standard position.

25. **A** = 38.9 m at 10.5°   26. **B** = 478 ft at 195.0°
27. **C** = 9.60 km at 310.0°   28. **D** = 5430 mi at 153.7°
29. **E** = 29.5 m at 101.5°   30. **F** = 154 mi at 273.2°

3.3 Addition of Vectors

Any given displacement can be the result of many different combinations of displacements. In Fig. 3.22, the displacement represented by the arrow labeled **R** for resultant is the result of either of the two paths shown. The resultant vector, **R**, is the sum of the vectors **A**, **B**, **C**, and **D**. It is also the sum of vectors **E** and **F**. That is,

$$\mathbf{A} + \mathbf{B} + \mathbf{C} + \mathbf{D} = \mathbf{R} \quad \text{and} \quad \mathbf{E} + \mathbf{F} = \mathbf{R}$$

Figure 3.22

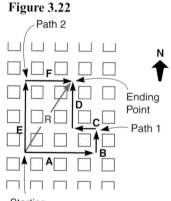

The resultant vector **R** is the graphic sum of the component sets of vectors **A**, **B**, **C**, and **D**, and **E** and **F**. That is, **A** + **B** + **C** + **D** = **R** and **E** + **F** = **R**.

To solve a vector addition problem graphically such as displacement:

1. Choose a suitable scale and calculate the length of each vector.
2. Draw the north–south reference line. Graph paper should be used.
3. Using a ruler and protractor, draw the first vector and then draw the other vectors so that the initial end of each vector is placed at the terminal end of the previous vector.
4. Draw the resultant vector from the initial end of the first vector to the terminal end of the last vector.
5. Measure the length of the resultant and use the scale to find the magnitude of the vector. Use a protractor to measure the angle of the resultant.

EXAMPLE 1

Find the resultant displacement of an airplane that flies $2\bar{0}$ mi due east, then $3\bar{0}$ mi due north, and then $1\bar{0}$ mi at $6\bar{0}°$ west of south.

We choose a scale of 1.0 cm = 5.0 mi so that the vectors are large enough to be accurate and small enough to fit on the paper. (Here each block represents 0.5 cm.) The length of the first vector is

$$|\mathbf{A}| = 2\bar{0} \text{ mi} \times \frac{1.0 \text{ cm}}{5.0 \text{ mi}} = 4.0 \text{ cm}$$

The length of the second vector is

$$|\mathbf{B}| = 3\bar{0} \text{ mi} \times \frac{1.0 \text{ cm}}{5.0 \text{ mi}} = 6.0 \text{ cm}$$

The length of the third vector is

$$|\mathbf{C}| = 1\bar{0} \text{ mi} \times \frac{1.0 \text{ cm}}{5.0 \text{ mi}} = 2.0 \text{ cm}$$

Draw the north–south reference line, and draw the first vector as shown in Fig. 3.23(a). The second and third vectors are then drawn as shown in Fig. 3.23(b) and 3.23(c).

Using a ruler, we find that the length of the resultant vector measures 5.5 cm [Fig. 3.23(d)]. Since 1.0 cm = 5.0 mi, this represents a displacement with magnitude

$$|\mathbf{R}| = 5.5 \text{ cm} \times \frac{5.0 \text{ mi}}{1.0 \text{ cm}} = 28 \text{ mi}$$

The angle between vector **R** and north measures 24°, so the resultant is 28 mi at 24° east of north.

Figure 3.23

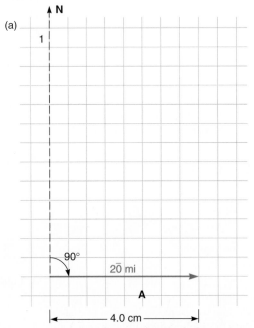

1. Draw the north–south reference line and the first vector: $2\bar{0}$ mi due east.

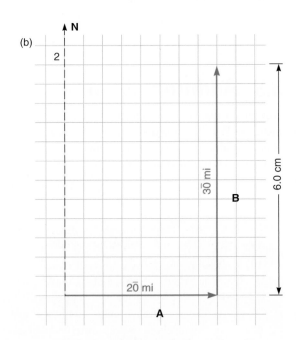

2. Draw the second vector: $3\bar{0}$ mi due north.

Figure 3.23 *(Continued)*

(c)

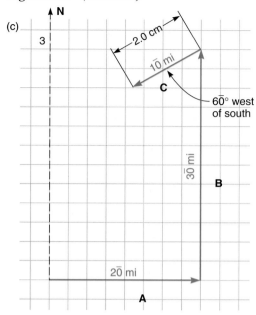

3. Draw the third vector: $1\bar{0}$ mi at $6\bar{0}°$ west of south.

(d)

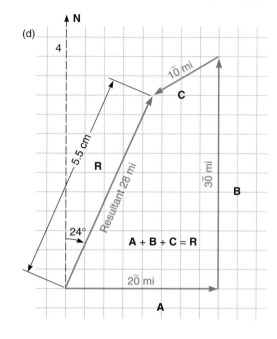

4. Draw the resultant vector, which is 28 mi at 24° east of north.

Scale: 1.0 cm = 5.0 mi

. . . .

Find the resultant of the displacements $15\bar{0}$ km due west, then $20\bar{0}$ km due east, and then 125 km due south.

> **EXAMPLE 2**

Choose a scale of 1.0 cm = $5\bar{0}$ km. The length of the first vector is

$$|\mathbf{A}| = 15\bar{0} \text{ km} \times \frac{1.0 \text{ cm}}{5\bar{0} \text{ km}} = 3.0 \text{ cm}$$

The length of the second vector is

$$|\mathbf{B}| = 20\bar{0} \text{ km} \times \frac{1.0 \text{ cm}}{5\bar{0} \text{ km}} = 4.0 \text{ cm}$$

The length of the third vector is

$$|\mathbf{C}| = 125 \text{ km} \times \frac{1.0 \text{ cm}}{5\bar{0} \text{ km}} = 2.5 \text{ cm}$$

Draw the north–south reference line, and draw the first vector as shown in Fig. 3.24(a). Then, draw the second and third vectors as shown in Fig. 3.24(b) and 3.24(c).

The length of the resultant vector measures 2.6 cm in Fig. 3.24(d). Since 1.0 cm = $5\bar{0}$ km,

$$|\mathbf{R}| = 2.6 \text{ cm} \times \frac{5\bar{0} \text{ km}}{1.0 \text{ cm}} = 130 \text{ km}$$

The angle between vector **R** and south measures 22°, so the resultant vector is 130 km at 22° east of south.

Figure 3.24

(a)

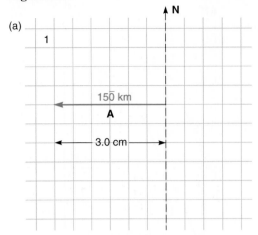

1. Draw the north–south reference line and the first vector: 15ō km due west.

(b)

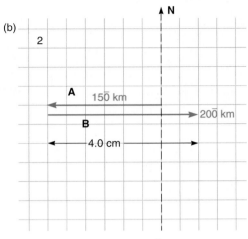

2. Draw the vector: 20ō km due east.

(c)

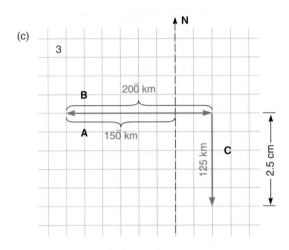

3. Draw the vector: 125 mi due south.

(d)

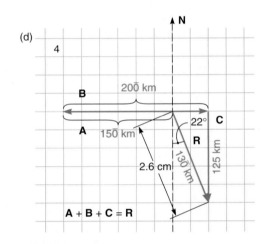

4. The length of the resultant is 2.6 cm, which represents 13ō km at 22° east of south.

Scale: 1.0 cm = 5ō km

· · · · · · · · · · · · · · · · · ·

Expressing the x- and y-components as signed numbers, we find the resultant vector of several vectors as follows:

1. Find the x-component of each vector and then find the sum of these x-components. This sum is the x-component of the resultant vector.
2. Find the y-component of each vector and then find the sum of these y-components. This sum is the y-component of the resultant vector.

EXAMPLE 3

Given vectors **A** and **B** in Fig. 3.25, graph and find the x- and y-components of the resultant vector **R**.

Graph resultant vector **R** by connecting the initial point of vector **A** to the end point of vector **B** [Fig. 3.26(a)]. The resultant vector **R** is shown in Fig. 3.26(b).

Find the x-component of **R** by finding and adding the x-components of **A** and **B**.

$$\mathbf{A}_x = +3$$
$$\mathbf{B}_x = \underline{+2}$$
$$\mathbf{R}_x = +5$$

Figure 3.25

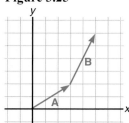

Figure 3.26

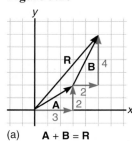

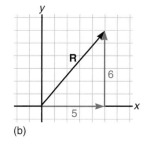

(a)   A + B = R   (b)

Find the *y*-component of **R** by finding and adding the *y*-components of **A** and **B**.

$$A_y = +2$$
$$B_y = +4$$
$$R_y = +6$$

Given vectors **A**, **B**, and **C** in Fig. 3.27, graph and find the *x*- and *y*-components of the resultant vector **R**.

Graph resultant vector **R** by connecting the initial point of vector **A** to the end point of vector **C** [Fig. 3.28(a)]. The resultant vector **R** is shown in Fig. 3.28(b).

EXAMPLE 4

Figure 3.27

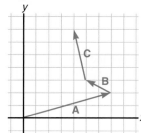

Figure 3.28

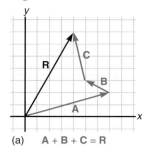

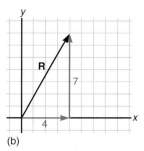

(a)   A + B + C = R   (b)

Find the *x*-component of **R** by finding and adding the *x*-components of **A**, **B**, and **C** as shown below. Find the *y*-component of **R** by finding and adding the *y*-components of **A**, **B**, and **C**.

Vector	*x*-component	*y*-component
A	+7	+2
B	−2	+1
C	−1	+4
R	+4	+7

Given vectors **A**, **B**, **C**, and **D** in Fig. 3.29, graph and find the *x*- and *y*-components of the resultant vector **R**.

Graph resultant vector **R** by connecting the initial point of vector **A** to the end point of vector **D** [Fig. 3.30(a)]. The resultant vector **R** is shown in Fig. 3.30(b).

EXAMPLE 5

Figure 3.29

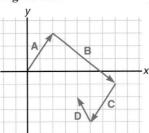

Figure 3.30

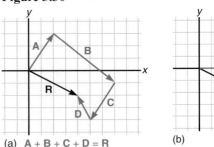

(a) A + B + C + D = R

(b)

Find the *x*-component of **R** by finding and adding the *x*-components of **A**, **B**, **C**, and **D** as shown below. Find the *y*-component of **R** by finding and adding the *y*-components of **A**, **B**, **C**, and **D**.

Vector	*x*-component	*y*-component
A	+2	+3
B	+5	−4
C	−2	−3
D	−1	+2
R	+4	−2

Two vectors are equal when they have the same magnitude and the same direction [Fig. 3.31(a)]. *Two vectors are opposites or negatives* of each other when they have the same magnitude but opposite directions [Fig. 3.31(b)].

Figure 3.31

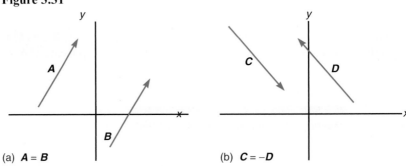

(a) **A** = **B**

(b) **C** = −**D**

To add two or more vectors in any position graphically, construct the first vector with its initial point at the origin and parallel to its given position. Then, construct the second vector with its initial point on the end point of the first vector and parallel to its given position. Then, construct the third vector with its initial point on the end point of the second vector and parallel to its given position. Continue this process until all vectors have been so constructed. The resultant vector is the vector joining the initial point of the first vector (origin) to the end point of the last vector. (The order of adding or constructing the given vectors does not matter.)

Given vectors **A**, **B**, and **C** in Fig. 3.32(a), graph and find the *x*- and *y*-components of the resultant vector **R**.

EXAMPLE 6

Figure 3.32

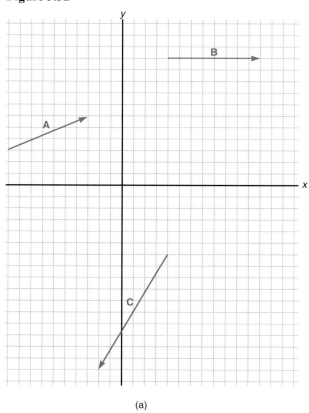

(a)

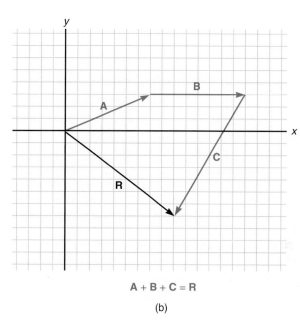

A + B + C = R

(b)

Construct vector **A** with its initial point at the origin and parallel to its given position as in Fig. 3.32(b). Next, construct vector **B** with its initial point on the end point of vector **A** and parallel to its given position. Then, construct vector **C** with its initial point on the end point of vector **B** and parallel to its given position. The resultant vector **R** is the vector with its initial point at the origin and its end point at the end point of vector **C**.

From the graph in Fig. 3.32(b), we read the *x*-component of **R** as +9 by counting the number of squares *to the right* between the *y*-axis and the end point of vector **R**. We read the *y*-component of **R** as −7 by counting the number of squares *below* between the *x*-axis and the end point of vector **R**.

Figure 3.33
$$R = v - w = v + (-w)$$

One vector may be subtracted from a second vector by adding its negative to the first. That is, $v - w = v + (-w)$. Construct **v** as usual. Then construct −**w** and find the resultant **R** as shown in Fig. 3.33.

Finding a Vector from Its Components

Find vector **R** in standard position with $R_x = +3.00$ m and $R_y = +4.00$ m.

EXAMPLE 7

First, graph the *x*- and *y*-components (Fig. 3.34) and complete the right triangle. The hypotenuse is the resultant vector. Find angle α as follows:

$$\tan \alpha = \frac{\text{side opposite } \alpha}{\text{side adjacent to } \alpha}$$

$$\tan \alpha = \frac{4.00 \text{ m}}{3.00 \text{ m}} = 1.333$$

$$\alpha = 53.1° \qquad \text{(see Appendix B, Section B.3)}$$

Figure 3.34

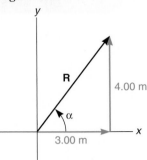

Find the magnitude of **R** using the Pythagorean theorem:

$$|\mathbf{R}| = \sqrt{|\mathbf{R}_x|^2 + |\mathbf{R}_y|^2}$$
$$|\mathbf{R}| = \sqrt{(3.00 \text{ m})^2 + (4.00 \text{ m})^2}$$
$$= 5.00 \text{ m}$$

That is, **R** = 5.00 m at 53.1°.

· · · · · · · · · · · · · · · · · ·

In general:

To find resultant vector **R** in standard position when its x- and y-components are given:

1. Complete the right triangle with the legs being the x- and y-components of the vector.
2. Find the acute angle α of the right triangle whose vertex is at the origin by using tan α.
3. Find angle θ in standard position as follows:

$$\theta = \alpha \qquad (\theta \text{ in first quadrant})$$
$$\theta = 180° - \alpha \qquad (\theta \text{ in second quadrant})$$
$$\theta = 180° + \alpha \qquad (\theta \text{ in third quadrant})$$
$$\theta = 360° - \alpha \qquad (\theta \text{ in fourth quadrant})$$

The Greek letter θ (theta) is often used to represent the measure of an angle.

4. Find the magnitude of the vector using the Pythagorean theorem:

$$\mathbf{R} = \sqrt{|\mathbf{R}_x|^2 + |\mathbf{R}_y|^2}$$

EXAMPLE 8

Figure 3.35

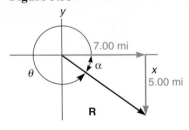

Find vector **R** in standard position whose x-component is +7.00 mi and y-component is −5.00 mi.

First, graph the x- and y-components (Fig. 3.35) and complete the right triangle. The hypotenuse is the resultant vector. Find angle α as follows:

$$\tan \alpha = \frac{\text{side opposite } \alpha}{\text{side adjacent to } \alpha}$$

$$\tan \alpha = \frac{5.00 \text{ mi}}{7.00 \text{ mi}} = 0.7143$$

$$\alpha = 35.5°$$

Then

$$\theta = 360° - \alpha \qquad \mathbf{R} \text{ is in the fourth quadrant.}$$
$$= 360° - 35.5°$$
$$= 324.5°$$

Find the magnitude of **R** using the Pythagorean theorem:

$$|\mathbf{R}| = \sqrt{|\mathbf{R}_x|^2 + |\mathbf{R}_y|^2}$$
$$|\mathbf{R}| = \sqrt{|7.00 \text{ mi}|^2 + |-5.00 \text{ mi}|^2}$$
$$= 8.60 \text{ mi}$$

That is, **R** = 8.60 mi at 324.5°.

· · · · · · · · · · · · · · · · · ·

Find vector **R** in standard position with $\mathbf{R}_x = -115$ km and $\mathbf{R}_y = +175$ km.

First, graph the x- and y-components (Fig. 3.36) and complete the right triangle. The hypotenuse is the resultant vector. Find angle α as follows:

EXAMPLE 9

$$\tan \alpha = \frac{\text{side opposite } \alpha}{\text{side adjacent to } \alpha}$$

$$\tan \alpha = \frac{175 \text{ km}}{115 \text{ km}} = 1.522$$

$$\alpha = 56.7°$$

Figure 3.36

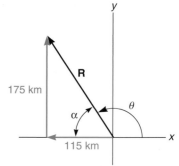

Then

$$\theta = 180° - \alpha \qquad \text{**R** is in the second quadrant.}$$
$$= 180° - 56.7°$$
$$= 123.3°$$

Find the magnitude of **R** using the Pythagorean theorem:

$$|\mathbf{R}| = \sqrt{|\mathbf{R}_x|^2 + |\mathbf{R}_y|^2}$$
$$|\mathbf{R}| = \sqrt{|-115 \text{ km}|^2 + |175 \text{ km}|^2}$$
$$= 209 \text{ km}$$

That is, **R** = 209 km at 123.3°.

To find the resultant vector **R** of any set of vectors, such as **R** = **A** + **B** + **C**, using right-triangle trigonometry:

1. Find the x-component of each vector and add: $\mathbf{R}_x = \mathbf{A}_x + \mathbf{B}_x + \mathbf{C}_x$.
2. Find the y-component of each vector and add: $\mathbf{R}_y = \mathbf{A}_y + \mathbf{B}_y + \mathbf{C}_y$.
3. Find the magnitude of the resultant vector **R** using the Pythagorean theorem $|\mathbf{R}| = \sqrt{|\mathbf{R}_x|^2 + |\mathbf{R}_y|^2}$.
4. Find the direction of the resultant vector **R** using right-triangle trigonometry by (a) first finding the acute α between the resultant vector and the x-axis and then finding angle θ in standard position or (b) expressing the direction of the resultant vector using some other reference.

A ship travels 105 km from port on a course of 55.0° west of north to an island. Then it travels 124 km due west to a second island. Then it travels 177 km on a course of 24.0° east of south to a third island. Find the displacement from the starting point to the ending point.

First, draw a vector diagram as in Fig. 3.37. Then, find the x- and y-components of each of the three vectors as follows:

EXAMPLE 10

Figure 3.37

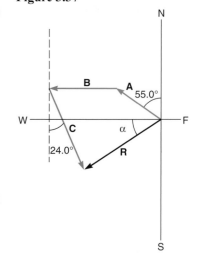

$|\mathbf{A}_x| = |\mathbf{A}| \cos 35.0°$ — The acute angle between vector **A** and the x-axis is $90° - 55.0° = 35.0°$.

$= (105 \text{ km})(\cos 35.0°)$
$= -86.0 \text{ km}$ — The x-component is in the negative x-direction.

$|\mathbf{A}_y| = |\mathbf{A}| \sin 35.0°$
$= (105 \text{ km})(\sin 35.0°)$
$= 60.2 \text{ km}$ — The y-component is in the positive y-direction.

$|\mathbf{B}_x| = |\mathbf{B}| = -124 \text{ km}$ — This x-component is in the negative x-direction.
$|\mathbf{B}_y| = |\mathbf{B}| = 0 \text{ km}$ — This y-component of due west is 0.

$|\mathbf{C}_x| = |\mathbf{C}| \cos 66.0°$ — The acute angle between vector **C** in standard position and the x-axis is $90° - 24.0° = 66.0°$.

$= (177 \text{ km})(\cos 66.0°)$
$= 72.0 \text{ km}$ — The x-component is in the positive x-direction.

$$|C_y| = |C| \sin 66.0°$$
$$= (177 \text{ km})(\sin 66.0°)$$
$$= -162 \text{ km} \qquad \text{The } y\text{-component is in the negative } y\text{-direction.}$$

Thus

$$R_x = A_x + B_x + C_x = -86.0 \text{ km} + (-124 \text{ km}) + 72.0 \text{ km} = -138 \text{ km}$$
$$R_y = A_y + B_y + C_y = 60.2 \text{ km} + 0 + (-162 \text{ km}) = -102 \text{ km}$$
$$|R| = \sqrt{|R_x|^2 + |R_y|^2}$$
$$= \sqrt{|-138 \text{ km}|^2 + |-102 \text{ km}|^2}$$
$$= 172 \text{ km}$$

$$\tan \alpha = \frac{102 \text{ km}}{138 \text{ km}} = 0.7391$$
$$\alpha = 36.5°$$

So, the displacement is 172 km at 36.5° south of west. That is, the ship stops at a port that is 172 km at 36.5° south of west from its starting point.

. . . .

PROBLEMS 3.3

Use graph paper to find the resultant of each displacement pair.

1. 35 km due east, then $5\bar{0}$ km due north
2. $6\bar{0}$ km due west, then $9\bar{0}$ km due south
3. $5\bar{0}0$ mi at 75° east of north, then $15\bar{0}0$ mi at $2\bar{0}°$ west of south
4. $2\bar{0}$ mi at 3° north of east, then 17 mi at 9° west of south
5. 67 km at 55° north of west, then 46 km at 25° south of east
6. 4.0 km at 25° west of south, then 2.0 km at 15° north of east

Use graph paper to find the resultant of each set of displacements.

7. $6\bar{0}$ km due south, then $9\bar{0}$ km at 15° north of west, and then 75 km at 45° north of east
8. 110 km at $5\bar{0}°$ north of east, then 170 km at $3\bar{0}°$ east of south, and then 145 km at $2\bar{0}°$ north of east
9. 1700 mi due north, then 2400 mi at $1\bar{0}°$ north of east, and then $20\bar{0}0$ mi at $2\bar{0}°$ south of west
10. $9\bar{0}$ mi at $1\bar{0}°$ west of north, then 75 mi at $3\bar{0}°$ west of south, and then 55 mi at $2\bar{0}°$ east of south
11. 75 km at 25° north of east, then 75 km at 65° south of west, and then 75 km due south
12. 17 km due north, then $1\bar{0}$ km at 7° south of east, and then 15 km at $1\bar{0}°$ west of south
13. 12 mi at 58° north of east, then 16 mi at 78° north of east, then $1\bar{0}$ mi at 45° north of east, and then 14 mi at $1\bar{0}°$ north of east
14. $1\bar{0}$ km at 15° west of south, then 27 km at 35° north of east, then 31 km at 5° north of east, and then 22 km at $2\bar{0}°$ west of north

Find the x- and y-components of each resultant vector **R** and graph the resultant vector **R**.

	Vector	x-component	y-component		Vector	x-component	y-component
15.	A	+2	+3	16.	A	+9	−5
	B	+7	+2		B	−4	−6
	R				R		
17.	A	−2	+13	18.	A	+10	−5
	B	−11	+1		B	−13	−9
	C	+3	−4		C	+4	+3
	R				R		

19.				20.			
	A	+17	+7		A	+1	+7
	B	−14	+11		B	+9	−4
	C	+7	+9		C	−4	+13
	D	−6	−15		D	−11	−4
	R				R		
21.	A	+1.5	−1.5	22.	A	+1	−1
	B	−3	−2		B	−4	−2
	C	+7.5	−3		C	+2	+4
	D	+2	+2.5		D	+5	−3
	R				E	+3	+5
					R		
23.	A	+1.5	+2.5	24.	A	−7	+15
	B	−2	−3		B	+13.5	−17.5
	C	+3.5	−7.5		C	−7.5	−20
	D	−4	+6		D	+6	+13.5
	E	−5.5	+2		E	+2.5	+2.5
	R				F	−11	+11.5
					R		

For each set of vectors, graph and find the *x*- and *y*-components of the resultant vector **R**.

25.

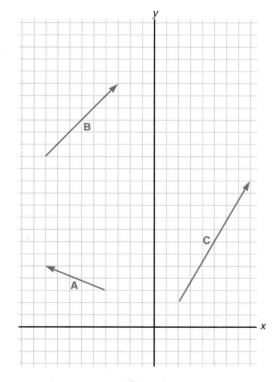

26.

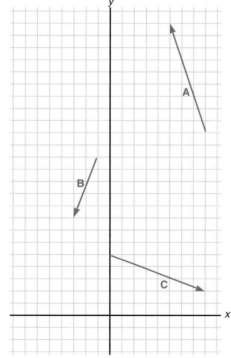

27.

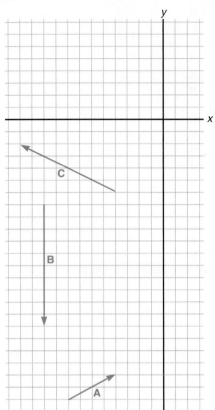

28.

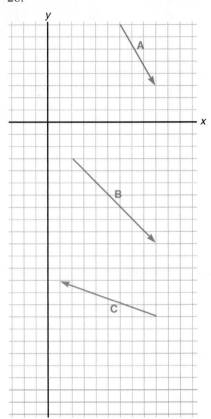

29.

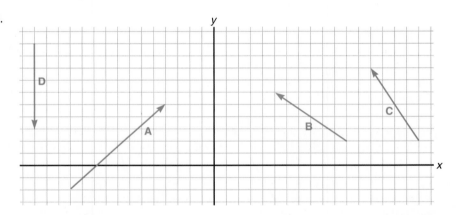

30.

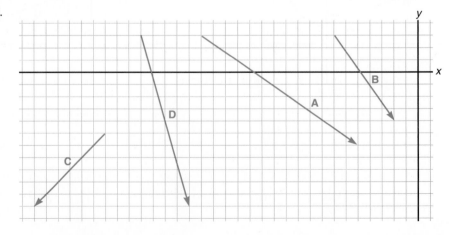

In Problems 31 through 42, find each resultant vector **R**. Give **R** in standard position.

31.
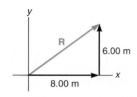

32.
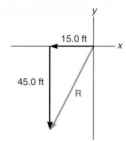

33.
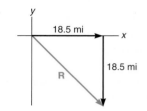

34.
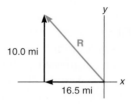

35.
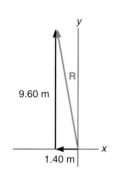

36.
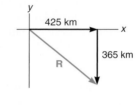

	x-component	y-component		x-component	y-component
37.	+19.5 m	−49.6 m	38.	−158 km	+236 km
39.	+14.7 mi	+16.8 mi	40.	−3240 ft	−1890 ft
41.	−9.65 m	+4.36 m	42.	+375 km	−408 km

43. A road grader must go around a pond by traveling $10\overline{0}$ m south and then $15\overline{0}$ m east. If the road grader could go directly from the beginning point to the end point, how far would it travel?

44. An earthmover must go north $35\overline{0}$ m and then west 275 m to avoid a pipeline hazard. What distance would it travel if it could go directly to the endpoint?

45. An airplane takes off and flies 225 km on a course of 25.0° north of west and then changes direction and flies 135 km due north where it lands. Find the displacement from its starting point to its landing point.

46. A ship travels 50.0 mi on a course of 15.0° south of east and then travels 85.5 mi on a course of 60.0° west of south. Find the displacement from its starting point to its ending point.

47. A ship travels 135 km from port on a course of 25.0° south of east to an island. It then travels 122 km on a course of 35.5° west of south to a second island. Then it travels 135 km on a course of 10.4° north of west to a third island. Find the displacement from its starting point to its ending point.

48. A ship travels 145 km from port on a course of 65.0° north of east to an island. It then travels 112 km on a course of 30.5° west of north to a second island. Then it travels 182 km on a course of 10.4° west of south to a third island. Then it travels 42.5 km due south to a fourth island. Find the displacement from its starting point to its ending point.

PHYSICS CONNECTIONS

Global Positioning Satellites

Navigators continually struggle to find better tools to help them determine their location. The first explorers used the sun and stars to help them steer a straight course, but this method of navigation only worked under clear skies. Magnetic compasses were developed, yet could only be used to determine longitude, not latitude. Finally, the mechanical clock, in conjunction with the compass, provided navigators with the most accurate method of determining location. Today, most navigators use a hand-held device that functions in concert with a series of 24 orbiting satellites. This network, the Global Positioning System (GPS), can determine your position and altitude anywhere on earth.

The GPS pinpoints your location by sending out radio signals to locate any 4 of the 24 orbiting GPS satellites. Once the satellites are found, the GPS measures the length of time it takes for a radio signal to reach the hand-held receiver. When the time is determined for each of 4 satellites, the distance is calculated, and the longitude, latitude, and altitude are displayed on the screen [Fig. 3.38(a)].

GPS was first developed solely for military use. Eventually, the GPS system was made available for civilian businesses. Shipping, airline, farming, surveying, and geological companies made use of the technology. Today, GPS receivers are affordable and are used by the general public [Fig. 3.38(b)]. More sophisticated receivers not only locate a position, but can also guide the navigator to a predetermined location. Several automobile manufacturers have included GPS receivers as an option in their cars. Such receivers come complete with voice commands such as, "Turn left at the next traffic light," as part of their option packages.

Figure 3.38 (a) The screen on the GPS receiver shows the position and strength of the signal between the receiver and the various satellites. At the time this photograph was taken, the receiver picked up 7 of the 12 overhead satellites, bringing the precision to within 20 ft of the actual location. (Photo by William Brouhle.) (b) Global Positioning Systems have allowed for an enormous step forward in navigation. The GPS receiver shown has monitored and recorded precisely where the person has traveled and is now helping the user find his way back to camp.

(a)   (b)

Glossary

Component Vector When two or more vectors are added, each of the vectors is called a component of the resultant, or sum, vector. (p. 73)

Displacement The net change in position of an object, or the direct distance and direction it moves; a vector. (p. 69)

Number Plane A plane determined by the horizontal line called the x-axis and a vertical line called the y-axis intersecting at a right angle at a point called the origin. These two lines divide the number plane into four quadrants. The x-axis contains positive numbers to the right of the origin and negative numbers to the left of the origin. The y-axis contains positive numbers above the origin and negative numbers below the origin. (p. 72)

Resultant Vector The sum of two or more vectors. (p. 73)

Scalar A physical quantity that can be completely described by a number (called its magnitude) and a unit. (p. 69)

Standard Position A vector is in standard position when its initial point is at the origin of the number plane. The vector is expressed in terms of its length and its angle θ, where θ is measured counterclockwise from the positive x-axis to the vector. (p. 74)

Vector A physical quantity that requires both magnitude (size) and direction to be completely described. (p. 69)

***x*-component** The horizontal component of a vector that lies along the x-axis. (p. 73)

***y*-component** The vertical component of a vector that lies along the y-axis. (p. 73)

Formulas

3.2   To find the x- and y-components of a vector **v** given in standard position (Fig. 3.39):
1. Complete the right triangle with the legs being the x- and y-components of the vector.
2. Find the lengths of the legs of the right triangle as follows:

$$|\mathbf{A}_x| = |\mathbf{A}|(\cos \alpha)$$
$$|\mathbf{A}_y| = |\mathbf{A}|(\sin \alpha)$$

3. Determine the signs of the x- and y- components.

Figure 3.39

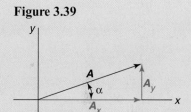

3.3   To find resultant vector **R** in standard position when its x- and y-components are given:
1. Complete the right triangle with the legs being the x- and y-components of the vector.
2. Find the acute angle α of the right triangle whose vertex is at the origin by using $\tan \alpha$.
3. Find angle θ in standard position as follows:

$$\theta = \alpha \qquad (\theta \text{ in first quadrant})$$
$$\theta = 180° - \alpha \qquad (\theta \text{ in second quadrant})$$
$$\theta = 180° + \alpha \qquad (\theta \text{ in third quadrant})$$
$$\theta = 360° - \alpha \qquad (\theta \text{ in fourth quadrant})$$

4. Find the magnitude of the vector using the Pythagorean theorem:

$$\mathbf{R} = \sqrt{|\mathbf{R}_x|^2 + |\mathbf{R}_y|^2}$$

To find the resultant vector **R** of any set of vectors, such as **R** = **A** + **B** + **C**, using right-triangle trigonometry:

1. Find the x-component of each vector and add: $\mathbf{R}_x = \mathbf{A}_x + \mathbf{B}_x + \mathbf{C}_x$.
2. Find the y-component of each vector and add: $\mathbf{R}_y = \mathbf{A}_y + \mathbf{B}_y + \mathbf{C}_y$.
3. Find the magnitude of the resultant vector **R** using the Pythagorean theorem
$$|\mathbf{R}| = \sqrt{|\mathbf{R}_x|^2 + |\mathbf{R}_y|^2}.$$

4. Find the direction of the resultant vector **R** using right-triangle trigonometry by (a) first finding the acute angle α between the resultant vector and the x-axis and then finding angle θ in standard position or (b) expressing the direction of the resultant vector using some other reference.

Review Questions

1. Displacement
   (a) can be interchanged with direction.
   (b) is a measurement of volume.
   (c) can be described only with a number.
   (d) is the net distance an object travels, showing direction and distance.
2. When adding vectors, the order in which they are added
   (a) is not important.
   (b) is important.
   (c) is important only in certain cases.
3. A vector is in standard position when its initial point is
   (a) at the origin.
   (b) along the x-axis.
   (c) along the y-axis.
4. Discuss number plane, origin, and axis in your own words.
5. Can every vector be described in terms of its components?
6. Can a vector have more than one set of component vectors?
7. Describe how to add two or more vectors graphically.
8. Describe how to find a resultant vector if given its x- and y-components.
9. Is a vector limited to a single position in the number plane?
10. Is the angle of a vector in standard position measured clockwise or counterclockwise?
11. What are the limits on the angle measure of a vector in standard position in the third quadrant?
12. Describe how to find the x- and y-components of a vector given in standard position.
13. Describe how to find a vector in standard position when the x- and y-components are given.

Review Problems

1. Find the x- and y-components of vector **R** which has a length of 13.0 cm at 30.0°.
2. Find the x- and y-components of vector **R**, which has a length of 10.0 cm at 60.0°.
3. Find the x- and y-components of vector **R**, which has a length of 20.0 cm at 30.0°.
4. Vector **R** has length 9.00 cm at 240.0°. Find its x- and y-components.
5. Vector **R** has length 9.00 cm at 40.0°. Find its x- and y-components.

6.   Vector **R** has length 18.0 cm at 305.0°. Find its x- and y-components.

7.   A hiker is plotting his course on a map with a scale of 1.00 cm = 3.00 km. If the hiker walks 2.50 cm north, then turns south and walks 1.50 cm, what is the actual displacement of the hiker in km?

8.   A hiker is plotting his course on a map with a scale of 1.00 cm = 3.00 km. If the hiker walks 1.50 cm north, then turns south and walks 2.50 cm, what is the actual displacement of the hiker in km?

9.   A co-pilot is charting her course on a map with a scale of 1.00 cm = 20.0 km. If the plane is charted to head 13.0 cm west, 9.00 cm north, and 2.00 cm east, what is the actual displacement of the plane in km?

10.   A co-pilot is charting her course on a map with a scale of 1.00 cm = 20.0 km. If the plane is charted to head 25.0° north of east for 16.0 cm, north for 6.00 cm, and west for 5.00 cm, what is the actual displacement of the plane in km?

11.   Vector **R** has x-component = +14.0 and y-component = +3.00. Find its length.

12.   Vector **R** has x-component = −5.00 and y-component = +10.0. Find its length.

13.   Vector **R** has x-component = +8.00 and y-component = −2.00. Find its length.

14.   Vector **R** has x-component = −3.00 and y-component = −4.00. Find its length.

15.   Vectors **A**, **B**, and **C** are given. Vector **A** has x-component = +3.00 and y-component = +4.00. Vector **B** has x-component = +5.00 and y-component = −7.00. Vector **C** has x-component = −2.00 and y-component = +1.00. Find the resultant vector **R**.

16.   Vectors **A**, **B**, and **C** are given. Vector **A** has x-component = +5.00 and y-component = +7.00. Vector **B** has x-component = +9.00 and y-component = −3.00. Vector **C** has x-component = −5.00 and y-component = +5.00. Find the x- and y-components of the resultant vector **R**.

17.   Vectors **A**, **B**, and **C** are given. Vector **A** has x-component = −3.00 and y-component = −4.00. Vector **B** has x-component = −5.00 and y-component = +7.00. Vector **C** has x-component = +2.00 and y-component = −1.00. Find the x- and y-components of the resultant vector **R**.

18.   Vectors **A**, **B**, and **C** are given. Vector **A** has x-component = −5.00 and y-component = −7.00. Vector **B** has x-component = −9.00 and y-component = +3.00. Vector **C** has x-component = +5.00 and y-component = −5.00. Find the x- and y-components of the resultant vector **R**.

Graph and find the x- and y-components of each resultant vector **R**, where **R** = **A** + **B** + **C** + **D**.

19.

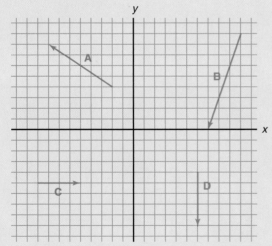

20.

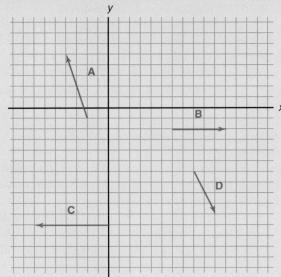

21. An airplane takes off and flies 245 km on a course of 45.0° south of west and then changes direction and flies 175 km due south, where it lands. Find the displacement from its starting point to its landing point.

22. A ship travels 155 km from port on a course of 35.0° south of west to an island. It then travels 142 km on a course of 55.5° east of south to a second island. Then it travels 138 km on a course of 9.4° north of east to a third island. Then it travels 185 km due east to a fourth island. Find the displacement from its starting point to its ending point.

APPLIED CONCEPTS

1. The New Clark Bridge is an elegant cable-stayed bridge. Its design requires cables to reach from the road deck up to the tower and back down to the road deck on the other side of the tower as shown in Fig. 3.40. In order to determine the best method for shipping the cables, the shipping company needs to know the lengths of the shortest and longest cables. Given the measurements in the diagram, determine the indicated total lengths BEC and AED, respectively.

    Figure 3.40

    Tower's height above the road deck = 176 ft

    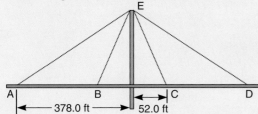

2. Frank just learned that the $80\overline{0}$-m section of Broadway that he uses to get to work will be closed for several days. Given the information from a map of Manhattan (Fig. 3.41), what is the distance of Frank's next shortest route?

    Figure 3.41

    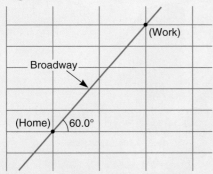

3. Power cables need to be suspended by the power company across a river to a new condominium development. Find the distance across the river in Fig. 3.42.

    Figure 3.42

    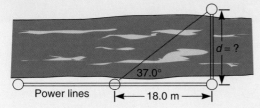

4. Bill has set his GPS to track his route. At the conclusion of his hike, the receiver indicates that he walked 3.50 mi north, 1.00 mi northeast, and 1.50 mi south. How far away is Bill from his original position?

5. With the airplane cruising at $30,\overline{0}00$ ft, the navigator indicates to the captain that the plane should continue traveling north for $50\overline{0}$ km and then turn to a heading of 45.0° east of north for $20\overline{0}$ km. What will be the resultant distance traveled?

CHAPTER 4

MOTION

Air Resistance

Acceleration
g =9.80m/s²

Motion is a change of position. Velocity and acceleration describe important kinds of motion. An analysis of motion helps introduce the real nature of physics—to understand the nature and behavior of the physical world.

Objectives

The major goals of this chapter are to enable you to:

1. Distinguish between speed and velocity.
2. Use vectors to illustrate and solve velocity problems.
3. Distinguish between velocity and acceleration.
4. Utilize vectors to illustrate and solve acceleration problems.
5. Analyze the motion of an object in free fall.
6. Solve two-dimensional motion problems.
7. Calculate the range of projectile motion.

4.1 Speed Versus Velocity

This chapter begins our study of mechanics, the study of motion. **Motion** can be defined as an object's change in position. How quickly the object changes its position is called its speed.

The ability to analyze and determine the speed of an object is important in many areas of science and technology. Automotive engineers are concerned not only with the motion of the entire vehicle, but also with the motion of the pistons, valves, driveshaft, and so on. The particular speeds of all the internal parts have a direct and very important effect on the motion of the vehicle.

Speed, as measured on a speedometer, is the distance traveled per unit of time. The speed of an automobile is represented in either miles per hour or kilometres per hour (Fig. 4.1). These units actually help define the formula for calculating speed:

Figure 4.1   A speedometer measures speed, but not velocity.

Copyright of Image Stock Imagery. Photo reprinted with permission

$$\text{speed} = \frac{\text{distance traveled}}{\text{time to move that distance}}$$

Speed is a scalar value, for it shows only the magnitude of the position change per unit of time and does not indicate a direction. The unit for speed is a distance unit divided by a time unit, such as miles per hour (mi/h), kilometres per hour (km/h), metres per second (m/s), and feet per second (ft/s). For example, if you drive $35\overline{0}$ mi in 7.00 h, your average speed is

$$\frac{35\overline{0}\ \text{mi}}{7.00\ \text{h}} = 50.0\ \text{mi/h}$$

Speed represents how fast something is moving, yet it does not indicate the direction in which it is traveling. Suppose you started driving from Chicago at a speed of 50 mi/h for 6 h. Where did you end your trip? You may have driven 50 mi/h southwest toward St. Louis, 50 mi/h northeast toward Detroit, 50 mi/h southeast toward Louisville, or 50 mi/h in a loop that brought you back to Chicago. Although speed may indicate how fast you are moving, it may not give you all the information you need to solve a problem.

Distance traveled must be distinguished from displacement. Whereas *distance* traveled may follow a path that is not straight, *displacement* is the net change of position of an object. It is represented by a straight line from the initial position to the final position and is a vector because it has both magnitude and direction.

The **velocity** of an object is the rate of motion in a particular direction. Velocity is a vector that not only represents the speed, but also indicates the direction of motion. The relationship may be expressed by the equation

$$v_{avg} = \frac{s}{t}$$

or

$$\boxed{s = v_{avg}t}$$

where s = displacement
         v_{avg} = average velocity
         t = time

This equation is used to find either average speed (a scalar quantity) or the magnitude of the velocity (a vector quantity). Remember that if indicating velocity, the direction must be included with the speed. Therefore, a speed of 50 mi/h would be written 50 mi/h northeast, 50 mi/h up, or 50 mi/h 30° east of south as a velocity.

Figure 4.2 shows an illustration of a car traveling at a constant velocity of 10 m/s to the right. Note that it travels 10 m to the right during each second.

Figure 4.2   The velocity, distance, and time for a car traveling at a constant velocity of 10 m/s to the right is shown in 1-s intervals.

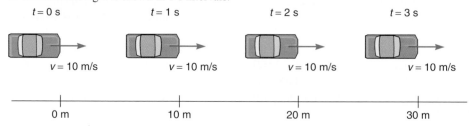

EXAMPLE 1

Find the average speed of an automobile that travels 160 km in 2.0 h.

Data:

$$s = 160 \text{ km}$$
$$t = 2.0 \text{ h}$$
$$v_{avg} = ?$$

Basic Equation:

$$s = v_{avg}t$$

Working Equation:

$$v_{avg} = \frac{s}{t}$$

Substitution:

$$v_{avg} = \frac{160 \text{ km}}{2.0 \text{ h}}$$
$$= 80 \text{ km/h}$$

An airplane flies $35\overline{0}0$ mi in 5.00 h. Find its average speed. ◀

EXAMPLE 2

Data:

$$s = 35\overline{0}0 \text{ mi}$$
$$t = 5.00 \text{ h}$$
$$v_{avg} = ?$$

Basic Equation:

$$s = v_{avg}t$$

Working Equation:

$$v_{avg} = \frac{s}{t}$$

Substitution:

$$v_{avg} = \frac{35\overline{0}0 \text{ mi}}{5.00 \text{ h}}$$
$$= 70\overline{0} \text{ mi/h}$$

· · · · · · · · · · · · · · · · ·

Find the velocity of a plane that travels $60\overline{0}$ km due north in 3 h 15 min. ◀

EXAMPLE 3

Data:

$$s = 60\overline{0} \text{ km}$$
$$t = 3 \text{ h } 15 \text{ min} = 3.25 \text{ h}$$
$$v_{avg} = ?$$

Basic Equation:

$$s = v_{avg}t$$

Working Equation:

$$v_{avg} = \frac{s}{t}$$

Substitution:

$$v_{avg} = \frac{60\overline{0} \text{ km}}{3.25 \text{ h}}$$
$$= 185 \text{ km/h}$$

The direction is north. Thus, the velocity is 185 km/h due north.

· · · · · · · · · · · · · · · · ·

Until now, our study of velocity has assumed a fixed observation point. The frame of reference can also be important for determining relative velocity. Paddling a canoe into a headwind may produce a net velocity of zero for the paddler. Another example is the flight of an airplane in which a crosswind, or in fact wind from any direction, will affect the airplane's velocity with respect to the ground. The airplane's final velocity is calculated by taking into account the velocity of the airplane in calm air and the velocity of any wind that the airplane encounters.

To find the sum (resultant vector) of velocity vectors, use the component method as outlined in Chapter 3.

EXAMPLE 4

A plane is flying due north (at 90°) at 265 km/h and encounters a wind from the east (at 180°) at 55.0 km/h. What is the plane's new velocity with respect to the ground in standard position? Assume that the plane's new velocity is the vector sum of the plane's original velocity and the wind velocity.

First, graph the plane's old velocity as the y-component and the wind velocity as the x-component (Fig. 4.3). The resultant vector is the plane's new velocity with respect to the ground. Find angle α as follows:

Figure 4.3

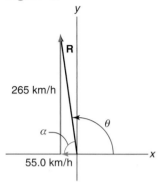

$$\tan \alpha = \frac{\text{side opposite } \alpha}{\text{side adjacent to } \alpha}$$

$$\tan \alpha = \frac{265 \text{ km/h}}{55.0 \text{ km/h}} = 4.818$$

$$\alpha = 78.3°$$

then

$$\theta = 180° - 78.3° = 101.7°$$

Find the magnitude of the new velocity (ground speed) using the Pythagorean theorem:

$$|\mathbf{R}| = \sqrt{|\mathbf{R}_x|^2 + |\mathbf{R}_y|^2}$$

$$|\mathbf{R}| = \sqrt{(55.0 \text{ km/h})^2 + (265 \text{ km/h})^2}$$

$$= 271 \text{ km/h}$$

That is, the new velocity of the plane is 271 km/h at 101.7°.

· · · · · · · · · · · · · · · · · ·

EXAMPLE 5

A plane is flying northwest (at 135.0°) at 315 km/h and encounters a wind from 30.0° south of west (at 30.0°) at 65.0 km/h. What is the plane's new velocity with respect to the ground in standard position? Assume that the plane's new velocity is the vector sum of the plane's original velocity and the wind velocity.

First, graph the plane's old velocity and the wind velocity as vectors in standard position (Fig. 4.4). The resultant vector is the plane's new velocity with respect to the ground.

Figure 4.4

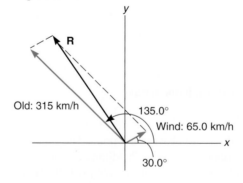

Then, find the x- and y-components of the plane's old velocity and the wind velocity using Fig. 4.5.

Figure 4.5

(a)

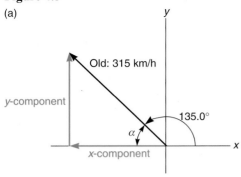

(b)

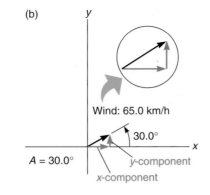

Plane: See Fig. 4.5(a). $\alpha = 180° - 135.0° = 45.0°$

x-component	**y-component**
$\cos \alpha = \dfrac{\text{side adjacent to } \alpha}{\text{hypotenuse}}$	$\sin \alpha = \dfrac{\text{side opposite } \alpha}{\text{hypotenuse}}$
$\cos 45.0° = \dfrac{x\text{-component}}{315 \text{ km/h}}$	$\sin 45.0° = \dfrac{y\text{-component}}{315 \text{ km/h}}$
$(315 \text{ km/h})(\cos 45.0°) = x\text{-component}$	$(315 \text{ km/h})(\sin 45.0°) = y\text{-component}$
$223 \text{ km/h} = x\text{-component}$	$223 \text{ km/h} = y\text{-component}$
Thus, x-component $= -223 \text{ km/h}$	y-component $= +223 \text{ km/h}$

Wind: See Fig. 4.5(b).

x-component	**y-component**
$\cos \alpha = \dfrac{\text{side adjacent to } \alpha}{\text{hypotenuse}}$	$\sin \alpha = \dfrac{\text{side opposite } \alpha}{\text{hypotenuse}}$
$\cos 30.0° = \dfrac{x\text{-component}}{65.0 \text{ km/h}}$	$\sin 30.0° = \dfrac{y\text{-component}}{65.0 \text{ km/h}}$
$(65.0 \text{ km/h})(\cos 30.0°) = x\text{-component}$	$(65.0 \text{ km/h})(\sin 30.0°) = y\text{-component}$
$56.3 \text{ km/h} = x\text{-component}$	$32.5 \text{ km/h} = y\text{-component}$
Thus, x-component $= +56.3 \text{ km/h}$	y-component $= +32.5 \text{ km/h}$

To find **R**:

	x-component	y-component	
Plane:	-223 km/h	$+223$ km/h	
Wind:	$+56.3$ km/h	$+32.5$ km/h	
Sum:	-167 km/h	$+256$ km/h	(Round each component sum to its least precise component.)

Figure 4.6

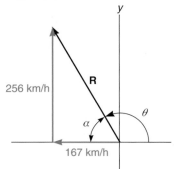

Find angle α from Fig. 4.6 as follows:

$$\tan \alpha = \frac{\text{side opposite } \alpha}{\text{side adjacent to } \alpha}$$

$$\tan \alpha = \frac{256 \text{ km/h}}{167 \text{ km/h}} = 1.533$$

$$\alpha = 56.9°$$

and

$$\theta = 180° - 56.9° = 123.1°$$

Find the magnitude of $\mathbf{R}$ using the Pythagorean theorem:

$$|\mathbf{R}| = \sqrt{|\mathbf{R}_x|^2 + |\mathbf{R}_y|^2}$$
$$|\mathbf{R}| = \sqrt{(167 \text{ km/h})^2 + (256 \text{ km/h})^2}$$
$$= 306 \text{ km/h}$$

That is, the new velocity of the plane is 306 km/h at 123.1°.

PHYSICS CONNECTIONS

Vectors Across Rivers

Crossing the Hudson River, which separates New York City from New Jersey, can be challenging. A working knowledge of velocity and vectors is absolutely essential, especially when attempting to cross the river in strong currents, brisk winds, driving rain, and dense fog. In addition, maneuvering between barges, cruise ships, recreational boaters, and driftwood can make the job even more difficult.

Figure 4.7 An example of how the velocity of a boat and the velocity of the current are combined so the resultant velocity is directed toward the desired location.

Figure 4.8 Although the boat is not pointed toward the dock, the combination of the boat's velocity (green vector) plus the current's velocity (blue vector) results in a perfect docking (red vector).

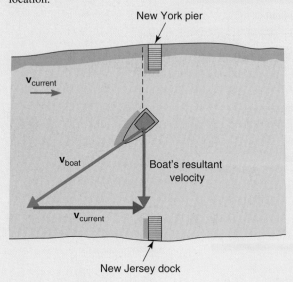

Ferry captains like Mike and John combine vectors every time they cross the river. Captain Mike said, "At times crossing the river can be quite tricky. Your ferry might be pointing directly across the river, but the current is pushing you farther down river. In order to combat this, you need to change the boat's heading so when your velocity and the current's velocity combine, you arrive at your planned destination" (Fig. 4.7).

Sometimes, when the current and wind are strong and headed in the same direction, ferryboats can appear to be heading up to 45° away from their destination, yet still travel directly across the river. In such situations, docking can be nerve-racking (Fig. 4.8).

The two experienced sea captains say vectors are even more important in the open seas. Captain Mike said, "Combining your boat's velocity vector with the current and wind vectors can mean the difference between arriving at your home port or at a port 100 miles away." These days the process is easier with the use of radar and computer navigation equipment and software. Looking at the monitor, Captain Mike said, "We can see the velocity of the current and our boat's intended velocity directly on the monitor. Instead of our combining the vectors, the computer can instantaneously combine them and provide the resultant velocity" (Fig. 4.9).

Figure 4.9 (a) Captain Mike combines velocity vectors every time he navigates across the Hudson River.

Figure 4.9 (b) Captain John's high-speed ferry is equipped with computers that automatically combine and display the boat's resultant velocity vector.

PROBLEMS 4.1

Find the average speed (in the given units) of an auto that travels each distance in the given time.

1. Distance of 150 mi in 3.0 h (in mi/h)
2. Distance of 190 m in 8.5 s (in m/s)
3. Distance of 8550 m in 6 min 35 s (in m/s)
4. Distance of 45 km in 0.50 h (in km/h)
5. Distance of 785 ft in 11.5 s (in ft/s)
6. Find the average speed (in mi/h) of a racing car that turns a lap on a 1.00-mi oval track in 30.0 s.
7. While driving at $9\overline{0}$ km/h, how far can you travel in 3.5 h?
8. While driving at $9\overline{0}$ km/h, how far (in metres) do you travel in 1.0 s?
9. An automobile is traveling at 55 mi/h. Find its speed
   (a) in ft/s. (b) in m/s. (c) in km/h.

SKETCH

12 cm² | w

4.0 cm

DATA
A = 12 cm², l = 4.0 cm, w = ?

BASIC EQUATION
A = lw

WORKING EQUATION
$w = \frac{A}{l}$

SUBSTITUTION
$w = \frac{12 \text{ cm}^2}{4.0 \text{ cm}} = 3.0$ cm

10. An automobile is traveling at 22.0 m/s. Find its speed
   (a) in km/h.　　　　(b) in mi/h.　　　　(c) in ft/s.
11. A semi-trailer truck traveling $10\overline{0}$ km/h continues for 2.75 h. How far does it go?
12. A flatbed truck travels for 3.85 h at 105 km/h. How far does it go?
13. The average speed of a garbage truck is 60.0 km/h. How long does it take for the truck to travel 265 km?
14. A highway maintenance truck has an average speed of 55.0 km/h. How far does it travel in 3.65 h?

Find the velocity for each displacement and time.

15. 160 km east in 2.0 h
16. $10\overline{0}$ km north in 3.0 h
17. $100\overline{0}$ mi south in 8.00 h
18. 31.0 mi west in 0.500 h
19. 275 km at $3\overline{0}°$ south of east in 4.50 h
20. 426 km at 45° north of west in 2.75 h
21. Milwaukee is 121 mi (air miles) due west of Grand Rapids. Maria drives 255 mi in 4.75 h from Grand Rapids to Milwaukee around Lake Michigan. Find (a) her average driving speed and (b) her average travel velocity.
22. Telluride, Colorado, is 45 air miles at 11° east of north of Durango. On a winter day, Chuck drove 120 mi from Durango to Telluride around a mountain in $4\frac{1}{4}$ h including a traffic delay. Find (a) his average driving speed and (b) his average travel velocity.

In Problems 23–30, assume that the plane's new velocity is the vector sum of the plane's original velocity and the wind velocity.

23. A plane is flying due north at 325 km/h and encounters a wind from the south at 45 km/h. What is the plane's new velocity with respect to the ground in standard position?
24. A plane is flying due west at 275 km/h and encounters a wind from the west at $8\overline{0}$ km/h. What is the plane's new velocity with respect to the ground in standard position?
25. A plane is flying due west at 235 km/h and encounters a wind from the north at 45.0 km/h. What is the plane's new velocity with respect to the ground in standard position?
26. A plane is flying due north at 185 mi/h and encounters a wind from the west at 35.0 mi/h. What is the plane's new velocity with respect to the ground in standard position?
27. A plane is flying southwest at 155 mi/h and encounters a wind from the west at 45.0 mi/h. What is the plane's new velocity with respect to the ground in standard position?
28. A plane is flying southeast at 215 km/h and encounters a wind from the north at 75.0 km/h. What is the plane's new velocity with respect to the ground in standard position?
29. A plane is flying at 25.0° north of west at $19\overline{0}$ km/h and encounters a wind from 15.0° north of east at 45.0 km/h. What is the plane's new velocity with respect to the ground in standard position?
30. A plane is flying at 36.0° south of west at $15\overline{0}$ mi/h and encounters a wind from 75.0° north of east at 55.0 mi/h. What is the plane's new velocity with respect to the ground in standard position?

4.2 Acceleration

When the dragster shown in Fig. 4.10 travels down a quarter-mile track, its velocity changes. Its velocity at the end of the race is much greater than its velocity near the start. The faster the velocity of the dragster changes, the less its travel time will be.

Figure 4.10 The velocity of the dragster changes in magnitude from zero at the start to its final velocity at the finish.

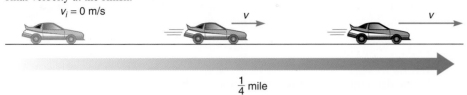

The faster its velocity changes, the larger its acceleration will be. **Acceleration** *is the change in velocity per unit time.* That is,

$$\text{average acceleration} = \frac{\text{change in velocity (or speed)}}{\text{elapsed time}}$$

$$= \frac{\text{final velocity} - \text{initial velocity}}{\text{time}}$$

This relationship can be expressed by the equation

$$a = \frac{\Delta v}{t} = \frac{v_f - v_i}{t}$$

or

$$\boxed{\Delta v = at}$$

where Δv = change in velocity (or speed)
a = acceleration
t = time

The Greek letter Δ (capital delta) is used to mean "change in."

A dragster starts from rest (velocity $= 0$ ft/s) and attains a speed of $15\overline{0}$ ft/s in 10.0 s. Find its acceleration.

EXAMPLE 1

Data:

$$\Delta v = 15\overline{0} \text{ ft/s} - 0 \text{ ft/s} = 15\overline{0} \text{ ft/s}$$
$$t = 10.0 \text{ s}$$
$$a = ?$$

Basic Equation:

$$\Delta v = at$$

Working Equation:

$$a = \frac{\Delta v}{t}$$

Substitution:

$$a = \frac{15\overline{0} \text{ ft/s}}{10.0 \text{ s}}$$

$$= 15.0 \frac{\text{ft/s}}{\text{s}} \text{ or } 15.0 \text{ feet per second per second}$$

Recall from arithmetic that to simplify fractions in the form

$$\frac{\dfrac{a}{b}}{\dfrac{c}{d}}$$

we divide by the denominator; that is, invert and multiply:

$$\frac{\dfrac{a}{b}}{\dfrac{c}{d}} = \frac{a}{b} \div \frac{c}{d} = \frac{a}{b} \cdot \frac{d}{c} = \frac{ad}{bc}$$

Use this idea to simplify the units 15.0 feet per second per second:

$$\frac{\dfrac{15.0 \text{ ft}}{s}}{\dfrac{s}{1}} = \frac{15.0 \text{ ft}}{s} \div \frac{s}{1} = \frac{15.0 \text{ ft}}{s} \cdot \frac{1}{s} = \frac{15.0 \text{ ft}}{s^2} \text{ or } 15.0 \text{ ft/s}^2$$

The units of acceleration are usually ft/s^2 or m/s^2.

····················

When the speed of an automobile increases from rest to 5 mi/h in the first second, to 10 mi/h in the next second, and to 15 mi/h in the third second, its acceleration is 5 $\frac{\text{mi/h}}{s}$. That is, its increase in speed is 5 mi/h during each second. In Fig. 4.11 an automobile increases in speed from 6 m/s to 9 m/s in the first second, to 12 m/s in the next second, and to 15 m/s in the third second, so, its acceleration is 3 $\frac{\text{m/s}}{s}$, usually written 3 m/s^2. This means that the speed of the automobile increases 3 m/s during each second.

Figure 4.11 This car is speeding up with a constant acceleration. Note how the distance covered and the velocity change during each time interval.

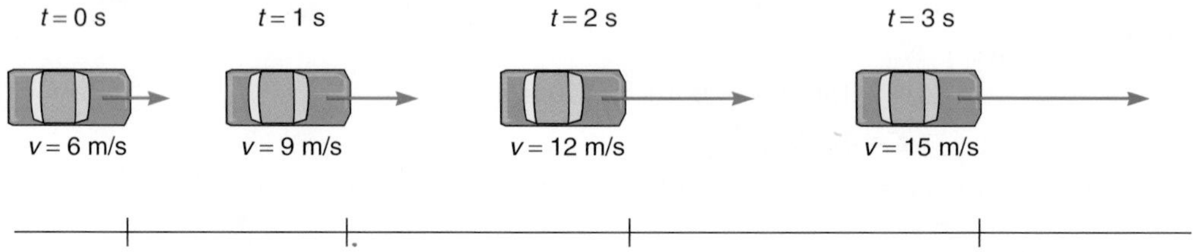

$t=0$ s	$t=1$ s	$t=2$ s	$t=3$ s
$v=6$ m/s	$v=9$ m/s	$v=12$ m/s	$v=15$ m/s

EXAMPLE 2

A car accelerates from 45 km/h to $\overline{80}$ km/h in 3.00 s. Find its acceleration (in m/s^2).

Data:
$$\Delta v = \overline{80} \text{ km/h} - 45 \text{ km/h} = 35 \text{ km/h}$$
$$t = 3.00 \text{ s}$$
$$a = ?$$

Basic Equation:
$$\Delta v = at$$

Working Equation:
$$a = \frac{\Delta v}{t}$$

Substitution:

$$a = \frac{35 \text{ km/h}}{3.00 \text{ s}} \times \frac{1000 \text{ m}}{1 \text{ km}} \times \frac{1 \text{ h}}{3600 \text{ s}}$$
$$= 3.2 \text{ m/s}^2$$

Note the use of the conversion factors to change the units km/h/s to m/s^2.

. . . .

A plane accelerates at 8.5 m/s^2 for 4.5 s. Find its increase in speed (in m/s). ◄

EXAMPLE 3

Data:

$$a = 8.5 \text{ m/s}^2$$
$$t = 4.5 \text{ s}$$
$$\Delta v = ?$$

Basic Equation:

$$\Delta v = at$$

Working Equation: Same

Substitution:

$$\Delta v = (8.5 \text{ m/s}^2)(4.5 \text{ s})$$
$$= 38 \text{ m/s}$$

$$\boxed{\frac{\text{m}}{\text{s}^2} \times \text{s} = \frac{\text{m}}{\text{s}}}$$

. . . .

Acceleration means more than just an increase in speed. In fact, since velocity is the speed of an object and its direction of motion, acceleration can mean speeding up, slowing down, or changing direction. The next example illustrates negative acceleration (sometimes called deceleration). **Deceleration** is an acceleration that usually indicates that an object is slowing down (Fig. 4.12). Acceleration when an object changes direction will be discussed in Chapter 9.

Figure 4.12 This car is slowing down with a constant acceleration of −10 m/s^2. Note how the distance covered and the velocity change during each unit of time interval.

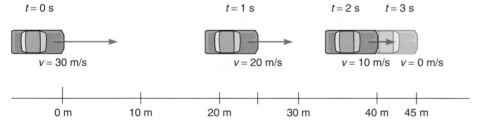

Sometimes the direction of the velocity or the acceleration of an object is understood and does not need to be stated explicitly. For example, if a car is accelerating on a straight road, both the direction of the velocity and the direction of the acceleration are along the road in the direction in which the car is moving. When the car begins to slow down, the direction of the velocity is understood to be along the road in the direction pointing ahead of the car, and the direction of its acceleration (deceleration) is understood to be along the road in the direction pointing behind the car.

EXAMPLE 4

A driver steps off the gas pedal and coasts at a rate of -3.00 m/s² for 5.00 s. Find the driver's new speed if she was originally traveling at a velocity of 20.0 m/s. (The negative acceleration indicates that the acceleration is in the opposite direction of the velocity; that is, the object is slowing down.)

Data:

$$a = -3.00 \text{ m/s}^2$$
$$t = 5.00 \text{ s}$$
$$v_i = 20.0 \text{ m/s}$$

Basic Equation:

$$\Delta v = at$$
$$v_f - v_i = at$$

Working Equation:

$$v_f = v_i + at$$

Substitution:

$$v_f = 20.0 \text{ m/s} + (-3.00 \text{ m/s}^2)(5.00 \text{ s})$$
$$= 5.0 \text{ m/s}$$

Figure 4.13 Motion of a high-speed train going from one station to another. When the speed increases, the acceleration is positive. When the speed is constant, the acceleration is zero. When the speed decreases, the acceleration is negative.

Acceleration has both magnitude and direction. Consider a high-speed train moving out of the station due east (positive direction). Its velocity increases in magnitude until it reaches its cruising speed (Fig. 4.13). Its acceleration is greatest at the start (from A to B), when its increase in speed is largest. When the train is moving at relatively constant velocity (from B to C), its acceleration is near zero. Then as the train approaches the next station (from C to D), its speed decreases as it decelerates.

PROBLEMS 4.2

An automobile changes speed as shown. Find its acceleration.

	Speed Change	Time Interval	Find a
1.	From 0 to 15 m/s	1.0 s	in m/s²
2.	From 0 to 18 m/s	3.0 s	in m/s²
3.	From $6\overline{0}$ ft/s to $7\overline{0}$ ft/s	1.0 s	in ft/s²
4.	From 45 m/s to 65 m/s	2.0 s	in m/s²
5.	From 25 km/h to $9\overline{0}$ km/h	5.6 s	in m/s²
6.	From $1\overline{0}$ mi/h to $5\overline{0}$ mi/h	3.5 s	in ft/s²

7. A dragster starts from rest and reaches a speed of 62.5 m/s in 10.0 s. Find its acceleration (in m/s²).
8. A car accelerates from 25 mi/h to 55 mi/h in 4.5 s. Find its acceleration (in ft/s²).
9. A train accelerates from $1\overline{0}$ km/h to $11\overline{0}$ km/h in 2 min 15 s. Find its acceleration (in m/s²).

A plane accelerates at 30.0 ft/s² for 3.30 s. Find its increase in speed

10. in ft/s.   11. in mi/h.

A rocket accelerates at 10.0 m/s² from rest for 20.0 s. Find its increase in speed

12. in m/s.   13. in km/h.
14. How long (in seconds) does it take for a rocket sled accelerating at 15.0 m/s² to change its speed from 20.0 m/s to 65.0 m/s?

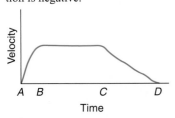

SKETCH

12 cm² w

4.0 cm

DATA

$A = 12$ cm², $l = 4.0$ cm, $w = ?$

BASIC EQUATION

$A = lw$

WORKING EQUATION

$w = \frac{A}{l}$

SUBSTITUTION

$w = \frac{12 \text{ cm}^2}{4.0 \text{ cm}} = 3.0$ cm

15. What is the acceleration of a road grader that goes from rest to 10.0 km/h in 5.20 s?
16. What is the acceleration of a compactor that goes from rest to 20.0 km/h in 4.80 s?
17. How long (in seconds) does it take for a truck accelerating at 1.50 m/s² to go from rest to 90.0 km/h?
18. How long (in seconds) does it take for a car accelerating at 3.50 m/s² to go from rest to 1$\overline{2}$0 km/h?
19. A bulldozer accelerates from rest to 3.00 m/s in 4.20 s. What is its acceleration?
20. A pickup truck pulling a trailer accelerates at 3.25 m/s² for 5.80 s. If it starts from rest, what is its final velocity?
21. The speed of a delivery van increases from 2.00 m/s at 1.00 s to 16.0 m/s at 4.50 s. What is its average speed?
22. A go-cart rolls backward down a driveway. We define forward speed as positive and backward speed as negative. The cart's speed changes from −2.00 m/s to −9.00 m/s in 2.00 s. What is its acceleration?
23. A stock car is moving at 25.0 m/s when the driver applies the brakes. If it stops in 3.00 s, what is its average acceleration?
24. If the car in Problem 23 took twice as long to stop, what would its acceleration be?
25. If the car in Problem 23 was going twice as fast but was able to stop in the same time, what would its acceleration be?
26. If the car in Problem 23 was going twice the speed and stopped in twice the time, what would its acceleration be?

4.3 Uniformly Accelerated Motion and Free Fall

Uniformly accelerated motion of an object occurs when its acceleration is constant; examples are a ball rolling down a straight incline, a car increasing its speed at a constant rate, and a ball dropped from a building. The following equations apply to uniformly accelerated motion and freely falling bodies. Some of the derivations are beyond the scope of this text.

ACCELERATED MOTION

1. $v_{avg} = \dfrac{v_f + v_i}{2}$

2. $a = \dfrac{v_f - v_i}{t}$

3. $v_f = v_i + at$

4. $s = v_i t + \frac{1}{2} at^2$

5. $s = \frac{1}{2}(v_f + v_i)t$

6. $2as = v_f^2 - v_i^2$

where s = displacement v_{avg} = average velocity
v_f = final velocity a = constant acceleration
v_i = initial velocity t = time

Now consider some problems using these equations, applying our problem-solving method.

The average velocity of a rolling freight car is 2.00 m/s. How long does it take for the car to roll 15.0 m?

EXAMPLE 1

Data:

$$s = 15.0 \text{ m}$$
$$v_{avg} = 2.00 \text{ m/s}$$
$$t = ?$$

Basic Equation:

$$s = v_{avg}t$$

Working Equation:

$$t = \frac{s}{v_{avg}}$$

Substitution:

$$t = \frac{15.0 \text{ m}}{2.00 \text{ m/s}}$$

$$= 7.50 \text{ s}$$

$$\boxed{\frac{\text{m}}{\text{m/s}} = \text{m} \div \frac{\text{m}}{\text{s}} = \text{m} \cdot \frac{\text{s}}{\text{m}} = \text{s}}$$

·················

EXAMPLE 2

A dragster starting from rest reaches a final velocity of 318 km/h. Find its average velocity.

Data:

$$v_i = 0$$
$$v_f = 318 \text{ km/h}$$
$$v_{avg} = ?$$

Basic Equation:

$$v_{avg} = \frac{v_f + v_i}{2}$$

Working Equation: Same

Substitution:

$$v_{avg} = \frac{318 \text{ km/h} + 0 \text{ km/h}}{2}$$

$$= 159 \text{ km/h}$$

·················

EXAMPLE 3

A train slowing to a stop has an average acceleration of -3.00 m/s^2. [Note that a minus $(-)$ acceleration is commonly called *deceleration*, meaning that the train is slowing down.] If its initial velocity is 30.0 m/s, how far does it travel in 4.00 s?

Data:

$$a = -3.00 \text{ m/s}^2$$
$$v_i = 30.0 \text{ m/s}$$
$$t = 4.00 \text{ s}$$
$$s = ?$$

Basic Equation:

$$s = v_i t + \tfrac{1}{2}at^2$$

Working Equation: Same

Substitution:

$$s = (30.0 \text{ m/s})(4.00 \text{ s}) + \tfrac{1}{2}(-3.00 \text{ m/s}^2)(4.00 \text{ s})^2$$

$$= 12\bar{0} \text{ m} - 24.0 \text{ m}$$

$$= 96 \text{ m}$$

·················

An automobile accelerates from 67.0 km/h to 96.0 km/h in 7.80 s. What is its acceleration (in m/s²)?

EXAMPLE 4

Data:

$$v_f = 96.0 \text{ km/h}$$
$$v_i = 67.0 \text{ km/h}$$
$$t = 7.80 \text{ s}$$
$$a = ?$$

Basic Equation:

$$a = \frac{v_f - v_i}{t}$$

Working Equation: Same

Substitution:

$$a = \frac{96.0 \text{ km/h} - 67.0 \text{ km/h}}{7.80 \text{ s}}$$

$$= \frac{29.0 \text{ km/h}}{7.80 \text{ s}}$$

$$= \frac{29.0 \frac{\cancel{km}}{\cancel{h}} \times \frac{1000 \text{ m}}{1 \cancel{km}} \times \frac{1 \cancel{h}}{3600 \text{ s}}}{7.80 \text{ s}}$$

$$= 1.03 \text{ m/s}^2$$

Freely falling bodies undergo constant acceleration. In a vacuum (in the absence of air resistance) a ball and a feather fall at the same rate. In 1971, astronaut David Scott demonstrated this during a moon mission by dropping a hammer and a feather simultaneously on the surface of the moon, where there is no atmosphere. Both objects fell at the same rate and landed at the same time.

TRY THIS ACTIVITY

Free Fall in a Vacuum

Drop a piece of paper and a book at the same time and note the relative time it takes for each to hit the floor. Now place that paper on top of the book as shown in Fig. 4.14. (**Note:** The top surface area of the book must be larger than that of the paper.) What happens to the time it takes the book and paper to fall? What does this show about objects falling in a vacuum? (A vacuum is a space in which there is no air resistance present.)

Figure 4.14   Place the paper on top of the book. The book must be larger than the paper.

The acceleration of a freely falling body, also called the **acceleration due to gravity**, is denoted by the symbol g, where $a = g = 9.80 \text{ m/s}^2$ (metric system) or $a = g = 32.2 \text{ ft/s}^2$ (U.S. system) on the earth's surface.

What does $a = 9.80 \text{ m/s}^2$ mean? When a ball is dropped from a building, the speed of the ball increases by 9.80 m/s during each second. Figure 4.15 shows the total distance traveled and the speed at 1-s intervals.

Figure 4.15 A ball falls with constant acceleration
$a = g = 9.80 \text{ m/s}^2$
with the speed and the distance traveled calculated at the given times.
Because the ball was dropped, $v_i = 0$ and the formulas for v_f and s are shown simplified. Note how the velocity and the distance traveled increase during each successive time interval.

Time	Distance Traveled	Speed
	$s = \frac{1}{2}at^2$	$v_f = at$
$t = 0$	0 m	0 m/s
$t = 1.00$ s	$s = \frac{1}{2}(9.80 \text{ m/s}^2)(1.00 \text{ s})^2$	$v_f = (9.80 \text{ m/s}^2)(1.00 \text{ s})$
	$s = 4.90$ m	$v_f = 9.80$ m/s
$t = 2.00$ s	$s = \frac{1}{2}(9.80 \text{ m/s}^2)(2.00 \text{ s})^2$	$v_f = (9.80 \text{ m/s}^2)(2.00 \text{ s})$
	$s = 19.6$ m	$v_f = 19.6$ m/s
$t = 3.00$ s	$s = \frac{1}{2}(9.80 \text{ m/s}^2)(3.00 \text{ s})^2$	$v_f = (9.80 \text{ m/s}^2)(3.00 \text{ s})$
	$s = 44.1$ m	$v_f = 29.4$ m/s
$t = 4.00$ s	$s = \frac{1}{2}(9.80 \text{ m/s}^2)(4.00 \text{ s})^2$	$v_f = (9.80 \text{ m/s}^2)(4.00 \text{ s})$
	$s = 78.4$ m	$v_f = 39.2$ m/s

TRY THIS ACTIVITY

Calculating Height

Drop a ball from a window that is at least two stories high (or from some other height) and time how long it takes the ball to fall to the ground. Use the formulas for accelerated motion to find the height. Measure the actual height with a tape measure. How does your calculated height compare with the actual height? What factors may have made your calculated height different from the actual height? Remember to use the problem-solving method to help you solve this problem.

We limit our discussion to uniformly accelerated motion because the mathematical tools needed to study other kinds of motion are beyond the scope of this book. We also need to assume that air resistance of a freely falling body is negligible for our calculations. However, air resistance is, in fact, an important factor in the design of machines that move through the atmosphere.

When the air resistance of a falling object equals its weight, the net force is zero and no further acceleration occurs. That is, a falling object reaches its **terminal speed**.

A rock is thrown straight down from a cliff with an initial velocity of 10.0 ft/s. Its final velocity when it strikes the water below is $31\bar{0}$ ft/s. The acceleration due to gravity is 32.2 ft/s^2. How long is the rock in flight?

EXAMPLE 5

Data:

$$v_i = 10.0 \text{ ft/s}$$
$$a = 32.2 \text{ ft/s}^2$$
$$v_f = 31\bar{0} \text{ ft/s}$$
$$t = ?$$

Note the importance of listing all the data as an aid to finding the basic equation.

Basic Equation:

$$v_f = v_i + at \quad \text{or} \quad a = \frac{v_f - v_i}{t} \qquad \text{(two forms of the same equation)}$$

Working Equation:

$$t = \frac{v_f - v_i}{a}$$

Substitution:

$$t = \frac{31\bar{0} \text{ ft/s} - 10.0 \text{ ft/s}}{32.2 \text{ ft/s}^2}$$

$$= \frac{30\bar{0} \text{ ft/s}}{32.2 \text{ ft/s}^2}$$

$$= 9.32 \text{ s}$$

$$\boxed{\frac{\text{ft/s}}{\text{ft/s}^2} = \frac{\text{ft}}{\text{s}} \div \frac{\text{ft}}{\text{s}^2} = \frac{\text{ft}}{\text{s}} \cdot \frac{\text{s}^2}{\text{ft}} = \text{s}}$$

When any object is thrown or hurled vertically upward, its upward speed is uniformly decreased by the force of gravity until it stops for an instant at its peak before falling back to the ground. As it is falling to the ground, it is uniformly accelerated by gravity the same as it would have been if dropped from its peak height. If an object is thrown vertically upward and if the initial velocity is known, the previous acceleration/gravity formulas may be used to find how high the object rises, how long it is in flight, and so on.

Note: When we consider a problem involving an object being thrown upward, we will consider an upward direction to be negative and the opposing gravity in its normal downward direction to be positive.

A baseball is thrown vertically upward with an initial velocity of 25.0 m/s (see Fig. 4.16).

EXAMPLE 6

(a) How high does it go?
(b) How long does it take to reach its maximum height?
(c) How long is it in flight?

Figure 4.16

$v_i = -25.0$ m/s

(a) Data:

$$v_i = -25.0 \text{ m/s}$$

(v_i is negative because the initial velocity is directed opposite gravity, g.)

$$v_f = 0$$

(At the instant of the ball's maximum height, its velocity is zero.)

$$a = g = 9.80 \text{ m/s}^2$$
$$s = ?$$

Basic Equation:

$$2as = v_f^2 - v_i^2$$

Working Equation:

$$s = \frac{v_f^2 - v_i^2}{2a}$$

Substitution:

$$s = \frac{0^2 - (-25.0 \text{ m/s})^2}{2(9.80 \text{ m/s}^2)}$$

$$\frac{(\text{m/s})^2}{\text{m/s}^2} = \frac{\text{m}^2/\text{s}^2}{\text{m/s}^2} = \frac{\text{m}^2}{\text{s}^2} \div \frac{\text{m}}{\text{s}^2} = \frac{\frac{\text{m}^2}{\text{m}^2}}{\text{s}^2} \times \frac{\text{s}^2}{\text{m}} = \text{m}$$

$$= -31.9 \text{ m}$$

(s being negative indicates an upward displacement.)

(b) Data:

$$v_i = -25.0 \text{ m/s}$$
$$v_f = 0$$
$$a = g = 9.80 \text{ m/s}^2$$
$$t = ?$$

Basic Equation:

$$v_f = v_i + at$$

Working Equation:

$$t = \frac{v_f - v_i}{a}$$

Substitution:

$$t = \frac{0 - (-25.0 \text{ m/s})}{9.80 \text{ m/s}^2}$$

$$\frac{\text{m/s}}{\text{m/s}^2} = \frac{\text{m}}{\text{s}} \div \frac{\text{m}}{\text{s}^2} = \frac{\text{m}}{\text{s}} \times \frac{\frac{\text{s}^2}{\text{s}^2}}{\text{m}} = \text{s}$$

$$= 2.55 \text{ s}$$

(c) The ball decelerates on the way up and accelerates on the way down at the same rate because the acceleration due to gravity is constant (9.80 m/s^2). Therefore, the time for the ball to reach its peak is the same as the time for it to fall to the ground. The total time in flight is $2(2.55 \text{ s}) = 5.10 \text{ s}$.

· · · · · · · · · · · · · · · · · ·

With what speed does the ball in Example 6 hit the ground? The answer is 25.0 m/s. Can you explain why?

Earlier, we assumed no air resistance. We know that two dense and compact objects, such a bowling ball and a marble, will fall at the same rate in air. We also know that two unlike objects, such as a marble and a feather, fall at different rates because of air resistance.

Figure 4.17 The sky diver in (a) has a different acceleration toward the ground than those in (b) as a result of different air resistance.

Courtesy of Peter Arnold, Inc. Reprinted with permission

(a)

Courtesy of Getty Images. Photo reprinted with permission

(b)

A parachute takes advantage of air resistance to slow a sky diver's descent [Fig. 4.17(a)]. What would happen if a parachute does not open [Fig. 4.17(b)]? Would the sky diver's velocity increase constantly until he or she hits the ground? As the velocity increases, the air resistance also increases. Since the gravitational pull and the air resistance are directed opposite each other, they tend to oppose or equalize each other. (Here, the velocity and acceleration are both directed downward, while the air resistance is directed upward.) This equalization occurs when the friction of the air's resistance equals the force of gravity. When this equalization occurs, the falling object stops accelerating and continues to fall at a constant velocity, called *terminal velocity.*

The terminal velocity or speed of a sky diver varies from 150 to 200 km/h, depending on the person's weight and position. A heavier person will attain a greater terminal speed than a lighter person because the larger weight results in a larger acceleration before the air resistance equals the weight. Body position also makes a difference. When a body is spread out like that of a bird gliding with outstretched wings, its surface area increases, which results in more air resistance. Terminal speed can be controlled by varying the body position. A light sky diver and a heavy sky diver can remain in close proximity to each other if the light person decreases his or her air resistance by falling head or feet first while the heavy person spreads out and increases his or her air resistance. A parachute greatly increases air resistance and reduces the terminal speed to approximately 15 to 25 km/h, which is slow enough for a safe landing.

In general, the terminal velocity of an object varies with its weight and its aerodynamic features, which include the following:

1. The shape of the object. (A symmetrical object is more aerodynamic than a nonsymmetrical one.)
2. The orientation of the object as it is traveling. (A sky diver slows the fall by spreading out his or her arms and legs parallel to the ground while falling. The speed of the fall increases if the person falls head or feet first.)
3. The smoothness of the surface. (A body with a smooth surface provides less air resistance than a body with a rough surface and falls or flies faster as a result.)

TRY THIS ACTIVITY

Air Resistance and Acceleration

Drop several objects of varying sizes, weights, and shapes outside a second-floor window. Which objects hit the ground faster than others? If gravity acts equally on all objects, what factors might cause the objects to fall at different rates?

SKETCH

$$12 \text{ cm}^2 \quad w$$

4.0 cm

DATA

$A = 12 \text{ cm}^2$, $l = 4.0$ cm, $w = ?$

BASIC EQUATION

$A = lw$

WORKING EQUATION

$w = \frac{A}{l}$

SUBSTITUTION

$w = \frac{12 \text{ cm}^2}{4.0 \text{ cm}} = 3.0$ cm

PROBLEMS 4.3

Substitute in the given equation and find the unknown quantity.

1. Given: $v_{avg} = \dfrac{v_f + v_i}{2}$

   $v_f = 6.20$ m/s

   $v_i = 3.90$ m/s

   $v_{avg} = ?$

2. Given: $a = \dfrac{v_f - v_i}{t}$

   $a = 3.07$ m/s^2

   $v_f = 16.8$ m/s

   $t = 4.10$ s

   $v_i = ?$

3. Given: $s = v_i t + \frac{1}{2}at^2$

   $t = 3.00$ s

   $a = 6.40$ m/s^2

   $v_i = 33.0$ m/s

   $s = ?$

4. Given: $2as = v_f^2 - v_i^2$

   $a = 8.41$ m/s^2

   $s = 4.81$ m

   $v_i = 1.24$ m/s

   $v_f = ?$

5. Given: $v_f = v_i + at$

   $v_f = 10.40$ ft/s

   $v_i = 4.01$ ft/s

   $t = 3.00$ s

   $a = ?$

6. The average velocity of a mini-bike is 15.0 km/h. How long does it take for the bike to go 35.0 m?

7. A sprinter starting from rest reaches a final velocity of 18.0 mi/h. What is her average velocity?

8. A coin is dropped with no initial velocity. Its final velocity when it strikes the earth is 50.0 ft/s. The acceleration due to gravity is 32.2 ft/s^2. How long does it take to strike the earth?

9. A front endloader accelerates from rest to 1.75 m/s in 2.50 s. How far does it travel in that time?

10. A mechanic test driving a car that she has just given a tune-up accelerates from rest to 50.0 m/s in 9.80 s. How far does she travel in that time?

11. A rocket lifting off from earth has an average acceleration of 44.0 ft/s^2. Its initial velocity is zero. How far into the atmosphere does it travel during the first 5.00 s, assuming that it goes straight up?

12. The final velocity of a truck is 74.0 ft/s. If it accelerates at a rate of 2.00 ft/s^2 from an initial velocity of 5.00 ft/s, how long will it take for it to attain its final velocity?

13. A truck accelerates from 85 km/h to 120 km/h in 9.2 s. Find its acceleration in m/s^2.

14. How long does it take a rock to drop 95.0 m from rest? Find the final speed of the rock.

15. An aircraft with a landing speed of 295 km/h lands on an aircraft carrier with a landing area 205 m long. Find the minimum constant deceleration required for a safe landing.

16. A ball is thrown downward from the top of a 43.0-ft building with an initial speed of 62.0 ft/s. Find its final speed as it strikes the ground.

17. A car is traveling at $7\overline{0}$ km/h. It then uniformly decelerates to a complete stop in 12 s. Find its acceleration (in m/s^2).

18. A car is traveling at $6\overline{0}$ km/h. It then accelerates at 3.6 m/s^2 to $9\overline{0}$ km/h.
     (a) How long does it take to reach the new speed?
     (b) How far does it travel while accelerating?

19. A rock is dropped from a bridge to the water below. It takes 2.40 s for the rock to hit the water.
     (a) Find the speed (in m/s) of the rock as it hits the water.
     (b) How high (in metres) is the bridge above the water?

20. A bullet is fired vertically upward from a gun and reaches a height of $70\overline{0}0$ ft.
     (a) Find its initial velocity.
     (b) How long does it take to reach its maximum height?
     (c) How long is it in flight?

21. A bullet is fired vertically upward from a gun with an initial velocity of $25\overline{0}$ m/s.
     (a) How high does it go?
     (b) How long does it take to reach its maximum height?
     (c) How long is it in flight?

22. A rock is thrown down with an initial speed of 30.0 ft/s from a bridge to the water below. It takes 3.50 s for the rock to hit the water.
     (a) Find the speed (in ft/s) of the rock as it hits the water.
     (b) How high is the bridge above the water?

23. John stands at the edge of a deck that is 25.0 m above the ground and throws a rock straight up with an initial speed of 10.0 m/s.
     (a) How long does it take to reach its maximum height?
     (b) What maximum height above the deck does it reach?
     (c) Assuming it misses the deck on its way down, at what speed does it hit the ground?
     (d) What total length of time is the rock in the air?

24. John stands at the edge of a deck that is 40.0 m above the ground and throws a rock straight up that reaches a height of 15.0 m above the deck.
     (a) What is the initial speed of the rock?
     (b) How long does it take to reach its maximum height?
     (c) Assuming it misses the deck on its way down, at what speed does it hit the ground?
     (d) What total length of time is the rock in the air?

25. John is standing on a steel beam 255.0 ft above the ground. Linda is standing 30.0 ft directly above John.
     (a) For John to throw a hammer up to Linda, at what initial speed must John throw the hammer for it to just reach Linda?
     (b) Suppose the hammer reaches the correct height, but Linda just misses catching it. How long does someone on the ground have to move out of the way from the time the hammer reaches its maximum height?
     (c) At what speed does the hammer hit the ground?

26. Kurt is standing on a steel beam 275.0 ft above the ground and throws a hammer straight up at an initial speed of 40.0 ft/s. At the instant he releases the hammer, he also drops a wrench from his pocket. Assume that neither the hammer nor the wrench hits anything while in flight.
     (a) Find the time difference between when the wrench and the hammer hit the ground.
     (b) Find the speed at which the wrench hits the ground.
     (c) Find the speed at which the hammer hits the ground.
     (d) How long does it take for the hammer to reach its maximum height?
     (e) How high above the ground is the wrench at the time the hammer reaches its maximum height?

27. One ball is dropped from a cliff. A second ball is thrown down 1.00 s later with an initial speed of 40.0 ft/s. How long after the second ball is thrown will the second ball overtake the first?

28. A car with velocity 2.00 m/s at $t = 0$ accelerates at 4.00 m/s^2 for 2.50 s. What is its velocity at $t = 2.50$ s?

29. A truck moving at 30.0 km/h accelerates at a constant rate of 3.50 m/s^2 for 6.80 s. Find its final velocity in km/h.

30. A bus accelerates from rest at a constant 5.50 m/s^2. How long will it take to reach 28.0 m/s?

31. A motorcycle slows from 22.0 m/s to 3.00 m/s with constant acceleration -2.10 m/s^2. How much time is required to slow down?

4.4 Projectile Motion

A **projectile** is a propelled object that travels through the air but has no capacity to propel itself. Up to this point, we have discussed projectiles either being thrown straight up or dropped straight down. We now discuss objects being thrown at an angle. This type of motion uses the same principles and formulas as in the previous section on uniformly accelerated motion. However, two dimensions are needed to analyze projectile motion; x will represent horizontal and y will represent vertical.

A baseball pop fly to right field, a car driving off a cliff, and water flowing out of a hose are all examples of projectile motion. **Projectile motion** is the movement of a projectile as it travels through the air influenced only by its initial velocity and gravitational acceleration.

Consider the example of a ball being rolled across a table at a constant 2.00 m/s. The ball moves 2.00 m for every second that it travels. Assuming no friction, the ball would continue to roll at that same speed (Fig. 4.18). As the ball approaches and rolls off the edge of the table, the ball continues to move horizontally at 2.00 m/s until it strikes the floor. Horizontally, there is nothing causing the ball to speed up or slow down, so it continues with that same horizontal motion.

Figure 4.18   A ball rolling across a table with a constant velocity

2.00 m/s

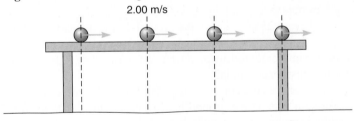

Figure 4.19   If a ball is simply dropped from the edge of a table, it will accelerate toward the ground, picking up speed and covering a greater and greater distance as time passes.

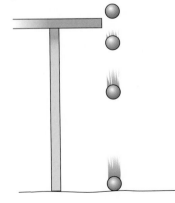

As the ball rolls off the table, gravity is accelerating the ball downward at a rate of $g = 9.80$ m/s^2 (Fig. 4.19). As a result, the ball increases its vertical speed by 9.80 m/s for every second it falls. Vertically, the problem can be treated as any other uniformly accelerated motion problem as seen in the previous section.

A projectile motion problem may be separated into the horizontal frame, the nongravitational acceleration component, and into the vertical frame, the gravitational acceleration component. Using formulas in both the horizontal and vertical frames allows you to solve problems such as finding the speed the ball was traveling as it came off the table, the distance the ball landed from the edge of the table, and the time the ball was in the air (Fig. 4.20).

Figure 4.20

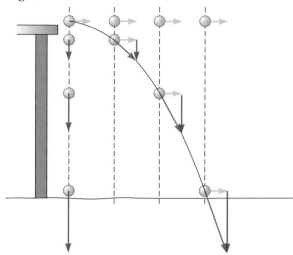

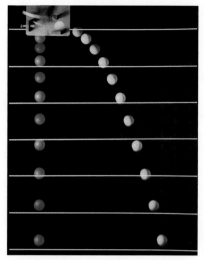

(a) This schematic shows the positions of a ball being dropped and a ball being projected horizontally from the same height at the same time. Note that the blue vertical component of the velocity of both balls is increasing and is the same for both balls at each instant, that the yellow horizontal component of the projected ball is constant at each instant, and that the incremental red resultant velocity of the projected ball is the resultant of each corresponding set of vertical and horizontal components, which results in the curved motion shown.

(b) Here a series of times flash photos shows that a dropped red ball and a yellow ball projected horizontally from the same height at the same time fall vertically at the same rate, and so they hit the ground at the same time, as demonstrated in the schematic in part (a).

TRY THIS ACTIVITY

Quarter and the Ruler Trick

Set up two coins and a ruler as shown in Fig. 4.21. Flick the ruler so the two coins are launched off the table at the same time. The coin closer to your stationary hand will travel more slowly than the coin farther away from your stationary hand. Which coin hits the ground first? Why?

Figure 4.21

A ball rolls at a constant speed of 0.700 m/s as it reaches the end of a 1.30-m-high table (Fig. 4.22). How far from the edge of the table does the ball land?

EXAMPLE 1

Sketch: **Figure 4.22**

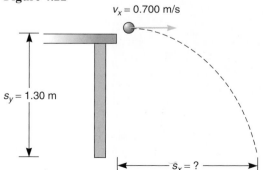

$v_x = 0.700$ m/s

$s_y = 1.30$ m

$s_x = ?$

Data:

$$v_{iy} = 0 \text{ m/s} \qquad\qquad v_x = 0.700 \text{ m/s}$$
$$s_y = 1.30 \text{ m} \qquad\qquad s_x = \,?$$

Basic Equations:

$$s_y = v_{iy}\, t + \tfrac{1}{2}a_y t^2 \qquad\qquad s_x = v_x t$$

Working Equations (with $v_{iy} = 0$):

$$t = \sqrt{\dfrac{2s_y}{a}} \qquad\qquad s_x = v_x t$$

Substitution:

$$t = \sqrt{\dfrac{2(1.30 \text{ m})}{9.80 \text{ m/s}^2}}$$
$$= 0.515 \text{ s}$$

$$s_x = (0.700 \text{ m/s})(0.515 \text{ s})$$
$$= 0.361 \text{ m}$$

· · · · · · · · · · · · · · · · ·

Projectiles launched at an angle need to be treated the same as a ball rolled off a table. However, unlike such a ball, which has an initial vertical velocity of zero, a projectile launched at an angle has an initial vertical velocity. The **range** is the horizontal distance that a projectile will travel before striking the ground. The range and the flight time may be found as follows.

1. Separate the original speed of the projectile into *horizontal* (*x*-component of the velocity) and *vertical components* (*y*-component of the velocity) using vectors and trigonometry (Fig. 4.23).
2. Use the equation $s_x = v_x t$ to find the range. The horizontal component of the velocity does not change because gravitational acceleration does not act in the horizontal direction (Fig. 4.24). (Gravity pulls objects down in only the vertical direction.)
3. Use the vertical component of the velocity and uniformly accelerated motion equations to determine how long the projectile will be in the air. Since gravity accelerates the projectile, use the following formula and solve for time: $v_f = v_i + at$.

Note: Since the vertical components of v_i and v_f are equal but opposite in direction and therefore have opposite signs, the time for the projectile going up is the same as the time for it going down.

Figure 4.23   The ball is kicked with a horizontal (yellow vector) and vertical (blue vector) velocity. The red vector represents the resultant of the horizontal and vertical velocities.

Figure 4.24   Velocity vectors are shown as a ball kicked into the air travels through its trajectory. Note that the yellow horizontal component remains constant at each instant while the blue vertical component decreases as the ball rises until the ball reaches its peak, at which the vertical component is zero, and then the vertical component increases as the ball falls.

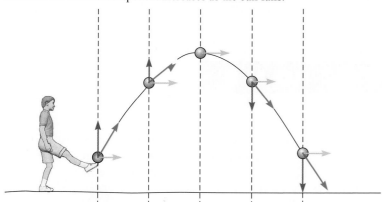

A baseball is hit and moves initially at an angle of 35.0° above the horizontal ground with a velocity of 25.0 m/s as shown in Fig. 4.25. (a) What are the vertical and horizontal components of the initial velocity of the ball? (b) How long will the ball be in the air? (c) What will be the range for this projectile?

EXAMPLE 2

Sketch: Figure 4.25

Data:

$$v = 25.0 \text{ m/s}$$
$$A = 35.0°$$

Basic Equations:

$$|\mathbf{v}_x| = |\mathbf{v}| \cos A$$
$$|\mathbf{v}_y| = |\mathbf{v}| \sin A$$
$$v_{fy} = v_{iy} + a_y t$$
$$s_x = v_x t$$

Working Equations: Same except for

$$t = \frac{v_{fy} - v_{iy}}{a_y}$$

Substitutions:

(a) $|\mathbf{v}_x| = (25.0 \text{ m/s})(\cos 35.0°)$

$\qquad = 20.5 \text{ m/s}$

$\qquad |\mathbf{v}_y| = (25.0 \text{ m/s})(\sin 35.0°)$

$\qquad = 14.3 \text{ m/s}$

(b) $\quad t = \dfrac{(14.3 \text{ m/s}) - (-14.3 \text{ m/s})}{9.80 \text{ m/s}^2}$

$\quad = 2.92 \text{ s}$

(c) $\quad s_x = (20.5 \text{ m/s})(2.92 \text{ s})$

$\quad = 59.9 \text{ m}$

....

PHYSICS CONNECTIONS

Orbiting Cannonballs?

Isaac Newton once said that if he could fire a cannonball with enough velocity, he could get it to circle the globe. Is this true? Can you really put something into orbit by launching it fast enough? In reality, there is too much air resistance and too many obstacles to allow this to happen. Theoretically, though, if we launch something with enough horizontal velocity, the earth itself would curve away before the cannonball strikes it. Figure 4.26 shows a cannonball launched with varying initial velocities. As the horizontal velocity of the cannonball increases, its range increases as well. In addition, the ball appears to fall farther due to the curvature of the earth. Finally, when the ball is launched with a large enough velocity, it completely misses the earth and achieves orbit.

Figure 4.26 Newton's diagram of a cannonball orbiting the earth

To place a satellite into orbit, a rocket or space shuttle must bring the satellite to a point above the earth's atmosphere where it will not experience any air resistance. The object is then given enough horizontal velocity so that although it is falling toward the earth, its horizontal velocity will prevent it from getting any closer to the surface. The concept of a falling object continuously missing the earth was a revolutionary concept developed by Isaac Newton over 300 years ago.

Communications satellites, the moon, and the astronauts in a space shuttle all are in a constant state of free fall but have the correct amount of horizontal velocity to prevent them from striking the earth. The speed required to keep a cannonball in orbit around the earth is approximately 17,700 mi/h. A space shuttle travels at approximately 17,400 mi/h because it orbits farther away from the earth.

PROBLEMS 4.4

Find the horizontal range for projectiles with the following speeds and angles.

	Angle	*Initial Speed*
1.	15.0°	35.0 m/s
2.	75.0°	35.0 m/s
3.	35.0°	35.0 m/s
4.	55.0°	35.0 m/s
5.	45.0°	35.0 m/s

6. Draw a conclusion about range and angles based on the answers to Problems 1 through 5.

7. Part of military training involves aiming and shooting a cannon. If a soldier sets the cannon at an angle of 62.0° and a launch velocity of 67.0 m/s, how far will the projectile travel horizontally?

8. A faulty fireworks rocket launches but never discharges. If the rocket launches with an initial velocity of 33.0 ft/s at an angle of 85.0°, how far away from the launch site does the rocket land?

9. An outfielder throws a baseball at a speed of $11\overline{0}$ ft/s at an angle of 25.0° above the horizontal to home plate 29$\overline{0}$ ft away. Will the ball reach the catcher on the fly or will it bounce first?

10. A bearing rolls off a 1.40-m-high workbench with an initial horizontal speed of 0.600 m/s. How far from the edge of the bench does the bearing land?

11. A mechanic's socket rolls off a 1.50-m-high bench with an initial horizontal speed of 0.800 m/s. How far from the edge of the bench does the socket hit the floor?

Glossary

Acceleration Change in velocity per unit time. (p. 107)

Acceleration Due to Gravity The acceleration of a freely falling object. On the earth's surface the acceleration due to gravity is 9.80 m/s^2 (metric) or 32.2 ft/s^2 (U.S.) (p. 114)

Deceleration An acceleration that indicates an object is slowing down. (p. 109)

Motion A change of position. (p. 99)

Projectile A propelled object that travels through the air but has no capacity to propel itself. (p. 120)

Projectile Motion The motion of a projectile as it travels through the air influenced only by its initial velocity and gravitational acceleration. (p. 120)

Range The horizontal distance that a projectile will travel before striking the ground. (p. 122)

Speed The distance traveled per unit of time. A scalar because it is described by a number and a unit, not a direction. (p. 99)

Terminal Speed The speed attained by a freely falling body when the air resistance equals its weight and no further acceleration occurs. (p. 115)

Velocity The rate of motion in a particular direction. The time rate of change of an object's displacement. Velocity is a vector that gives the direction of travel and the distance traveled per unit of time. (p. 100)

Formulas

4.1 $s = v_{avg}t$

4.2 $\Delta v = at$

4.3 $v_{avg} = \dfrac{v_f + v_i}{2}$ $s = v_i t + \frac{1}{2}at^2$

$a = \dfrac{v_f - v_i}{t}$ $s = \frac{1}{2}(v_f + v_i)t$

$v_f = v_i + at$ $2as = v_f^2 - v_i^2$

Review Questions

1. Velocity is
   (a) the distance traveled per unit of time.
   (b) the same as speed.
   (c) direction of travel and distance traveled per unit of time.
   (d) only the direction of travel.

2. A large heavy rock and a small marble are dropped at the same time from the roof of a three-story building. Neglecting air resistance, which object will strike the ground first?
   (a) The marble.   (b) The rock.
   (c) They both strike the ground at the same time.

3. One ball is thrown horizontally while another is dropped vertically. Which ball will strike the ground first?
   (a) Both strike the ground at the same time.
   (b) The horizontally thrown ball strikes first.
   (c) The vertically dropped ball strikes first.

4. At what launch angle with the ground does a projectile have the greatest horizontal range?
   (a) 0°   (b) 45°   (c) 60°   (d) 90°

5.   Where in a projectile's path would its speed be the least?
      (a)   Just as it is launched.   (b)   Just before it lands.
      (c)   It has the same speed throughout
            its entire motion.   (d)   At the top of its path.
6.   Explain your answer to Question 2.
7.   Explain your answer to Question 3.
8.   Distinguish between velocity and speed.
9.   Is velocity always constant?
10.   Why are vectors important in measuring motion? Provide two examples where vectors are used to help measure motion.
11.   Give three familiar examples of acceleration.
12.   Distinguish among acceleration, deceleration, and average acceleration.
13.   State the values of the acceleration due to gravity for freely falling bodies in both the metric and U.S. systems.

Review Problems

SKETCH

12 cm^2 w

4.0 cm

DATA

A = 12 cm^2, l = 4.0 cm, w = ?

BASIC EQUATION

A = lw

WORKING EQUATION

w = $\frac{A}{l}$

SUBSTITUTION

w = $\frac{12 \text{ cm}^2}{4.0 \text{ cm}}$ = 3.0 cm

1.   A boat travels at 17.0 mi/h for 1.50 h. How far does the boat travel?
2.   A commercial jet flies at $55\overline{0}$ mi/h for $300\overline{0}$ mi. For how much time does the jet fly?
3.   A plane flies north at 215 km/h. A wind from the east blows at 69 km/h. What is the plane's new velocity with respect to the ground in standard position?
4.   A glider flies southeast (at 320.0°) at 25.0 km/h. A wind blows at 12.0 km/h from 15.0° south of west. What is the new velocity of the glider with respect to the ground in standard position?
5.   A runner starts from rest and attains a speed of 8.00 ft/s after 2.00 s. What is the runner's acceleration?
6.   A race car goes from rest to 150 km/h with an acceleration of 6.0 m/s^2. How many seconds does it take?
7.   A sailboat has an initial velocity of 10.0 km/h and accelerates to 20.0 km/h. Find its average velocity.
8.   A skateboarder starts from rest and accelerates at a rate of 1.30 m/s^2 for 3.00 s. What is his final velocity?
9.   A plane has an average velocity of $50\overline{0}$ km/h. How long does it take to travel 1.5×10^4 km?
10.   A train has a final velocity of 110 km/h. It accelerated for 36 s at 0.50 m/s^2. What was its initial velocity?
11.   A boulder is rolling down a hill at 8.00 m/s before it comes to rest 17.0 s later. What is its average velocity?
12.   A truck accelerates from rest to 120 km/h in 13 s. Find its acceleration.
13.   An airplane reaches a velocity of 71.0 m/s when it takes off. What must its acceleration be if the runway is 1.00 km long?
14.   An airplane accelerates at 3.00 m/s^2 from a velocity of 21.0 m/s over a distance of 535 m. What is its final velocity?
15.   A bullet is fired vertically upward and reaches a height of 2150 m.
      (a)   Find its initial velocity.
      (b)   How long does it take to reach its maximum height?
      (c)   How long is it in flight?
16.   A rock is thrown down with an initial speed of 10.0 m/s from a bridge to the water below. It takes 2.75 s for the rock to hit the water.
      (a)   Find the speed of the rock as it hits the water.
      (b)   How high is the bridge above the water?
17.   A shot put is hurled at 9.43 m/s at an angle of 55.0°. Ignoring the height of the shot putter, what is the range of the shot?
18.   An archer needs to hit a bull's eye on a target at eye level 60.0 ft away. If the archer fires the arrow from eye level with a speed of 47.0 ft/s at an angle of 25.0° above the horizontal, will the arrow hit the target?

APPLIED CONCEPTS

1. Amy walks at an average speed of 1.75 m/s toward her airport gate. When she comes within 57.5 m of her gate, she gets onto and continues to walk on a people mover at the same rate. (a) If she arrives at the gate 15.3 s after getting on the people mover, how fast was she moving relative to the ground? (b) What was the speed of the people mover?

2. A novice captain is pointing his ferryboat directly across the river at a speed of 15.7 mi/h. If he does not pay attention to the current that is headed downriver at 5.35 mi/h, what will be his resultant speed and direction? (Consider that the current and the boat's initial heading are perpendicular to each other.)

3. Anette is a civil engineer and needs to determine the length of a highway on-ramp before construction begins. If the average vehicle takes 10.8 s to go from 20.0 mi/h to 60.0 mi/h, how long should she design the separate merge lane to be so a car can reach a speed of 60.0 mi/h before merging?

4. As a movie stunt coordinator, you need to be sure a stunt will be safe before it is performed. If a stuntwoman is to run horizontally off the roof of a three-story building and land on a foam pad 7.35 m away from the base of the building, how fast should she run as she leaves the roof? (Each story is 4.00 m.)

5. As a newspaper delivery boy, Jason needs to know his projectile motion to throw a paper horizontally from a height of 1.40 m to a door that is 13.5 m away. What must the paper's velocity be for it to reach the door?

Force=Mass×Acceleration

$F = ma$

F

a

Classical physics is sometimes called Newtonian physics in honor of Sir Isaac Newton, who lived from 1642 to 1727 and formulated three laws of motion that summarize much of the behavior of moving bodies. Forces may cause motion. Inertia tends to resist the influence of an applied force. Forces, inertia, friction, and how they relate to motion are considered now.

Objectives

The major goals of this chapter are to enable you to:

1. Relate force and the law of inertia.
2. Apply the law of acceleration.
3. Identify components of friction.
4. Analyze forces in one dimension.
5. Distinguish among weight, mass, and gravity.
6. Analyze how the law of action and reaction is used.

5.1 Force and the Law of Inertia

As discussed in the previous chapter, if an object changes its velocity, we say it accelerates. But what causes an object to accelerate? Let's take an example of a soccer ball at rest on a field. What must you do to accelerate the ball? Similarly, if your car is approaching a red stoplight, what must you do to make the car accelerate to rest? The answer in both instances is to apply a force.

A **force** is any push or pull. Forces tend to either change the motion of an object or prevent the object from changing its motion. Force is a vector quantity and therefore has both magnitude and direction. The force tends to produce acceleration in the direction of its application. Therefore, if you want to accelerate the soccer ball, you need to kick it in the direction you want the ball to move. To get the car to slow down, you apply the brakes, which creates a force in the opposite direction of the car's motion and causes a negative acceleration.

Not all forces result in acceleration. For example, if you attempt to push a chest, it may not move because another force, in this case a frictional force, matches your pushing force, preventing you from moving it (Fig. 5.1). This concept of concurrent forces will be covered in Chapter 7.

The units for measuring force are the newton (N) in the metric system and the pound (lb) in the U.S. system. The conversion factor is

$$4.45 \text{ N} = 1 \text{ lb}$$

Let's examine the relationship between forces and motion. There are three relationships or laws that were discovered by **Isaac Newton** during the late seventeenth century. The three laws are often called Newton's laws. The first law, called the **law of inertia**, is as follows:

Isaac Newton (1642–1727),

physicist, mathematician, and astronomer, was born in England. He is credited with discovering the laws of motion and gravitation, studying the nature of light and finding that white light is a mixture of colors which can be separated by refraction, inventing the calculus, and devising the first reflecting telescope. The metric unit of force, the newton, is named after him.

LAW OF INERTIA: NEWTON'S FIRST LAW
A body that is in motion continues in motion with the same velocity (at constant speed and in a straight line) and a body at rest continues at rest unless an unbalanced (outside) force acts upon it.

If an automobile is stopped (at rest) on level ground, it resists being moved. That is, a person is required to exert a tremendous push to get it moving. Similarly, if an automobile is

Figure 5.1 The pushing force and the frictional force cancel each other out, resulting in zero acceleration.

moving—even slowly—it takes a large force to stop it. This property of resisting a change in motion is called inertia. **Inertia** is the property of a body that causes it to remain at rest if it is at rest or to continue moving with a constant velocity unless an unbalanced force acts upon it. When the accelerating force of an automobile engine is no longer applied to a moving car, the car will slow down. This is not a violation of the law of inertia because there are forces being applied to the car through air resistance, friction in the bearings, and the rolling resistance of the tires [Fig. 5.2(a)]. If these forces could be removed, the auto would continue moving with a constant velocity. Anyone who has tried to stop quickly on ice knows the effect of the law of inertia when frictional forces are small [Fig. 5.2(b)].

Figure 5.2

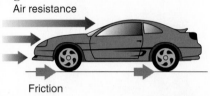

Air resistance

Friction

(a) Air resistance and friction slow the car.

(b) Inertia makes it hard to stop a car on ice.

The engine of a train makes use of the concept of inertia in incrementally starting a train that has far too much inertia to start moving all at once. The train is set in motion one car at a time. The couplers are loosely connected, which allows each car to start moving separately from the others. Then the inertia of each moving car aids in getting the rest of the cars moving. With use of this technique trains up to 1 mi long can be set in motion.

TRY THIS ACTIVITY

Inertia Tricks

Place a card on top of a glass. Then place a quarter on top of the card as in Fig. 5.3(a). Quickly flick the card horizontally. The inertia of the coin tends to keep it at rest horizontally. The force that causes the coin to move is the vertical force of gravity, which pulls it straight down into the glass as in Fig. 5.3(b).

Figure 5.3 When the card is flicked, the inertia of the quarter keeps it at rest until it falls into the glass.

(a)   (b)

How could you remove a tablecloth from under a set of dishes without removing the dishes from the table? The trick to keeping the dishes on the table is to use a very smooth tablecloth without any hem and very quickly jerk the tablecloth backward in a slightly downward direction. We suggest that you practice with heavy objects on plastic plates. Remember that the more mass placed on the plates, the greater is the inertia.

Some objects more than others tend to resist changes in their motion. It is much easier to push a small automobile than to push a large truck into motion (Fig. 5.4). **Mass** *is a measure of the inertia of a body*; that is, a measure of the resistance a body has to changing its motion. The common units of mass are the kilogram (kg) in the metric system and the slug in the U.S. system. The conversion factor is 1 kg = 0.0685 slug.

Figure 5.4   A larger body (in mass) has a greater resistance to a change in its motion than does a smaller one.

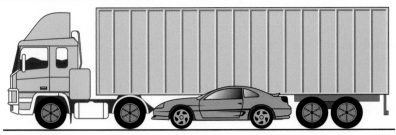

5.2 Force and the Law of Acceleration

The second law of motion, called the **law of acceleration**, relates the applied force, the mass, and the acceleration of an object.

> **LAW OF ACCELERATION: NEWTON'S SECOND LAW**
> The total force acting on a body is equal to the mass of the body times its acceleration.

In equation form this law is

$$F = ma$$

where F = total force
  m = mass
  a = acceleration

The formula states that when a force is applied to an object, the force causes the object to accelerate. The stronger the force, the larger is the acceleration. The weaker the force, the smaller is the acceleration. In addition, when pushed with the same force, a more massive object will accelerate less and a less massive object will accelerate more.

If the mass is kept constant,

   $F \sim a$ (The force is directly proportional to the acceleration.)

If the force is kept constant,

   $m \sim 1/a$ (The mass is inversely proportional to the acceleration.)

In SI units, the mass unit is the kilogram (kg) and the acceleration unit is metre/second/second (m/s^2). The force required to accelerate 1 kg of mass at a rate of 1 m/s^2 is

$$F = ma$$
$$= (1 \text{ kg})(1 \text{ m/s}^2)$$
$$= 1 \text{ kg m/s}^2$$

The SI force unit is the newton (N), named in honor of Isaac Newton, and is defined as

$$1 \text{ N} = 1 \text{ kg m/s}^2$$

In the U.S. system, the mass unit is the slug and the acceleration unit is foot/second/second (ft/s^2). The force required to accelerate 1 slug of mass at the rate of 1 ft/s^2 is

$$F = ma$$
$$= (1 \text{ slug})(1 \text{ ft/s}^2)$$
$$= 1 \text{ slug ft/s}^2$$

The U.S. force unit is the pound (lb) and is defined as

$$1 \text{ lb} = 1 \text{ slug ft/s}^2$$

Note: The other metric unit of force is the dyne. One dyne is the force required to accelerate 1 g of mass at the rate of 1 cm/s^2. The dyne is not an SI unit, and its use is less common.

EXAMPLE 1

What force is necessary to produce an acceleration of 6.00 m/s^2 on a mass of 5.00 kg?

Data:

$$m = 5.00 \text{ kg}$$
$$a = 6.00 \text{ m/s}^2$$
$$F = ?$$

Basic Equation:

$$F = ma$$

Working Equation: Same

Substitution:

$$F = (5.00 \text{ kg})(6.00 \text{ m/s}^2)$$
$$= 30.0 \text{ kg m/s}^2$$
$$= 30.0 \text{ N} \quad (1 \text{ N} = 1 \text{ kg m/s}^2)$$

. . . .

EXAMPLE 2

What force is necessary to produce an acceleration of 2.00 ft/s^2 on a mass of 3.00 slugs?

Data:

$$m = 3.00 \text{ slugs}$$
$$a = 2.00 \text{ ft/s}^2$$
$$F = ?$$

Basic Equation:

$$F = ma$$

Working Equation: Same

Substitution:

$$F = (3.00 \text{ slugs})(2.00 \text{ ft/s}^2)$$
$$= 6.00 \text{ slug ft/s}^2$$
$$= 6.00 \text{ lb} \quad (1 \text{ lb} = 1 \text{ slug ft/s}^2)$$

. . . .

EXAMPLE 3

Find the acceleration produced by a force of $50\overline{0}$ N applied to a mass of 20.0 kg.

Data:

$$F = 50\overline{0} \text{ N}$$
$$m = 20.0 \text{ kg}$$
$$a = ?$$

Basic Equation:

$$F = ma$$

Working Equation:

$$a = \frac{F}{m}$$

Substitution:

$$a = \frac{50\overline{0} \text{ N}}{20.0 \text{ kg}}$$

$$= 25.0 \frac{\text{N}}{\text{kg}}$$

$$= 25.0 \frac{\cancel{\text{N}}}{\cancel{\text{kg}}} \times \frac{1 \text{ kg m/s}^2}{1 \cancel{\text{N}}}$$

$$= 25.0 \text{ m/s}^2$$

Note: We use a conversion factor to obtain acceleration units.

················

PROBLEMS 5.2

Find the total force necessary to give each mass the given acceleration.

1. $m = 15.0$ kg, $a = 2.00$ m/s^2
2. $m = 4.00$ kg, $a = 0.500$ m/s^2
3. $m = 111$ slugs, $a = 6.70$ ft/s^2
4. $m = 91.0$ kg, $a = 6.00$ m/s^2
5. $m = 28.0$ slugs, $a = 9.00$ ft/s^2
6. $m = 42.0$ kg, $a = 3.00$ m/s^2
7. $m = 59.0$ kg, $a = 3.90$ m/s^2
8. $m = 2.20$ slugs, $a = 1.53$ ft/s^2

Find the acceleration of each mass with the given total force.

9. $m = 19\overline{0}$ kg, $F = 76\overline{0}0$ N
10. $m = 7.00$ slugs, $F = 12.0$ lb
11. $m = 3.60$ kg, $F = 42.0$ N
12. $m = 0.790$ kg, $F = 13.0$ N
13. $m = 11\overline{0}$ kg, $F = 57.0$ N
14. $m = 84.0$ kg, $F = 33.0$ N
15. $m = 9.97$ slugs, $F = 13.9$ lb
16. $m = 21\overline{0}$ kg, $F = 41.0$ N
17. Find the total force necessary to give an automobile of mass 1750 kg an acceleration of 3.00 m/s^2.
18. Find the acceleration produced by a total force of 93.0 N on a mass of 6.00 kg.
19. Find the total force necessary to give an automobile of mass 12$\overline{0}$ slugs an acceleration of 11.0 ft/s^2.
20. Find the total force necessary to give a rocket of mass 25,0$\overline{0}$0 slugs an acceleration of 28.0 ft/s^2.
21. A forklift has a mass of 975 kg. What force must be applied to give it an acceleration of 2.50 m/s^2?
22. A power wheelbarrow has a mass of 432 kg. What force must be applied to give it an acceleration of 1.75 m/s^2?
23. What is the rate of deceleration of a 14$\overline{0}$0-kg SUV that is going 75.0 km/h and then slows to 25.0 km/h in 8.20 s?
24. An earthmover slows from 15.0 km/h to 3.00 km/h in 2.70 s. What is its rate of deceleration?
25. Find the total force necessary to give a 14$\overline{0}$ kg mass an acceleration of 41.0 m/s^2.
26. Find the acceleration produced by a total force of 30$\overline{0}$ N on a mass of 0.750 kg.
27. Find the mass of an object with acceleration 15.0 m/s^2 when an unbalanced force of 90.0 N acts on it.

SKETCH

12 cm^2 w

4.0 cm

DATA

$A = 12$ cm^2, $l = 4.0$ cm, w = ?

BASIC EQUATION

$A = lw$

WORKING EQUATION

$w = \frac{A}{l}$

SUBSTITUTION

$w = \frac{12 \text{ cm}^2}{4.0 \text{ cm}} = 3.0$ cm

28. An automobile has a mass of $10\overline{0}$ slugs. The passengers it carries have a mass of 5.00 slugs each.
    (a) Find the acceleration of the auto and one passenger if the total force acting on them is $150\overline{0}$ lb.
    (b) Find the acceleration of the auto and six passengers if the total force is again $150\overline{0}$ lb.

29. Find the acceleration produced by a force of 6.75×10^6 N on a rocket of mass 5.27×10^5 kg.

30. An astronaut has a mass of 80.0 kg. His space suit has a mass of 15.5 kg. Find the acceleration of the astronaut during his space walk when his backpack propulsion unit applies a force to him (and his suit) of 85.0 N.

31. A discus thrower exerts a force of $14\overline{0}$ N on the discus. (a) If the discus has an acceleration of 19.0 m/s^2, what is the mass of the discus? (b) If the mass of the discus is doubled and the applied force remains the same, what is the new acceleration? (c) If the force is doubled and the mass is unchanged, how is the acceleration affected?

32. A scooter and rider together have a mass of 275 kg. (a) If the scooter slows with an acceleration of -4.50 m/s^2, what is the net force on the scooter and rider? (b) Describe the direction of the force and state the meaning of the $(-)$ sign.

33. A pickup truck with mass of 1230 kg moving at 105 km/h stops within a distance of 53.0 m. (a) What is the direction and size of the force that acts on the truck? (b) How much more slowing force would be required to stop the truck in half the distance?

5.3 Friction

Friction is a force that resists the relative motion of two objects in contact caused by the irregularities of the two surfaces sliding or rolling across each other, which tend to catch on each other (Fig. 5.5). In general, it is found that if two rough surfaces are polished, the frictional force between them is lessened. However, there is a point beyond which this decrease in friction is not observed. If two objects are polished such that the surfaces are very smooth, then the frictional force actually increases. (Two panes of glass is an example.) This is related to the fact that friction can also be caused by the adhesion of molecules of one surface to the molecules of the other surface. This adhesive force is similar to the electric forces that hold atoms together in solids.

Figure 5.5   Friction resists motion of objects in contact with each other.

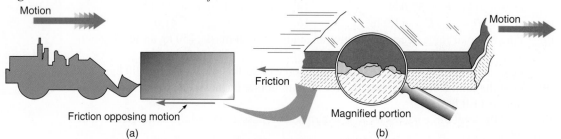

Static friction is the force that opposes the start of the relative motion of two objects in contact with each other. It is sometimes called starting friction. Once the touching objects are in motion relative to each other, the friction is generally less and is called *kinetic friction* or sliding friction.

Friction is both a necessity and a hindrance in our everyday lives. Without friction, walking, driving, swimming and many other normal activities would not be possible. Experiments with frictional forces indicate the following general characteristics:

1. ***Friction is a force that always acts parallel to the surface in contact and opposite to the direction of motion.*** If there is no motion, friction acts in the direction opposite any force that tends to produce motion [Fig. 5.6(a)]. The resistance to motion is the frictional force.

Figure 5.6 Friction increases as the force between the surfaces increases.

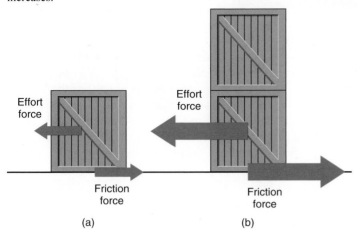

Effort force

Effort force

Friction force

Friction force

(a)

(b)

2. ***Static friction is greater than kinetic friction.*** When you push a large box across the floor, you probably notice that it takes more force to start it moving than to keep it moving. This is due to inertia. A box at rest tends to remain at rest, whereas a moving box tends to continue moving. Pushing someone on a sled is a good way to experience the difference between static and kinetic friction.

3. ***Friction increases as the force between the surfaces increases.*** It is much easier to slide a light crate than a heavy one across the floor [Fig. 5.6(b)]. *The area of contact is not relevant.* Friction depends only on the nature of the materials in contact and the force pressing them together.

The characteristics of friction can be described by the following equation:

$$F_f = \mu F_N$$

where F_f = frictional force
        F_N = **normal force** (force perpendicular to the contact surface)
        μ = coefficient of friction

The **coefficient of friction** is the ratio between the frictional force and the normal force of the object. The coefficient describes how rough or smooth the two surfaces are when they are in contact with each other. A higher coefficient of friction indicates two rough surfaces, whereas a lower number indicates two smooth surfaces.

Representative values for the coefficients of friction for some surfaces are given in Table 5.1. Values may vary with surface conditions.

Table 5.1   Coefficients of Friction (μ)

Material	Static Friction	Kinetic Friction
Steel on steel	0.58	0.20
Steel on steel (lubricated)	0.13	0.13
Glass on glass	0.95	0.40
Hardwood on hardwood	0.40	0.25
Steel on concrete		0.30
Aluminum on aluminum	1.9	
Rubber on dry concrete	2.0	1.0
Rubber on wet concrete	1.5	0.97
Aluminum on wet snow	0.4	0.02
Steel on Teflon	0.04	0.04

TRY THIS ACTIVITY

How to Find μ

Establish your own chart of coefficients of friction for various pairs of surfaces. Take any fairly massive object, perhaps a textbook, and measure its normal force by weighing it with a spring scale. (We will only be doing this activity on horizontal surfaces so the normal force is the same as the weight of the object.) To determine the coefficient of friction between the two surfaces, slowly pull horizontally on the spring scale until the object moves at a constant velocity. As the object moves, the reading on the scale gives the applied pulling force, which is also the force of friction. Record your data in a table and compare. The rougher materials should have a larger coefficient of friction than the smoother materials.

In general:

To reduce kinetic friction:

1. Use smoother surfaces.
2. Use lubrication to provide a thin film between surfaces.
3. Use Teflon to greatly reduce friction between surfaces when an oil lubricant is not desirable, such as in electric motors.
4. Substitute rolling friction for sliding friction. Rolling friction is the resistance that occurs when an object, such as a wheel or a tire, rolls on a surface. It is usually much smaller than sliding friction. Using ball bearings and roller bearings greatly reduces friction.

EXAMPLE 1

A force of 170 N is needed to keep a 530-N wooden box sliding on a wooden floor. What is the coefficient of kinetic friction?

Sketch:

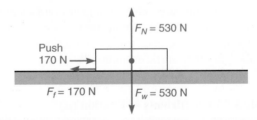

Data:

$$F_f = 170 \text{ N}$$
$$F_N = 530 \text{ N}$$
$$\mu = ?$$

Basic Equation:

$$F_f = \mu F_N$$

Working Equation:

$$\mu = \frac{F_f}{F_N}$$

Substitution:

$$\mu = \frac{170 \text{ N}}{530 \text{ N}}$$
$$= 0.32$$

Note that μ does not have a unit because the force units always cancel.

· · · · · · · · · · · · · · · ·

PHYSICS CONNECTIONS

Friction and Antilock Brakes

Since the invention of the automobile, engineers have worked to design brakes that reduce the stopping distance for automobiles. The most impressive advance in automobile braking technology is the antilock braking system (ABS). ABS technology is found on most new automobiles and works to prevent changing the friction between the tires and the road to sliding or kinetic friction. The ratio of the coefficients of static friction to kinetic friction of rubber on dry cement is 2.0 to 1.0.

Automobiles stop by using friction to slow down during normal braking situations. This friction takes place while the tires are in contact with the pavement. Locking the wheels or braking on ice or a film of water can quickly change static friction between the road and the tires to kinetic friction between the tires and the road. Sliding tires cause cars to go out of control and result in longer stopping distances.

Antilock braking systems use computerized sensors to monitor the rotational speed of the tires while braking. If the sensors detect a sudden decrease in the turning speed of the tires (indicating a skid), the control unit repeatedly releases and then restores the pressure to the brakes at a rate of up to 15 times per static. In essence, the ABS pulses the brakes on and off to keep the tires from sliding. Maintaining the static frictional force throughout braking keeps the car in control and reduces its stopping distance.

PROBLEMS 5.3

1. A cart on wheels weighs 2400 N. The coefficient of rolling friction between the wheels and floor is 0.16. What force is needed to keep the cart rolling uniformly?
2. A wooden crate weighs 780 lb. What force is needed to start the crate sliding on a wooden floor when the coefficient of static friction is 0.40?
3. A piano weighs 4700 N. What force is needed to start the piano rolling across the floor when the coefficient of static friction is 0.23?
4. A force of 850 N is needed to keep the piano in Problem 3 rolling uniformly. What is the coefficient of rolling friction?
5. A dog sled weighing 750 lb is pulled over level snow at a uniform speed by a dog team exerting a force of 60 lb. Find the coefficient of friction.
6. A horizontal conveyor belt system has a coefficient of kinetic friction of 0.65. The motor driving the system can deliver a maximum force of 2.5×10^6 N. What maximum total weight can be placed on the conveyor system?
7. A tow truck can deliver 2500 lb of pulling force. What is the maximum-weight truck that can be pulled by the tow truck if the coefficient of rolling friction of the truck is 0.10?
8. A snowmobile is pulling a large sled across a snow-covered field. The weight of the sled is 3560 N. If the coefficient of friction of the sled is 0.12, what is the pulling force supplied by the snowmobile?
9. An automobile weighs 12,000 N and has a coefficient of static friction of 0.13. What force is required to start the auto rolling?
10. A light truck weighs 14,000 N with a coefficient of static friction of 0.140. What force is required to start the truck rolling?

SKETCH

| 12 cm² | w |

4.0 cm

DATA

$A = 12$ cm², $l = 4.0$ cm, $w = ?$

BASIC EQUATION

$A = lw$

WORKING EQUATION

$w = \frac{A}{l}$

SUBSTITUTION

$w = \frac{12 \text{ cm}^2}{4.0 \text{ cm}} = 3.0$ cm

11. A stake truck weighs 20,0̄00 N with a coefficient of static friction of 0.130. What force is required to start the truck rolling?

12. If the coefficient of rolling friction of the auto in Problem 11 is 0.080, what force is required to keep it moving once it is in motion?

13. An alloy block is placed on a smooth composite table. If a force of 14.0 N is required to keep the 40.0-N block moving at a constant velocity, what is the coefficient of kinetic friction for the table and block?

14. If a 20.0-N casting is placed on the block in Problem 13, what force is necessary to keep the block and casting moving at constant velocity?

15. Rubber tires and wet blacktop have a coefficient of kinetic friction of 0.500. A pickup truck with mass 75̄0 kg traveling 30.0 m/s skids to a stop. (a) What is the size and direction of the frictional force that the road exerts on the truck? (b) Find the acceleration of the truck. (c) How far would the truck travel before coming to rest?

16. The coefficient of friction in Problem 15 is 0.700 if the tires do not skid. (a) Would the force of friction be greater than, less than, or equal to that in Problem 15? (b) Would the truck in (a) stop in a shorter, a longer, or an equal distance compared to the truck in Problem 15?

5.4 Total Forces in One Dimension

In the examples used to illustrate the law of acceleration, we discussed only total forces. We need to remember that forces are vectors and have magnitude and direction. The total force acting on an object is the resultant of the separate forces.

> When forces act in the same or opposite directions (in one dimension), the total, or net, force can be found by adding the forces that act in one direction and subtracting the forces that act in the opposite direction.

It is often useful to draw the forces as vectors.

EXAMPLE 1

Two workers push in the same direction (to the right) on a crate. The force exerted by one worker is 15̄0 lb. The force exerted by the other is 175 lb. Find the net force exerted.

Sketch:

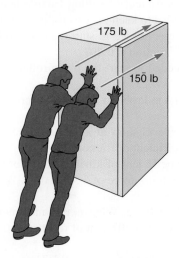

175 lb

15̄0 lb

Both forces act in the same direction, so the total force is the sum of the two.
Note: The Greek letter Σ (sigma) means "sum of."

$$\Sigma \mathbf{F} = 175 \text{ lb} + 15\bar{0} \text{ lb}$$
$$= 325 \text{ lb to the right}$$

The same two workers push the crate to the right, and the motion is opposed by a static frictional force of $30\bar{0}$ lb. Find the net force.

EXAMPLE 2

Sketch:

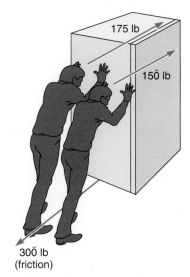

175 lb

$15\bar{0}$ lb

$30\bar{0}$ lb
(friction)

The workers push in one direction and static friction pushes in the opposite direction, so we add the forces exerted by the workers and subtract the frictional force.

$$\Sigma \mathbf{F} = 175 \text{ lb} + 15\bar{0} \text{ lb} - 30\bar{0} \text{ lb}$$
$$= 25 \text{ lb to the right}$$

The crate in Example 2 has a mass of 5.00 slugs. What is its acceleration when the workers are pushing against the frictional force?

EXAMPLE 3

Data:

$$F = 25 \text{ lb (from Example 2)}$$
$$m = 5.00 \text{ slugs}$$
$$a = ?$$

Basic Equation:

$$F = ma$$

Working Equation:

$$a = \frac{F}{m}$$

Substitution:

$$a = \frac{25 \text{ lb}}{5.00 \text{ slugs}}$$
$$= 5.0 \frac{\cancel{lb}}{\cancel{slugs}} \times \frac{1 \cancel{slug} \text{ ft/s}^2}{1 \cancel{lb}}$$
$$= 5.0 \text{ ft/s}^2$$

Note: We use a conversion factor to obtain acceleration units.

EXAMPLE 4

Two workers push in the same direction on a large pallet. The force exerted by one worker is 645 N. The force exerted by the other worker is 755 N. The motion is opposed by a frictional force of 1175 N. Find the net force.

$$\Sigma F = 645 \text{ N} + 755 \text{ N} - 1175 \text{ N}$$
$$= 225 \text{ N}$$

. . . .

PROBLEM SOLVING

SKETCH

```
┌──────────────┐
│  12 cm²      │ w
└──────────────┘
     4.0  cm
```

DATA

$A = 12 \text{ cm}^2$, $l = 4.0 \text{ cm}$, $w = ?$

BASIC EQUATION

$A = lw$

WORKING EQUATION

$w = \frac{A}{l}$

SUBSTITUTION

$w = \frac{12 \text{ cm}^2}{4.0 \text{ cm}} = 3.0 \text{ cm}$

Figure 5.7

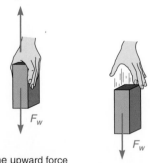

100 lb   500 lb

PROBLEMS 5.4

Find the net force including its direction when each force acts in the direction indicated.

1. 17.0 N to the left, 20.0 N to the right.
2. 265 N to the left, 85 N to the right.
3. 100.0 N to the left, 75.0 N to the right, and 10.0 N to the right.
4. 190 lb to the left, 87 lb to the right, and 49 lb to the right.
5. 346 N to the right, 247 N to the left, and 103 N to the left.
6. 37 N to the right, 24 N to the left, 65 N to the right, and 85 N to the right.
7. Find the acceleration of an automobile of mass 100 slugs acted upon by a driving force of 500 lb that is opposed by a frictional force of 100 lb (Fig. 5.7).
8. Find the acceleration of an automobile of mass 1500 kg acted upon by a driving force of 2200 N that is opposed by a frictional force of 450 N.
9. A truck of mass 13,100 kg is acted upon by a driving force of 8900 N. The motion is opposed by a frictional force of 2230 N. Find the acceleration.
10. A speedboat of mass 30.0 slugs has a 300-lb force applied by the propellers. The friction of the water on the hull is a force of 100 lb. Find the acceleration.
11. A truck with a mass of 14,000 kg is pushed with a force of 9200 N. If the frictional force is 2150 N, what is the truck's acceleration?
12. A trailer has a mass of 5000 kg. It is pulled by a truck with a force of 8750 N. If the frictional force is 2000 N, what is its acceleration?
13. A refrigeration unit on a job site must be slid into place. If the frictional force of 975 N opposes the motion and two workers apply a total force of 1095 N to the unit, what is the net force on the unit?
14. A light truck of 2000 kg mass has to be pushed with a force of 1975 N. If the frictional force is 550 N, what is its acceleration?

5.5 Gravity and Weight

Figure 5.8 Balancing gravity in holding a brick.

(a) The upward force of the hand equals the downward force of the weight.

(b) The downward force of the weight is now greater.

The **weight** of an object is the amount of *gravitational pull* exerted on an object by the earth. If this force is not balanced by other forces, an acceleration is produced. When you hold a brick in your hand as in Fig. 5.8, you exert an upward force on the brick that balances the downward force (weight). If you remove your hand, the brick moves downward due to the unbalanced force. The velocity of the falling brick increases, but the acceleration (rate of change of the velocity) is constant.

The acceleration of all objects near the surface of the earth is the same if air resistance is ignored. We call this acceleration due to the gravitational pull of the earth g. Its value is 9.80 m/s^2 in the metric system and 32.2 ft/s^2 in the U.S. system.

The *weight* of an object is the force exerted by the earth (or by another large body) and gives the object an acceleration g. This force can be found using $F = ma$, where $a = g$. If we abbreviate weight by F_w, the equation for weight is

$$\boxed{F_w = mg}$$

where F_w = weight
  m = mass
  g = acceleration due to gravity
  g = 9.80 m/s² (metric)
  g = 32.2 ft/s² (U.S.)

Find the weight of 5.00 kg.

EXAMPLE 1

Data:

$$m = 5.00 \text{ kg}$$
$$g = 9.80 \text{ m/s}^2$$
$$F_w = ?$$

Basic Equation:

$$F_w = mg$$

Working Equation: Same

Substitution:

$$F_w = (5.00 \text{ kg})(9.80 \text{ m/s}^2)$$
$$= 49.0 \text{ kg m/s}^2$$
$$= 49.0 \text{ N} \qquad (1 \text{ N} = 1 \text{ kg m/s}^2)$$

Find the weight of 12.0 slugs.

EXAMPLE 2

Data:

$$m = 12.0 \text{ slugs}$$
$$g = 32.2 \text{ ft/s}^2$$
$$F_w = ?$$

Basic Equation:

$$F_w = mg$$

Working Equation: Same

Substitution:

$$F_w = (12.0 \text{ slugs})(32.2 \text{ ft/s}^2)$$
$$= 386 \text{ slug ft/s}^2$$
$$= 386 \text{ lb} \qquad (1 \text{ lb} = 1 \text{ slug ft/s}^2)$$

Mass Versus Weight

Note that the mass of an object remains the same, but its weight varies according to the gravitational pull. For example, an astronaut of mass 75.0 kg has a weight of

$$F_w = mg = (75.0 \text{ kg})(9.80 \text{ m/s}^2) = 735 \text{ N}$$

on the earth. If that astronaut lands on the moon, where the acceleration due to gravity is less than it is on the earth, the astronaut will still have the same 75.0 kg mass but will weigh significantly less than 735 N. (The moon has less acceleration due to gravity than the earth in part because the moon is less massive than the earth. A full explanation will be given in Chapter 11.) The following example shows the astronaut's weight on the moon.

EXAMPLE 3

Find the 75.0-kg astronaut's weight on the moon, where $g = 1.63 \text{ m/s}^2$.

Data:

$$m = 75.0 \text{ kg}$$
$$g = 1.63 \text{ m/s}^2$$
$$F_w = ?$$

Basic Equation:

$$F_w = mg$$

Working Equation: Same

Substitution:

$$F_w = (75.0 \text{ kg})(1.63 \text{ m/s}^2)$$
$$= 122 \text{ N} \quad (1 \text{ N} = 1 \text{ kg m/s}^2)$$

Note that the astronaut's *mass* on the moon remains 75.0 kg.

....

Mass Versus Volume

Do not confuse mass and volume. The volume of an object is the measure of the space it occupies. Volume is measured in cubic units such as cm^3, ft^3, or L. The mass of an object is the amount of inertia or the amount of material it contains. The more mass contained in an object, the greater its inertia and the more force it takes to move it or change its motion. Compare the masses of two boxes of identical size, one filled with books and one empty. The box filled with books has more mass and requires more force to move it.

As an astronaut goes from the earth to the moon, his or her weight changes but mass and volume remain the same. Weight and mass are directly proportional in a given place as we saw earlier.

PROBLEMS 5.5

SKETCH

12 cm² | w

4.0 cm

DATA

$A = 12 \text{ cm}^2, l = 4.0 \text{ cm}, w = ?$

BASIC EQUATION

$A = lw$

WORKING EQUATION

$w = \frac{A}{l}$

SUBSTITUTION

$w = \frac{12 \text{ cm}^2}{4.0 \text{ cm}} = 3.0 \text{ cm}$

Find the weight for each mass.

1. $m = 30.0 \text{ kg}$ 2. $m = 60.0 \text{ kg}$
3. $m = 10.0 \text{ slugs}$ 4. $m = 9.00 \text{ kg}$

Find the mass for each weight.

5. $F_w = 17.0 \text{ N}$ 6. $F_w = 21.0 \text{ lb}$
7. $F_w = 12,\overline{0}00 \text{ N}$ 8. $F_w = 25,\overline{0}00 \text{ N}$
9. $F_w = 6.7 \times 10^{12} \text{ N}$ 10. $F_w = 5.5 \times 10^6 \text{ lb}$
11. Find the weight of an 1150-kg automobile.
12. Find the weight of an 81.5-slug automobile.
13. Find the mass of a 2750-lb automobile.
14. What is the mass of a 20,$\overline{0}$00-N truck?
15. What is the mass of a 7500-N trailer?
16. Find the mass of an 11,500-N automobile.
17. Find the weight of a 1350-kg automobile (a) on the earth and (b) on the moon.
18. Maria weighs 115 lb on the earth. What are her (a) mass and (b) weight on the moon?
19. John's mass is 65.0 kg on the earth. What are his (a) mass and (b) weight on the moon?
20. What is your weight in newtons and in pounds?
21. What is your mass in kilograms and in slugs?
22. What are your U.S. mass and weight on the moon?
23. What are your metric mass and weight on the moon?
24. John's mass is 65.0 kg on the earth. What are his U.S. (a) mass and (b) weight 40$\overline{0}$0 mi above the surface of the earth, where $g = 7.85 \text{ ft/s}^2$?

25. Maria weighs 115 lb on the earth. What are her U.S. (a) mass and (b) weight on Jupiter, where $g = 85.0$ ft/s^2?
26. John's mass is 65.0 kg on the earth. What are his metric (a) mass and (b) weight on Mars, where $g = 3.72$ m/s^2?
27. What are your metric mass and weight on Jupiter, where $g = 25.9$ m/s^2?
28. What are your metric mass and weight on Mars, where $g = 3.72$ m/s^2?
29. An automobile transmission weighs 995 N. What is its mass?
30. A power wheelbarrow weighs 210 N. What is its mass?

5.6 Law of Action and Reaction

When an automobile accelerates, we know that a force is being applied to it. What applies this force? You may think that the tires exert this force on the auto. This is not correct, because the tires move along with the auto and there must be a force applied to them also. The ground below the tires actually supplies the force that accelerates the car (Fig. 5.9). This force is called a *reaction* to the force exerted by the tires on the ground, which is called the *action force*. The third law of motion, the **law of action and reaction**, can be stated as follows:

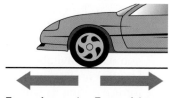

Figure 5.9 The ground supplies the force to accelerate the car.

Force of ground on tires (reaction)   Force of tires on ground (action)

$F_1 = -F_2$

> ## LAW OF ACTION AND REACTION: NEWTON'S THIRD LAW
> For every force applied by object *A* to object *B* (action), there is an equal but opposite force exerted by object *B* to object *A* (reaction).

When a bullet is fired from a handgun (action), the recoil felt is the reaction. These forces are shown in Fig. 5.10. Note that the action and reaction forces *never* act on the same object.

For every interaction, the forces always occur in pairs and are equal and opposite. When you sit on a chair, your weight pushes *down* on the chair; the chair pushes *up* with a force equal to your weight. If the chair pushed up with a force less than your weight, you would fall through it. If the chair pushed up with a force greater than your weight, you would be pushed up above the seat.

Most interactions depend on force. What would happen if you were standing in a small boat and tried to jump across to the nearby boat dock? You would fall into the water. Why? The force you would exert against the boat as you jumped would push it away, and the equal and opposite force the boat would exert on you would not result in much forward motion for you.

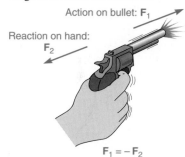

Figure 5.10 The magnitude of the reaction force always equals the magnitude of the action force.

Action on bullet: F_1

Reaction on hand: F_2

$F_1 = -F_2$

TRY THIS ACTIVITY

Balloon Rocket

Blow up a balloon and release it. What causes the balloon to accelerate? What causes it to stop accelerating? Use Newton's Third Law of Motion to describe how the balloon accelerates forward.

To create a straight path for the balloon, tape the balloon to a straw that is on a string that serves as a guide wire between two points or people as shown in Fig. 5.11.

Figure 5.11 A balloon rocket

PHYSICS CONNECTION

Shuttle Launch

Newton's Second and Third Laws of motion play a vital role during the launch of the Space Shuttle. (See Fig. 5.12.) Just as a massive gun recoils as a less-massive bullet is fired, the massive Shuttle recoils or "lifts off" as the less-massive, high-velocity gaseous exhaust is ejected from the rocket engines.

In order to overcome the force of gravity that the earth applies to all objects, the Space Shuttle must carry enough fuel in its external tank and solid rocket boosters to overcome the gravitational pull of the earth. To do so, the Shuttle carries more than 4.4 million pounds of rocket fuel for use during its launch. Compare this to the weight of the Space Shuttle itself, which is 170,000 pounds, and it is clear that the Shuttle uses a tremendous amount of fuel to lift off.

In order to take advantage of Newton's Third Law and send the Shuttle into space, the gaseous exhaust from the burned fuel is ejected from the Shuttle's rocket boosters at speeds of nearly 6000 mi/h. As the rocket fuel is burned and its gaseous exhaust is ejected out of the rocket, the overall weight of the shuttle's fuel decreases. According to Newton's Second Law, if the same force is applied but the mass is reduced, the acceleration increases.

Figure 5.12   The gas particles are expelled at a high velocity, causing the shuttle to recoil or launch into space.

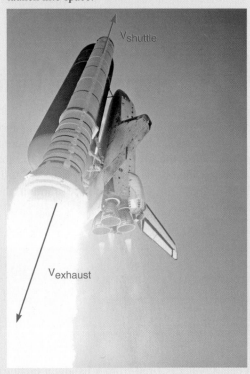

Glossary

Coefficient of Friction The ratio between the frictional force and the normal force of an object. The number represents how rough or smooth two surfaces are when moving across one another. (p. 135)

Force A push or a pull that tends to change the motion of an object or prevent an object from changing motion. Force is a vector quantity and thus has both magnitude and direction. (p. 129)

Friction A force that resists the relative motion of two objects in contact caused by the irregularities of two surfaces sliding or rolling across each other. (p. 134)

Inertia The property of a body that causes it to remain at rest if it is at rest or to continue moving with a constant velocity unless an unbalanced force acts upon it. (p. 130)

Law of Acceleration The total force acting on a body is equal to the mass of the body times its acceleration. (Newton's second law). (p. 131)

Law of Action and Reaction For every force applied by object A to object B (action), there is an equal but opposite force exerted by object B on object A (reaction). (Newton's third law). (p. 143)

Law of Inertia A body that is in motion continues in motion with the same velocity (at constant speed and in a straight line) and a body at rest continues at rest unless an unbalanced (outside) force acts upon it (Newton's first law). (p. 129)

Mass A measure of the inertia of a body. (p. 130)

Normal Force Force perpendicular to the contact surface. (p. 135)

Weight The amount of gravitational pull exerted on an object by the earth or by another large body. (p. 140)

Formulas

5.2 $F = ma$

5.3 $F_f = \mu F_N$

5.5 $F_w = mg$

where $g = 9.80 \text{ m/s}^2$ (metric)

$g = 32.2 \text{ ft/s}^2$ (U.S.)

Review Questions

1. Force
   (a) is a vector quantity.
   (b) may be different from weight.
   (c) does not always cause motion.
   (d) all of the above.
2. The metric weight of a 10-lb bag of sugar is approximately
   (a) 4.45 N.
   (b) 44.5 N.
   (c) 445 N.
   (d) none of the above.
3. Mass and weight
   (a) are the same.
   (b) are different.
   (c) do not change wherever you are.
4. According to Newton's second law, the law of acceleration,
   (a) acceleration is equal to mass times force.
   (b) mass is equal to mass times acceleration.
   (c) force is equal to mass times acceleration.
   (d) none of the above.

5. Friction
    (a) always acts parallel to the surface of contact and opposite to the direction of motion.
    (b) acts in the direction of motion.
    (c) is smaller when starting than moving.
    (d) is an imaginary force.
6. Cite three examples of forces acting without motion being produced.
7. (a) Does a pound of feathers have more inertia than a pound of lead?
    (b) Does the pound of feathers have more mass than the pound of lead?
8. How is inertia a factor in multicar pileups?
9. Using your own words, state Newton's first law, the law of inertia.
10. Distinguish between velocity and acceleration.
11. When the same force is applied to two different masses, which will have a greater acceleration?
12. Is 3 pounds heavier than 10 newtons?
13. Explain how life would be easier or more difficult without friction.
14. Explain how the weight of an astronaut is different on the moon than on the earth. Would the astronaut's mass be different?
15. Explain the difference between action and reaction forces.
16. State Newton's third law of motion, the law of action and reaction, in your own words.

Review Problems

SKETCH

4.0 cm

DATA

$A = 12 \text{ cm}^2, l = 4.0 \text{ cm}, w = ?$

BASIC EQUATION

$A = lw$

WORKING EQUATION

$w = \frac{A}{l}$

SUBSTITUTION

$w = \frac{12 \text{ cm}^2}{4.0 \text{ cm}} = 3.0 \text{ cm}$

1. A crate of mass 6.00 kg is moved by a force of 18.0 N. What is its acceleration?
2. A 825-N force is required to pedal a bike with an acceleration of 11.0 m/s². What is the mass of the bike and person?
3. A block of mass 0.89 slug moves with a force of 17.0 lb. Find the block's acceleration.
4. What is the force necessary for a 2400-kg truck to accelerate at a rate of 8.0 m/s²?
5. Two movers push a piano across a frictionless surface. One pushes with 29.0 N of force and the other mover exerts 35.0 N. What is the total force?
6. A 340-N box has a frictional force of 57 N. Find the coefficient of kinetic friction.
7. A truck pulls a trailer with a frictional force of 870 N and a coefficient of friction of 0.23. What is the trailer's normal force?
8. A steel box is slid along a steel surface. It has a normal force of 57 N. What is the frictional force?
9. A rock of a mass 13.0 kg is dropped from a cliff. Find its weight.
10. A projectile has a mass of 0.37 slug. Find its weight.
11. What force is required to produce an acceleration of 4.00 m/s² on a wrecking ball with a mass of 50.0 kg?
12. Find the total force necessary to give a 2$\overline{8}$0-kg motorcycle an acceleration of 3.20 m/s².
13. A force of 175 N is needed to keep a 64$\overline{0}$-N stationary engine on wooden skids from sliding on a wooden floor. What is the coefficient of static friction?
14. A crated garden tractor weighs 375 N. What force is needed to start the crate sliding on a wooden floor when the coefficient of static friction is 0.40?
15. Find the acceleration of a forklift of mass 14$\overline{0}$0 kg pushed by a force of 21$\overline{0}$0 N that is opposed by a frictional force of 425 N.
16. What is the weight of a 375-kg air compressor?
17. What is the mass of a 405-N welder?
18. What is the mass of a 12.0-N hammer?

APPLIED CONCEPTS

1. Engineers at Boeing developing specs for their "next-generation" 737 aircraft needed to know the acceleration of the 737-900 during a typical take-off. (a) What acceleration would they calculate given the plane's 78,200-kg mass and its maximum engine force of 121,000 N? (b) How fast would the plane be traveling after the first $50\overline{0}$ m of runway? (c) How fast would it travel after the first $150\overline{0}$ m of runway?

2. The Apollo spacecrafts were launched toward the moon using the Saturn rocket, the most powerful rocket available. Each rocket had five engines producing a total of 33.4×10^6 N of force to launch the 2.77×10^6-kg spacecraft toward the moon. (a) Find the average acceleration of the spacecraft. (b) Calculate the altitude of the rocket 2.50 min after launch—the point when the spacecraft loses its first stage.

3. Kirsten's mass is 3.73 slugs. Being the physics fan that she is, she decides to see what her apparent weight will be during an elevator ride. Beginning at rest, the elevator accelerates upward at 4.50 ft/s^2 for 3.00 s and then continues at a constant upward velocity. Finally, as the elevator comes to a stop at the top floor, the elevator slows down (accelerates downward but continues to move upward) at a rate of -5.5 ft/s^2 (the negative sign represents the downward direction). Find Kirsten's weight while the elevator is (a) at rest, (b) speeding up, (c) moving at a constant velocity, and (d) slowing down. The next time you ride in an elevator, concentrate on when you feel heavier and when you feel lighter.

4. A motorcycle racer traveling at 145 km/h loses control in a corner of the track and slides across the concrete surface. The combined mass of the rider and bike is 243 kg. The steel of the motorcycle rubs against the concrete road surface. (a) What is the frictional force between the road and the motorcycle and rider? (b) What would be the acceleration of the motorcycle and rider during the wipeout? (c) Assuming there were no barriers to stop the motorcycle and rider, how long would it take the bike and the rider to slow to a stop?

5. The motorcycle and rider are sliding with the same acceleration as found in Problem 4. If the motorcycle and rider have been sliding for 4.55 s, what will be the force applied to the motorcycle and the rider when they strike the side barrier and come to rest in another 0.530 s?

CHAPTER 6

MOMENTUM

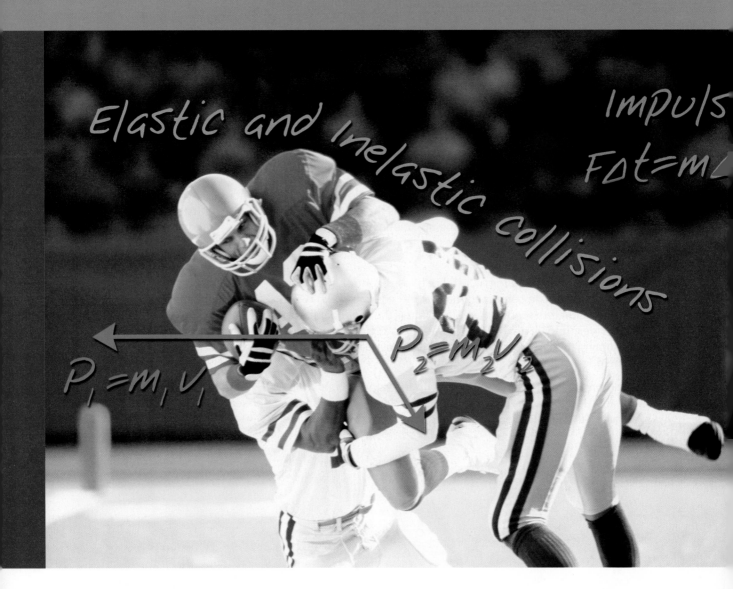

Momentum and impulse are important concepts in describing and understanding the motion of objects and the related effects on those objects. The law of conservation of momentum is an important law of physics, which helps us analyze how two objects interact with each other when they are in contact with each other and when they collide.

Objectives

The major goals of this chapter are to enable you to:

1. Use momentum and impulse in describing motion.
2. State the law of conservation of momentum and apply it to physical problems.
3. Analyze elastic and inelastic collisions of two objects.

6.1 Momentum and Impulse

We know that it is much more difficult to stop a large truck than a small car traveling at the same speed. The truck has more *inertia* and is more difficult to bring to a stop or to begin moving than the car. Momentum is a measure of the amount of inertia and motion an object has or of the difficulty in bringing a moving object to rest. **Momentum** *equals the product of the mass times the velocity of an object.*

$$p = mv$$

where p = momentum
   m = mass
   v = velocity

The momentum of a train makes it impossible to stop within a short distance, and this explains why it cannot stop at a railroad crossing when the engineer sees someone stopped or stalled at it.

The units of momentum are kg m/s in the metric system and slug ft/s in the U.S. system. Momentum is a vector quantity whose direction is the same as the velocity.

Find the momentum of an auto with mass 105 slugs traveling 60.0 mi/h. ◄

EXAMPLE 1

Data:

$$m = 105 \text{ slugs}$$
$$v = 60.0 \text{ mi/h} = 88.0 \text{ ft/s}$$
$$p = ?$$

Basic Equation:

$$p = mv$$

Working Equation: Same

Substitution:

$$p = (105 \text{ slugs})(88.0 \text{ ft/s})$$
$$= 9240 \text{ slugs ft/s}$$

EXAMPLE 2

Find the momentum of an auto with mass 1350 kg traveling 75.0 km/h.

Data:

$$m = 1350 \text{ kg}$$

$$v = 75.0 \; \frac{\text{km}}{\text{h}} \times \frac{1000 \text{ m}}{1 \text{ km}} \times \frac{1 \text{ h}}{3600 \text{ s}} = 20.8 \text{ m/s}$$

$$p = ?$$

Basic Equation:

$$p = mv$$

Working Equation: Same

Substitution:

$$p = (1350 \text{ kg})(20.8 \text{ m/s})$$

$$= 28{,}100 \text{ kg m/s}$$

EXAMPLE 3

Find the velocity that a bullet of mass 1.00×10^{-2} kg would have to have so that it has the same momentum as a lighter bullet of mass 1.80×10^{-3} kg and velocity 325 m/s.

Sketch:

$m_1 = 1.00 \times 10^{-2}$ kg $m_2 = 1.80 \times 10^{-3}$ kg

$v_1 = ?$ $v_2 = 325$ m/s

Data:

Heavier Bullet	Lighter Bullet
$m_1 = 1.00 \times 10^{-2}$ kg	$m_2 = 1.80 \times 10^{-3}$ kg
$v_1 = ?$	$v_2 = 325$ m/s
$p_1 = ?$	$p_2 = ?$

Basic Equations:

$$p_1 = m_1 v_1$$

$$p_2 = m_2 v_2$$

We want

$$p_1 = p_2$$

or

$$m_1 v_1 = m_2 v_2$$

Working Equation:

$$v_1 = \frac{m_2 v_2}{m_1}$$

Substitution:

$$v_1 = \frac{(1.80 \times 10^{-3} \text{ kg})(325 \text{ m/s})}{1.00 \times 10^{-2} \text{ kg}}$$

$$= 58.5 \text{ m/s}$$

The **impulse** on an object is the product of the force applied and the time interval during which the force acts on the object. That is,

$$\text{impulse} = Ft$$

where F = force
t = time interval during which the force acts

How are impulse and momentum related? Recall that

$$a = \frac{v_f - v_i}{t}$$

If we substitute this equation into Newton's second law of motion, we have

$$F = ma$$

$$F = m\left(\frac{v_f - v_i}{t}\right)$$

$$F = \frac{mv_f - mv_i}{t} \qquad \text{Remove parentheses.}$$

$$Ft = mv_f - mv_i \qquad \text{Multiply both sides by } t.$$

Note that mv_f is the final momentum and mv_i is the initial momentum. That is,

$$\text{impulse} = \Delta p \text{ (change in momentum)} = Ft = mv_f - mv_i$$

Note: The Greek letter Δ ("delta") is used to designate "change in."

The impulse is the measure of the change in momentum of an object in response to an exerted force. To change an object's momentum or motion, a force must be applied to the object for a given period of time. The amount of force and the length of time the force is applied will determine the change in momentum. A common example that illustrates this relationship is a golf club hitting a golf ball (Fig. 6.1). When a golf ball is on the tee, it has zero momentum because its velocity is zero. To give it or change its momentum (impulse), you apply a force for a given period of time. During the time that the club and ball are in contact, the force of the swinging club is transferring most of its momentum to the ball. The impulse given to the ball is the product of the *force* with which the ball is hit and the length of *time* that the club and ball are in direct contact. You can increase its momentum by increasing the *force* (by swinging the golf club faster) or increasing the *time* (by keeping the golf club in contact with the ball longer, which shows the importance of "followthrough").

Figure 6.1   When a person hits a golf ball with a golf club, the club applies a force F during the time t that the club is in contact with the ball. The impulse (change in momentum) is $Ft = mv_f - mv_i = mv_f$ because $v_i = 0$.

(a)   (b)

EXAMPLE 4

A 17.5-g bullet is fired at a muzzle velocity of 582 m/s from a gun with a mass of 8.00 kg and a barrel length of 75.0 cm.

(a) How long is the bullet in the barrel?
(b) What is the force on the bullet while it is in the barrel?
(c) Find the impulse exerted on the bullet while it is in the barrel.
(d) Find the bullet's momentum as it leaves the barrel.

Sketch:

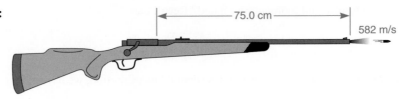

75.0 cm

582 m/s

(a) Data:

$$s = 75.0 \text{ cm} = 0.750 \text{ m}$$
$$v_f = 582 \text{ m/s}$$
$$v_i = 0 \text{ m/s}$$
$$v_{avg} = \frac{v_f + v_i}{2} = \frac{582 \text{ m/s} + 0 \text{ m/s}}{2} = 291 \text{ m/s}$$
$$t = ?$$

Basic Equation:

$$s = v_{avg}t$$

Working Equation:

$$t = \frac{s}{v_{avg}}$$

Substitution:

$$t = \frac{0.750 \text{ m}}{291 \text{ m/s}}$$
$$= 0.00258 \text{ s}$$

Note: This is the length of time that the force is applied to the bullet.

(b) Data:

$$t = 0.00258 \text{ s}$$
$$m = 17.5 \text{ g} = 0.0175 \text{ kg}$$
$$v_f = 582 \text{ m/s}$$
$$v_i = 0 \text{ m/s}$$
$$F = ?$$

Basic Equation:

$$Ft = mv_f - mv_i$$

Working Equation:

$$F = \frac{mv_f - mv_i}{t}$$

Substitution:

$$F = \frac{(0.0175 \text{ kg})(582 \text{ m/s}) - (0.0175 \text{ kg})(0 \text{ m/s})}{0.00258 \text{ s}}$$

$$= 3950 \text{ kg m/s}^2$$

$$= 3950 \text{ N} \qquad (1 \text{ N} = 1 \text{ kg m/s}^2)$$

(c) Data:

$$t = 0.00258 \text{ s}$$
$$F = 3950 \text{ N}$$
$$\text{impulse} = ?$$

Basic Equation:

$$\text{impulse} = Ft$$

Working Equation: Same

Substitution:

$$\text{impulse} = (3950 \text{ N})(0.00258 \text{ s})$$

$$= 10.2 \text{ N s}$$

$$= 10.2 \ (\text{kg m/s}^2)(\text{s}) \qquad (1 \text{ N} = 1 \text{ kg m/s}^2)$$

$$= 10.2 \text{ kg m/s}$$

(d) Data:

$$m = 17.5 \text{ g} = 0.0175 \text{ kg}$$
$$v = 582 \text{ m/s}$$
$$p = ?$$

Basic Equation:

$$p = mv$$

Working Equation: Same

Substitution:

$$p = (0.0175 \text{ kg})(582 \text{ m/s})$$

$$= 10.2 \text{ kg m/s}$$

Note: The impulse equals the change in momentum.

TRY THIS ACTIVITY

Scrambled Eggs

Figure 6.2

Drop a raw egg from a height of a few feet onto a surface that can be cleaned. Observe the motion of the egg as it hits the surface and note the time the egg takes to come to rest. Drop another raw egg from the same height into a suspended bed sheet. Again observe the motion of the egg as it hits the bed sheet and note the time the egg takes to come to rest (Fig. 6.2). Explain the connection between what happened to these eggs and how airbags in automobiles work.

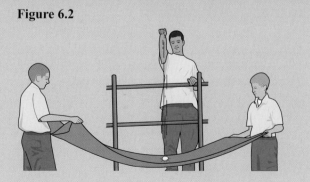

One of the most important laws of physics, the **law of conservation of momentum**, is the following:

LAW OF CONSERVATION OF MOMENTUM
When no outside forces are acting on a system of moving objects, the total momentum of the system remains constant.

For example, consider a 35-kg boy and a 75-kg man standing next to each other on ice skates on "frictionless" ice (Fig. 6.3). The man pushes on the boy, which gives the boy a velocity of 0.40 m/s. What happens to the man? Initially, the total momentum was zero because the initial velocity of each was zero. According to the law of conservation of momentum, the total momentum must still be zero. That is,

$$m_{boy}v_{boy} + m_{man}v_{man} = 0$$
$$(35 \text{ kg})(0.40 \text{ m/s}) + (75 \text{ kg})v_{man} = 0$$
$$v_{man} = -0.19 \text{ m/s}$$

Figure 6.3   Momentum is conserved by the lighter boy moving faster than the heavier man.

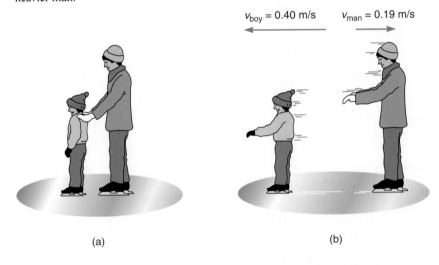

Note: The minus sign indicates that the man's velocity and the boy's velocity are in opposite directions.

Rocket propulsion is another illustration of conservation of momentum. **Wernher von Braun** was a pioneering rocket scientist. As in the example of the skaters, the total momentum of a rocket on the launch pad is zero. When the rocket engines are fired, hot exhaust gases (actually gas molecules) are expelled downward through the rocket nozzle at tremendous speeds. As the rocket takes off, the sum of the total momentums of the rocket and the gas particles must remain zero. The total momentum of the gas particles is the sum of the products of each mass and its corresponding velocity and is directed down. The momentum of the rocket is the product of its mass and its velocity and is directed up.

When the rocket is in space, its propulsion works in the same manner. The conservation of momentum is still valid except that when the rocket engines are fired, the total momentum is a nonzero constant. This is because the rocket has velocity.

Actually, repair work is more difficult in space than it is on the earth because of the conservation of momentum and the "weightlessness" of objects in orbit. On the earth, when a hammer is swung, the person is coupled to the earth by frictional forces, so that the person's mass includes that of the earth. In space orbit, because the person is weightless, there is no friction to couple him or her to the spaceship. A person in space has roughly the same problem driving a nail as a person on the earth would have wearing a pair of "frictionless" roller skates.

A change in momentum takes force and time because

$$\text{change in momentum} = \text{impulse} = Ft$$

As we noted earlier in this section, it is more difficult to stop a large truck than a small car traveling at the same speed and impossible to stop a rapidly moving train within a short distance. These events can be explained in terms of the **impulse–momentum theorem** as follows.

If the mass of an object is constant, then a change in its velocity results in a change in its momentum. That is,

$$\Delta p = m\Delta v$$

The impulse of an object equals its change in momentum. That is,

$$F\Delta t = \Delta p$$

Then,

IMPULSE–MOMENTUM THEOREM

$$F\Delta t = \Delta p = m\Delta v = mv_f - mv_i$$

What force is required to slow a 1450-kg car traveling 115 km/h to 45.0 km/h within 3.00 s? How far does the car travel during its deceleration?

EXAMPLE 5

Data:

$$m = 1450 \text{ kg}$$

$$v_f = 45\frac{\text{km}}{\text{h}} \times \frac{1 \text{ h}}{3600 \text{ s}} \times \frac{1000 \text{ m}}{1 \text{ km}} = 12.5 \text{ m/s}$$

$$v_i = 115\frac{\text{km}}{\text{h}} \times \frac{1 \text{ h}}{3600 \text{ s}} \times \frac{1000 \text{ m}}{1 \text{ km}} = 31.9 \text{ m/s}$$

$$\Delta t = 3.00 \text{ s}$$

$$F = ?$$

Basic Equation:

$$F\Delta t = mv_f - mv_i$$

Working Equation:

$$F = \frac{mv_f - mv_i}{\Delta t}$$

Substitution:

$$F = \frac{(1450 \text{ kg})(12.5 \text{ m/s}) - (1450 \text{ kg})(31.9 \text{ m/s})}{3.00 \text{ s}}$$

$$= -9380 \text{ kg m/s}^2 = -9380 \text{ N}$$

Note: The negative sign indicates a deceleration force.

Basic Equation:

$$s = \tfrac{1}{2}(v_f + v_i)t$$

Working Equation: Same

Substitution:

$$s = \tfrac{1}{2}(12.5 \text{ m/s} + 31.9 \text{ m/s})(3.00 \text{ s})$$
$$= 66.6 \text{ m}$$

· · · · · · · · · · · · · · · · · ·

PHYSICS CONNECTIONS

Airbags

During an automobile front-end collision, passengers will continue to travel forward until the dashboard, seat belt, or airbag applies a force on them to stop them. Airbags are designed to provide a cushion-like effect to gradually bring passengers to rest. Airbags increase the time it takes to bring passengers to a stop and reduce the force of the impact (Fig. 6.4). Airbags used in conjunction with seat belts help prevent death and serious injury.

Airbags expand from the steering wheel or dashboard when a sudden impulse or a change in momentum of the vehicle triggers a sensor that is connected to a heating element. The heating element causes a chemical reaction with a propellant that fills the airbag with nitrogen gas within $\frac{1}{20}$ s. This short inflation time gives the airbag enough time to inflate before the passenger strikes it. Within $\frac{1}{2}$ s, the collision is completed and the airbag deflates.

Airbags are designed to strike the average seat-belted man in the midsection of the body. An airbag, which expands at a rate of 150 mi/h, can be quite dangerous if the bag strikes short individuals in the face. Injuries to women and children caused by airbags are a serious problem. Efforts are being made to automatically adjust airbag deployment to make airbags safer for all passengers. Airbags are also used for side-impact collisions.

Figure 6.4 An airbag increases the time it takes to bring a passenger to a stop in a collision by reducing the force of the impact applied to the passenger.

Photo Courtesy of Insurance Institute for Highway Safety. Reprinted with Permission

PROBLEMS 6.1

Find the momentum of each object.

1. $m = 2.00$ kg, $v = 40.0$ m/s
2. $m = 5.00$ kg, $v = 90.0$ m/s
3. $m = 17.0$ slugs, $v = 45.0$ ft/s
4. $m = 38.0$ kg, $v = 97.0$ m/s
5. $m = 3.8 \times 10^5$ kg, $v = 2.5 \times 10^3$ m/s
6. $m = 3.84$ kg, $v = 1.6 \times 10^5$ m/s
7. $F_w = 1.50 \times 10^5$ N, $v = 4.50 \times 10^4$ m/s
8. $F_w = 3200$ lb, $v = 60$ mi/h (change to ft/s)
9. (a) Find the momentum of a heavy automobile of mass 180 slugs traveling 70.0 ft/s.
   (b) Find the velocity of a light auto of mass 80.0 slugs so that it has the same momentum as the auto in part (a).
   (c) Find the weight (in lb) of each auto in parts (a) and (b).
10. (a) Find the momentum of a bullet of mass 1.00×10^{-3} slug traveling 700 ft/s.
    (b) Find the velocity of a bullet of mass 5.00×10^{-4} slug so that it has the same momentum as the bullet in part (a).
11. (a) Find the momentum of an automobile of mass 2630 kg traveling 21.0 m/s.
    (b) Find the velocity (in km/h) of a light auto of mass 1170 kg so that it has the same momentum as the auto in part (a).
12. A ball of mass 0.50 kg is thrown straight up at 6.0 m/s.
    (a) What is the initial momentum of the ball?
    (b) What is the momentum of the ball at its peak?
    (c) What is the momentum of the ball as it hits the ground?
13. A bullet with mass 60.0 g is fired with an initial velocity of 575 m/s from a gun with mass 4.50 kg. What is the speed of the recoil of the gun?
14. A cannon is mounted on a railroad car. The cannon shoots a 1.75-kg ball with a muzzle velocity of 300 m/s. The cannon and the railroad car together have a mass of 4500 kg. If the ball, cannon, and railroad car are initially at rest, what is the recoil velocity of the car and cannon?
15. A 125-kg pile driver falls from a height of 10.0 m to hit a piling.
    (a) What is its speed as it hits the piling?
    (b) With what momentum does it hit the piling?
16. A person is traveling 75.0 km/h in an automobile and throws a bottle of mass 0.500 kg out the window.
    (a) With what momentum does the bottle hit a roadway sign?
    (b) With what momentum does the bottle hit an oncoming automobile traveling 85.0 km/h in the opposite direction?
    (c) With what momentum does the bottle hit an automobile passing and traveling 85.0 km/h in the same direction?
17. A 75.0-g bullet is fired with a muzzle velocity of 460 m/s from a gun with mass 3.75 kg and barrel length of 66.0 cm.
    (a) How long is the bullet in the barrel?
    (b) What is the force on the bullet while it is in the barrel?
    (c) Find the impulse exerted on the bullet while it is in the barrel.
    (d) Find the bullet's momentum as it leaves the barrel.
18. A 60.0-g bullet is fired at a muzzle velocity of 525 m/s from a gun with mass 4.50 kg and a barrel length of 55.0 cm.
    (a) How long is the bullet in the barrel?
    (b) What is the force on the bullet while it is in the barrel?
    (c) Find the impulse exerted on the bullet while it is in the barrel.
    (d) Find the bullet's momentum as it leaves the barrel.
19. (a) What force is required to stop a 1250-kg car traveling 95.0 km/h within 4.00 s?
    (b) How far does the car travel during its deceleration?
20. (a) What force is required to slow a 1350-kg car traveling 90.0 km/h to 25.0 km/h within 4.00 s?
    (b) How far does the car travel during its deceleration?

SKETCH

12 cm² w

4.0 cm

DATA
$A = 12$ cm², $l = 4.0$ cm, $w = ?$

BASIC EQUATION
$A = lw$

WORKING EQUATION
$w = \frac{A}{l}$

SUBSTITUTION
$w = \frac{12 \text{ cm}^2}{4.0 \text{ cm}} = 3.0$ cm

(c) How long does it take for the car to come to a complete stop at this same rate of deceleration?

21. What force is required to stop a 3000-kg truck going 35.0 km/h within 5.00 s?

22. What force is needed to stop a piece of heavy equipment moving 10.0 km/h in 6.00 s if its mass is 5000 kg?

6.2 Collisions

Collisions in One Dimension

The collision of two objects is an excellent example that demonstrates the law of conservation of momentum. Whenever objects collide in the absence of any external forces, the total momentum of the objects *before* the collision equals the total momentum *after* the collision. That is,

$$\text{total momentum}_{\text{before collision}} = \text{total momentum}_{\text{after collision}}$$

We will now study collisions in one dimension (along a straight line) by discussing the two extreme types, perfectly elastic and inelastic.

Elastic Collisions

In an **elastic collision**, two objects collide and return to their original shape without being permanently deformed. This happens when two billiard balls collide.

EXAMPLE 1

One ball of mass 0.600 kg traveling 9.00 m/s to the right collides with a second ball of mass 0.300 kg traveling 8.00 m/s to the left. After the collision, the heavier ball is traveling 2.33 m/s to the left. What is the velocity of the lighter ball after the collision?

Sketch:

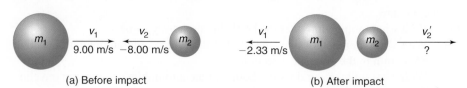

(a) Before impact   (b) After impact

Data:

$$m_1 = 0.600 \text{ kg}$$
$$m_2 = 0.300 \text{ kg}$$
$$v_1 = 9.00 \text{ m/s} \qquad \text{(right is positive direction)}$$
$$v_2 = -8.00 \text{ m/s} \qquad \text{(left is negative direction)}$$
$$v_1' = -2.33 \text{ m/s}$$
$$v_2' = ?$$

Basic Equation:

$$m_1 v_1 + m_2 v_2 = m_1 v_1' + m_2 v_2'$$

Working Equation:

$$v_2' = \frac{m_1 v_1 + m_2 v_2 - m_1 v_1'}{m_2}$$

Substitution:

$$v_2' = \frac{(0.600\,\text{kg})(9.00\,\text{m/s}) + (0.300\,\text{kg})(-8.00\,\text{m/s}) - (0.600\,\text{kg})(-2.33\,\text{m/s})}{0.300\,\text{kg}}$$

$$= 14.66\,\text{m/s} \qquad \text{(to the right)}$$

. . . .

Inelastic Collisions

In an **inelastic collision**, two objects collide and couple together. This happens when two railroad cars collide and couple together and move along the tracks.

A 1.75×10^4-kg railroad car traveling 8.00 m/s to the east collides and couples with a stopped 2.25×10^4-kg railroad car. What is the velocity of the joined railroad cars after the collision?

EXAMPLE 2

Sketch:

(a) Before impact   (b) After impact

Data:

$$m_1 = 1.75 \times 10^4\,\text{kg}$$
$$m_2 = 2.25 \times 10^4\,\text{kg}$$
$$v_1 = 8.00\,\text{m/s}$$
$$v_2 = 0\,\text{m/s}$$
$$v' = ?$$

Basic Equation:

$$m_1 v_1 + m_2 v_2 = (m_1 + m_2)v'$$

Working Equation:

$$v' = \frac{m_1 v_1 + m_2 v_2}{m_1 + m_2}$$

Substitution:

$$v' = \frac{(1.75 \times 10^4\,\text{kg})(8.00\,\text{m/s}) + (2.25 \times 10^4\,\text{kg})(0\,\text{m/s})}{1.75 \times 10^4\,\text{kg} + 2.25 \times 10^4\,\text{kg}}$$

$$= 3.50\,\text{m/s (east)}$$

. . . .

Collisions of Equal Masses in Two Dimensions

If the two colliding objects do not join together to form a single mass but ricochet off each other, the collision is elastic. The same principles of conservation of momentum apply to elastic collisions in two dimensions; that is, the total momentum in the system must be the same before and after the collision. The following example shows how such problems can be solved using the above principles.

T R Y   T H I S   A C T I V I T Y

Air Hockey Physics

Physics laboratory experiments often use air tracks or low-friction carts to study the conservation of momentum throughout collisions. Air hockey tables are typically more accessible for students and provide the low-friction surface that is needed to study the conservation of momentum. If you have access to an air hockey table, try the following collisions:

For elastic collisions, make sure that the pucks strike one another "head on" by aiming one puck directly toward the center of a stationary puck (Fig. 6.5). Make observations about the velocity of both pucks before and after the collision.

Figure 6.5   For collisions in one dimension, aim the puck directly at the center of the stationary puck as indicated by the blue velocity vector in the photo.

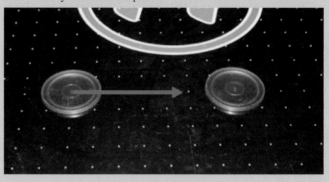

To observe an elastic collision for objects with different masses, place two pucks on top of one another with some double-sided tape between them so they remain secure to one another. Repeat the previous experiment by aiming a single puck at the doubled pucks and note the changes in velocity for both sets of pucks before and after the collision.

For inelastic collisions, wrap some double-sided tape around the sides of each of two pucks so they can stick together when they collide. Again, note the velocity of both pucks before and after the collision.

EXAMPLE 3

A 2.00-kg mass A is moving in an easterly direction at a velocity of 5.00 m/s. It crashes into a stationary mass B, which also has a mass of 2.00 kg. Mass A is deflected 30.0° north of its original path, and mass B is thrust in a direction 90.0° to the right of the final path of mass A.

(a)   What is the momentum of mass A after the collision?
(b)   What is the momentum of mass B after the collision?
(c)   What is the velocity of mass A after the collision?
(d)   What is the velocity of mass B after the collision?

Sketch:

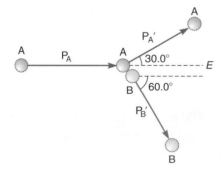

Data:

$$m_A = 2.00 \text{ kg}$$
$$v_A = 5.00 \text{ m/s}$$
$$m_B = 2.00 \text{ kg}$$
$$v_B = 0.00 \text{ m/s}$$

Basic Equation:

$$p = p'$$

Working Equation:

$$p_A + p_B = p'_A + p'_B$$

Before the collision:

Substitution:

$$p_A = m_A v_A \qquad p_B = 0$$
$$= (2.00 \text{ kg})(5.00 \text{ m/s})$$
$$= 10.0 \text{ kg m/s}$$

Use vector addition to find p'_A and p'_B and after the collision.

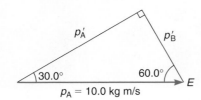

(a) Mass A

$$\cos 30.0° = \frac{p'_A}{p_A}$$
$$p'_A = p_A \cos 30.0°$$
$$= (10.0 \text{ kg m/s})(\cos 30.0°)$$
$$= 8.66 \text{ kg m/s}$$

(b) Mass B

$$\sin 30.0° = \frac{p'_B}{p_A}$$
$$p'_B = p_A \sin 30.0°$$
$$= (10.0 \text{ kg m/s})(\sin 30.0°)$$
$$= 5.00 \text{ kg m/s}$$

(c) Also, $p = mv$
so, $p'_A = m_A v'_A$
$$v'_A = \frac{p'_A}{m_A}$$
$$= \frac{8.66 \text{ kg m/s}}{2.00 \text{ kg}}$$
$$= 4.33 \text{ m/s}$$

(d) Also, $p = mv$,
so, $p'_B = m_B v'_B$
$$v'_B = \frac{p'_B}{m_B}$$
$$= \frac{5.00 \text{ kg m/s}}{2.00 \text{ kg}}$$
$$= 2.50 \text{ m/s}$$

. . . .

The law of conservation of momentum holds for all isolated, closed systems, regardless of the directions of the masses before and after the collision.

What appears to be a special case in Example 3 when the angle of deflection between the masses is 90° is actually verifiable experimentally. When the masses are equal and one is at rest before the collision, the angle of deflection between them is always 90°. The concept of conservation of momentum applies not only in games like billiards but also in nuclear physics in collisions between identical subatomic particles.

Example 3 also shows that since momentum is a vector quantity, momentum along the x-axis p_x must be conserved, so p_{A_x} (before the collision) equals $p'_A \cos 30.0° + p'_B \cos 60.0°$ (after the collision). Similarly, momentum along the y-axis is also conserved, so p_y (zero in the example before the collision) equals $p'_A \sin 30.0° + p'_B \sin 60.0°$ (after the collision). The sum of the x-components before the collision must equal the sum of the x-components after the collision and the sum of the y-components before the collision must equal the sum of the y-components after the collision.

TRY THIS ACTIVITY

Two-Dimensional Air Hockey Physics

The advantage of using an air hockey table to model the conservation of momentum is that it can easily be used to create two-dimensional collisions (Fig. 6.6). Repeat the previous Try This Activity with elastic and inelastic collisions, but now make sure the moving puck is aimed off center from the stationary puck. Carefully note the angle between the objects after they collide (the holes in the table can be used as guidelines for measuring the angle).

To add a level of complexity, create a two-dimensional collision with pucks of two different masses. Finally, attempt an inelastic collision at an angle. Note what happens. Get creative with the collisions, and make predictions and observe what actually happens and how it reinforces what you know about the conservation of momentum.

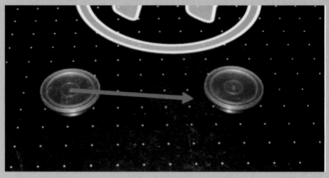

Figure 6.6   For collisions in two dimensions, aim the puck off center of the stationary puck as indicated by the blue velocity vector in the photo.

Collisions that demonstrate both elastic and inelastic characteristics as well as collisions in three-dimensional space will not be discussed in this text.

PHYSICS CONNECTION

Football Positions

The mass of football players has a significant role in the position they play on the football field. The function of offensive linemen is to protect the quarterback as defensive linemen attempt to cross the line of scrimmage (Fig. 6.7) and tackle the quarterback before a pass or a handoff can be made. Linemen make their way through the opposing team's line by using their momentum. Since linemen are positioned at the line of scrimmage, they don't have the opportunity to gain a lot of speed; as a result, players take advantage of their large mass to increase their momentum. According to the National Football League, the average weight of a lineman is 295 lb.

On the other hand, the function of a running back is to carry the football as far into the defensive territory as possible while avoiding tackles from the opposing team. Thus, a running back tends not to be as massive as a lineman and therefore can change velocity, and thus momentum, more easily than can a lineman attempting to run at such high speeds. According to the National Football League, the average weight of a running back is 240 lb.

Figure 6.7   Players on the line of scrimmage are typically more massive than those at other positions.

PROBLEMS 6.2

Assume a frictionless surface in each of the following problems.

1. One ball of mass 0.500 kg traveling 6.00 m/s to the right collides with a ball of mass 0.200 kg initially at rest. After the collision, the heavier ball is traveling 2.57 m/s to the right. What is the velocity of the lighter ball after the collision?

2. A ball of mass 625 g traveling 4.00 m/s to the right collides with another ball of equal mass that is initially at rest. The first ball is at rest after the collision. (a) What is the velocity of the second ball after the collision? (b) What is the velocity of the second ball if the mass of the two balls of equal mass changes?

3. A 0.600-kg ball traveling 4.00 m/s to the right collides with a 1.00-kg ball traveling 5.00 m/s to the left. After the collision, the lighter ball is traveling 7.25 m/s to the left. What is the velocity of the heavier ball after the collision?

4. A 90.0-g disk traveling 3.00 m/s to the right collides with a 75.0-g disk traveling 8.00 m/s to the left. After the collision, the heavier disk is traveling 7.00 m/s to the left. What is the velocity of the lighter disk after the collision?

5. A 98.0-kg parts cart with rubber bumpers rolling 1.20 m/s to the right crashes into a similar cart of mass 125 kg moving left at 0.750 m/s. After the collision, the lighter cart is traveling 0.986 m/s to the left. What is the velocity of the heavier cart after the collision?

6. A 75.0-kg paint cart with rubber bumpers is rolling 0.965 m/s to the right and strikes a second cart of mass 85.0 kg moving 1.30 m/s to the left. After the collision, the heavier cart is traveling 0.823 m/s to the right. What is the velocity of the lighter cart after the collision?

7. A railroad car of mass 2.00×10^4 kg is traveling north 6.00 m/s and collides with a railroad car of mass 1.50×10^4 kg traveling south 4.00 m/s. Find the velocity of the railroad cars that become coupled after the collision.

8. Find the velocity of the railroad cars in Problem 7 if the lighter car is initially at rest.

9. One cart of mass 12.0 kg is moving 6.00 m/s to the right on a frictionless track and collides with a cart of mass 4.00 kg moving in the opposite direction 3.00 m/s. Find the final velocity of the carts that become stuck together after the collision.

10. One cart of mass 15.0 kg is moving 5.00 m/s to the right on a frictionless track and collides with a cart of mass 3.00 kg. The final velocity of the carts that become stuck together after the collision is 1.50 m/s to the right. Find the velocity of the second cart before the collision.

11. A 1650-kg automobile moving south 12.0 m/s collides with a 2450-kg automobile moving north on an icy road. The automobiles stick together and move 3.00 m/s to the north after the collision. What is the speed of the heavier automobile before the collision?

12. A 16.0-g bullet is shot into a wooden block at rest with mass 4550 g on a frictionless surface. The block moves 1.20 m/s after the bullet strikes and becomes lodged in the block. Find the speed of the bullet before striking the block.

13. A 2450-kg automobile moving north 12.0 m/s collides with a 1650-kg automobile moving 8.00 m/s on an icy road. The automobiles stick together and move after the collision. Find the velocity of the automobiles after the collision if the automobiles were traveling in (a) opposite directions and (b) the same direction before the collision.

14. Ball A with a mass of 0.500 kg is moving east at a velocity of 0.800 m/s. It strikes ball B, also of mass 0.500 kg, which is stationary. Ball A glances off B at an angle of 40.0° north of its original path. Ball B is pushed along a path perpendicular to the final path of ball A.
    (a) What is the momentum of ball A after the collision?
    (b) What is the momentum of ball B after the collision?
    (c) What is the velocity of ball A after the collision?
    (d) What is the velocity of ball B after the collision?

15. A vehicle with a mass of 1000 kg is going east at a velocity of 30.0 m/s. It collides with a stationary vehicle of the same mass and is deflected 35.0° north of its original

course. The second vehicle's final path is 90° to the right of the final path of the first vehicle.

(a) What is the momentum of the first vehicle after the collision?
(b) What is the momentum of the second vehicle after the collision?
(c) What is the velocity of the first vehicle after the collision?
(d) What is the velocity of the second vehicle after the collision?

16. Two vehicles of equal mass collide at a 90° intersection. If the momentum of vehicle A is 1.20×10^5 kg km/h east and the momentum of vehicle B is 8.50×10^4 kg km/h north, what is the resulting momentum of the final mass?

17. A vehicle with mass of 950 kg is driving east with velocity 12.0 m/s. It crashes into a stationary vehicle of the same mass. Assume an elastic collision. The first vehicle is deflected at an angle of 40.0° north of its original path. The second vehicle's path is 90° to the right of the first vehicle's final path.

(a) What is the momentum of the first vehicle after the crash?
(b) What is the momentum of the second vehicle after the crash?
(c) What is the velocity of the first vehicle after the crash?
(d) What is the velocity of the second vehicle after the crash?

Glossary

Elastic Collision A collision in which two objects return to their original shape without being permanently deformed. (p. 158)

Impulse The product of the force exerted and the time interval during which the force acts on the object. Impulse equals the change in momentum of an object in response to the exerted force. (p. 151)

Impulse–Momentum Theorem If the mass of an object is constant, then a change in its velocity results in a change of its momentum. That is,
$F\Delta t = \Delta p = m\Delta v = mv_f - mv_i$. (p. 155)

Inelastic Collision A collision in which two objects couple together. (p. 159)

Law of Conservation of Momentum When no outside forces are acting on a system of moving objects, the total momentum of the system remains constant. (p. 154)

Momentum A measure of the amount of inertia and motion an object has or the difficulty in bringing a moving object to rest. Momentum equals the mass times the velocity of an object. (p. 149)

Formulas

6.1 $p = mv$
impulse $= Ft$
impulse $=$ change in momentum
impulse–momentum theorem

$$F\Delta t = \Delta p = m\Delta v = mv_f - mv_i$$

6.2   total momentum $_{\text{before collision}}$ $=$ total momentum $_{\text{after collision}}$

Review Questions

1. Momentum is
    (a) equal to speed times weight.
    (b) equal to mass times velocity.
    (c) the same as force.
2. Impulse is
    (a) a force applied to an object.
    (b) the initial force applied to an object.
    (c) the initial momentum applied to an object.
    (d) the change in momentum due to a force being applied to an object during a given time.
3. Why do a slow-moving loaded truck and a speeding rifle bullet each have a large momentum?
4. How are impulse and change in momentum related?
5. Why is "followthrough" important in hitting a baseball or a golf ball?
6. Describe in your own words the law of conservation of momentum.
7. Describe conservation of momentum in terms of a rocket being fired.
8. One billiard ball striking another is an example of a(n) _____ collision.
9. One moving loaded railroad car striking and coupling with a parked empty railroad car and then both moving on down the track is an example of a(n) _____ collision.
10. A father and 8-year-old son are standing on ice skates in an ice arena. The father then pushes the son on the back to give him a quick start. What do we know about the momentum of each person?

Review Problems

1. A truck with mass 1475 slugs travels 57.0 mi/h. Find its momentum.
2. A projectile with mass 27.0 kg is fired with a momentum of 5.50 kg m/s. Find its velocity.
3. A box is pushed with a force of 125 N for 2.00 min. What is the impulse?
4. What is the momentum of a bullet of mass 0.034 kg traveling at 250 m/s?
5. A 4.00-g bullet is fired from a 4.50-kg gun with a muzzle velocity of 625 m/s. What is the speed of the recoil of the gun?
6. A 150-kg pile driver falls from a height of 7.5 m to hit a piling.
   (a) What is its speed as it hits the piling?
   (b) With what momentum does it hit the piling?
7. A 15.0-g bullet is fired at a muzzle velocity of 3250 m/s from a high-powered rifle with a mass of 4.75 kg and barrel of length 75.0 cm.
   (a) How long is the bullet in the barrel?
   (b) What is the force on the bullet while it is in the barrel?
   (c) Find the impulse exerted on the bullet while it is in the barrel.
   (d) Find the bullet's momentum as it leaves the barrel.
8. What force is required to slow a 1250-kg car traveling 115 km/h to 30.0 km/h within 3.50 s? (a) How far does the car travel during its deceleration? (b) How long does it take for the car to come to a complete stop at this same rate of deceleration?
9. One ball of mass 575 g traveling 3.50 m/s to the right collides with another ball of mass 425 g that is initially at rest. After the collision, the lighter ball is traveling 4.03 m/s. What is the velocity of the heavier ball after the collision?
10. A railroad car of mass 2.25×10^4 kg is traveling east 5.50 m/s and collides with a railroad car of mass 3.00×10^4 kg traveling west 1.50 m/s. Find the velocity of the railroad cars that become coupled after the collision.
11. A 195-g ball traveling 4.50 m/s to the right collides with a 125-g ball traveling 12.0 m/s to the left. After the collision, the heavier ball is traveling 8.40 m/s to the left. What is the velocity of the lighter ball after the collision?
12. Two trucks of equal mass collide at a 90° intersection. If the momentum of truck A is 9.50×10^4 kg km/h east and the momentum of truck B is 1.05×10^5 kg km/h north, what is the resulting momentum of the final mass, assuming the trucks remain joined together following the crash?
13. Ball A, of mass 0.35 kg, has a velocity 0.75 m/s east. It strikes a stationary ball, also of mass 0.35 kg. Ball A deflects off B at an angle of 37.0° north of A's original path. Ball B moves in a line 90° right of the final path of A.
    (a) Find ball A's momentum after the collision.
    (b) Find ball B's momentum after the collision.
    (c) Find the velocity of A after the collision.
    (d) Find the velocity of B after the collision.

APPLIED CONCEPTS

1. A coach knows it is vital that the volleyballs be fully inflated before a match. (a) Calculate the impulse on a spiked 0.123-slug volleyball when the incoming velocity of the ball is −11.5 ft/s and the outgoing velocity is 57.3 ft/s. (b) Using physics terms, explain what would happen to the outgoing velocity and the impulse on the ball if it were not fully inflated.

2. An automobile accident causes both the driver and passenger front airbags to deploy. (a) If the vehicle was traveling at a speed of 88.6 km/h and is now at rest, find the change in momentum for both the 68.4-kg adult driver and the 34.2-kg child passenger. (b) The adult took 0.564 s and the child took 0.260 s to come to rest. Find the force that the airbag exerted on each individual. Explain why airbags tend to be dangerous for children.

3. Several African tribes engage in a ritual much like bungee jumping, in which a tree vine is used instead of a bungee cord. (a) A 70.8-kg person falls from a cliff with such a vine attached to his ankles. Find the force applied to his ankles if it takes 0.355 s to change his velocity from −18.5 m/s to rest (the negative sign represents the downward direction). (b) Find the force applied to the person's ankles when he takes 1.98 s to change his velocity from −18.5 m/s to +9.75 m/s using a manufactured bungee cord (remember that a bungee cord causes the jumper to bounce back upward). (c) Using physics terms, describe why it is safer to use a bungee cord than a tree vine.

4. Sally, who weighs 125 lb, knows that getting out of a 65.5-lb canoe can be a difficult experience. (a) What happens to the canoe's velocity if she attempts to step out of the canoe and onto the dock with a velocity of 3.50 ft/s? (b) If the canoe were heavier, would it be easier or harder to step out of it?

5. An automobile accident investigator needs to determine the initial westerly velocity of a Jeep ($m = 1720$ kg) that may have been speeding before colliding head-on with a Volkswagen ($m = 1510$ kg) that was moving with a velocity of 75.7 km/h east. The speed limit on this road is 90 km/h. After the collision, the Jeep and the Volkswagen stuck together and continued to travel with a velocity of 15.5 km/h west. (a) Find the initial westerly velocity of the Jeep. (b) Was the Jeep speeding?

CHAPTER 7
CONCURRENT AND PARALLEL FORCES

N ot all forces cause motion. A body that is static, or not moving, may be in equilibrium. Huge forces may be acting on a bridge without producing motion. We will consider concurrent forces (forces acting at the same point) in equilibrium.

When forces act nonconcurrently (that is, not at the same point), they may tend to produce rotational motion. We will consider torque (an applied force that causes a rotation), parallel force problems, equilibrium, and the concept of center of gravity.

Objectives

The major goals of this chapter are to enable you to:

1. Find the vector sum of concurrent forces.
2. Analyze equilibrium in one dimension.
3. Analyze concurrent force situations using force diagrams.
4. Distinguish compression and tension.
5. Apply the torque equation to rotational problems.
6. Solve parallel force problems.
7. Express the conditions of equilibrium using torque concepts.
8. Use the center of gravity to solve parallel force problems.

7.1 Forces in Two Dimensions

Concurrent forces are those forces that are applied to or act at the same point, as in Fig. 7.1. When two or more forces act at the same point, the **resultant force** is the sum of the forces applied at that point. The resultant force is the single force that has the same effect as two or more forces acting together.

As we saw in Section 5.4, when forces act in the same or opposite directions (in one dimension), the total, or net, force can be found by adding the forces that act in one direction and subtracting the forces that act in the opposite direction. What is the result when the forces are acting in two dimensions? In Chapter 3, addition of two vectors was shown by connecting the end point of the first vector to the initial point of the second vector as shown in Fig. 7.2. This is often called the *vector triangle method.*

This sum may also be obtained by constructing a parallelogram using the two vectors as adjacent sides and then constructing the opposite sides parallel as shown in Fig. 7.3. The diagonal of the parallelogram is the resultant, or sum, of the two vectors. This is often called the *parallelogram method.*

Figure 7.1 Concurrent forces are applied to or act at the same point.

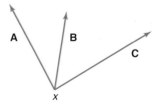

Figure 7.2 Vector triangle method of adding two vectors

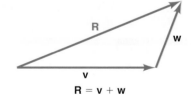

$$\mathbf{R} = \mathbf{v} + \mathbf{w}$$

Figure 7.3 Parallelogram method of adding two vectors

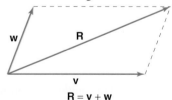

$$\mathbf{R} = \mathbf{v} + \mathbf{w}$$

In Fig. 7.4, two people on opposite banks are pulling a boat up a small river. Note that the effort forces must be equal to keep the boat in the middle of the river, the direction of the equal effort forces is along the ropes, and the direction of the resultant force **R** is upriver. What would happen if the effort forces were not equal?

Figure 7.4

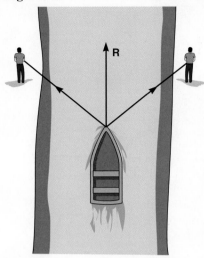

EXAMPLE 1

Two workers move a large crate by applying two ropes at the same point. The first worker applies a force of 525 N while the second worker applies a force of 763 N at the same point at right angles as shown in Fig. 7.5. Find the resultant force.

Figure 7.5

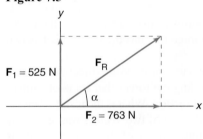

To find $\mathbf{F}_R$, find the x- and y-components of each vector and add the components as follows:

Vector	x-component	y-component
$\mathbf{F}_1$	0 N	525 N
$\mathbf{F}_2$	763 N	0 N
$\mathbf{F}_R$	763 N	525 N

Find angle α as follows:

$$\tan \alpha = \frac{\text{side opposite } \alpha}{\text{side adjacent to } \alpha} = \frac{|\mathbf{F}_{Ry}|}{|\mathbf{F}_{Rx}|}$$

$$\tan \alpha = \frac{525 \text{ N}}{763 \text{ N}} \qquad \text{(In a parallelogram, opposite sides are equal.)}$$

$$= 0.6881$$

$$\alpha = 34.5°$$

Find the magnitude of $\mathbf{F}_R$ using the Pythagorean theorem:

$$|\mathbf{F}_R| = \sqrt{|\mathbf{F}_{Rx}|^2 + |\mathbf{F}_{Ry}|^2}$$
$$|\mathbf{F}_R| = \sqrt{(763\ \text{N})^2 + (525\ \text{N})^2}$$
$$= 926\ \text{N}$$

That is, $\mathbf{F}_R = 926$ N at $34.5°$.

· · · · · · · · · · · · · · · · ·

Two workers move a large crate by applying two ropes at the same point. The first worker applies a force of 525 N while the second worker applies a force of 763 N at the same point as shown in Fig. 7.6. Find the resultant force.

EXAMPLE 2

Figure 7.6

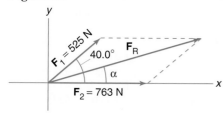

To find $\mathbf{F}_R$, find the x- and y-components of each vector and add the components as follows:

Vector	x-component	y-component
$\mathbf{F}_1$	$|\mathbf{F}_1| \cos \alpha =$ (525 N) cos 40.0° = 402 N	$|\mathbf{F}_1| \sin \alpha =$ (525 N) sin 40.0° = 337 N
$\mathbf{F}_2$	763 N	0 N
$\mathbf{F}_R$	1165 N	337 N

Find angle α as follows:

$$\tan \alpha = \frac{|\mathbf{F}_{Ry}|}{|\mathbf{F}_{Rx}|} = \frac{337\ \text{N}}{1165\ \text{N}} = 0.2893$$
$$\alpha = 16.1°$$

Find the magnitude of $\mathbf{F}_R$ using the Pythagorean theorem:

$$|\mathbf{F}_R| = \sqrt{|\mathbf{F}_{Rx}|^2 + |\mathbf{F}_{Ry}|^2}$$
$$|\mathbf{F}_R| = \sqrt{(1165\ \text{N})^2 + (337\ \text{N})^2}$$
$$= 1210\ \text{N}$$

That is, $\mathbf{F}_R = 1210$ N at $16.1°$.

· · · · · · · · · · · · · · · · ·

Forces of $\mathbf{F}_1 = 375$ N, $\mathbf{F}_2 = 575$ N, and $\mathbf{F}_3 = 975$ N are applied at the same point. The angle between $\mathbf{F}_1$ and $\mathbf{F}_2$ is $60.0°$ and the angle between $\mathbf{F}_2$ and $\mathbf{F}_3$ is $80.0°$. $\mathbf{F}_2$ is between $\mathbf{F}_1$ and $\mathbf{F}_3$. Find the resultant force.

EXAMPLE 3

First, draw a force diagram as in Fig. 7.7. Place the point of application at the origin and one of the forces on the x-axis for ease in computing the components.

Figure 7.7

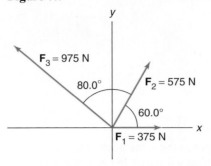

To find $\mathbf{F_R}$, find the x- and y-components of each vector and add the components as follows:

Vector	x-component	y-component
$\mathbf{F_1}$	375 N	0 N
$\mathbf{F_2}$	$\|\mathbf{F_2}\| \cos \alpha =$ $(575 \text{ N}) \cos 60.0° = \quad 288 \text{ N}$	$\|\mathbf{F_2}\| \sin \alpha =$ $(575 \text{ N}) \sin 60.0° = 498 \text{ N}$
$\mathbf{F_3}$	$\|\mathbf{F_3}\| \cos \alpha =$ $-(975 \text{ N}) \cos 40.0° = -747 \text{ N}$	$\|\mathbf{F_3}\| \sin \alpha =$ $(975 \text{ N}) \sin 40.0° = 627 \text{ N}$
Note for $\mathbf{F_3}$: $\alpha = 180° - 140.0° = 40.0°$		
$\mathbf{F_R}$	-84 N	1125 N

Find angle α of the resultant vector as follows:

$$\tan \alpha = \frac{|\mathbf{F_{Ry}}|}{|\mathbf{F_{Rx}}|} = \frac{1125 \text{ N}}{84 \text{ N}} = 13.39$$

$$\alpha = 85.7°$$

Note: The x-component of $\mathbf{F_R}$ is negative and its y-component is positive; this means that $\mathbf{F_R}$ is in the second quadrant. Its angle in standard position is $180° - 85.7° = 94.3°$.
Find the magnitude of $\mathbf{F_R}$ using the Pythagorean theorem:

$$|\mathbf{F_R}| = \sqrt{|\mathbf{F_{Rx}}|^2 + |\mathbf{F_{Ry}}|^2}$$
$$|\mathbf{F_R}| = \sqrt{(84 \text{ N})^2 + (1125 \text{ N})^2}$$
$$= 1130 \text{ N}$$

That is, $\mathbf{F_R} = 1130$ N at $94.3°$, or $94.3°$ from $\mathbf{F_1}$.
The resultant vector is shown in Fig. 7.8.

Figure 7.8

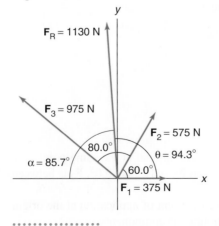

TRY THIS ACTIVITY

Tension Forces

An easy way to experiment with concurrent forces in cables is to suspend a 1.0-kg mass from two equal-length strings (the actual length of the strings is not important) (see Fig. 7.9). Attach a spring scale at the end of each string and observe the reading on the scales as they suspend the mass vertically. In this position, each spring scale should have the same reading, which is half the weight of the suspended mass.

Now, slowly separate the two strings from one another, gradually creating a larger and larger angle between them. Use the spring scales to observe the tension force in the strings and use a protractor to determine the angle between the two strings. What happens to the tension force as the angle between the suspending cables increases? What is the resultant upward force from the two strings?

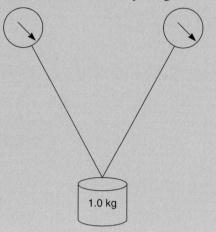

Figure 7.9 Two spring scales suspending a mass by two cables that are separated from the vertical at equal angles

1.0 kg

PROBLEMS 7.1

Find the sum of each set of forces acting at the same point in a straight line.

1. 355 N (right); 475 N (right); 245 N (left); 555 N (left)
2. 703 N (right); 829 N (left); 125 N (left); 484 N (left)
3. Forces of 225 N and 175 N act at the same point.
   (a) What is the magnitude of the maximum net force the two forces can exert together?
   (b) What is the magnitude of the minimum net force the two forces can exert together?
4. Three forces with magnitudes of 225 N, 175 N, and 125 N act at the same point.
   (a) What is the magnitude of the maximum net force the three forces can exert together?
   (b) What is the magnitude of the minimum net force the three forces can exert together?

Find the sum of each set of vectors. Give angles in standard position.

5.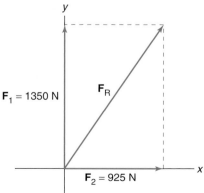

6.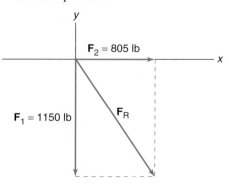

SKETCH

| 12 cm² | w |

4.0 cm

DATA
A = 12 cm², l = 4.0 cm, w = ?

BASIC EQUATION
A = lw

WORKING EQUATION
$w = \frac{A}{l}$

SUBSTITUTION
$w = \frac{12 \text{ cm}^2}{4.0 \text{ cm}} = 3.0$ cm

PHYSICS CONNECTIONS

The Cable-Stayed Bridge

All bridges are designed and constructed according to the needs of the community, the desired aesthetics, the costs, and the geographic and geological conditions around the bridge site. One of the most popular, attractive, and cost-effective designs is the cable-stayed bridge. The physical strength and relatively low cost of the design made the cable-stayed bridge ideal for the midlength span across the Mississippi River at Alton, Illinois (Fig. 7.10).

Cable-stayed bridges support the roadbed by attaching one end of multiple cables directly to the deck, passing them through a vertical tower, and attaching them to the deck on the opposite side of the tower. Through the use of lighter, stronger

Figure 7.10 The new cable-stayed design of the New Clark Bridge at Alton, Illinois

materials, engineers are able to avoid the need for the heavy and expensive steel and massive anchorages that are needed to support more traditional suspension bridges.

The combination of compression, tension, shear, and bending forces keeps the cable-stayed New Clark Bridge static. This particular cable-stayed bridge was designed to replace a deteriorating truss bridge that the community had outgrown. The New Clark Bridge meets the needs of the growing community and a busy shipping channel, is aesthetically pleasing, and is economically viable. The bridge also met the geographic and geological conditions as dictated by the Mississippi River and surrounding landscape.

7. If forces of $10\overline{0}0$ N acting in a northerly direction and $15\overline{0}0$ N acting in an easterly direction both act on the same point, what is the resultant force?

8. If two forces of $10\overline{0}$ N and 50.0 N, respectively, act in a westerly direction on a point and a force of 175 N acts in a northerly direction on the same point, what is the resultant force?

Find the sum of each set of vectors. Give angles in standard position.

9.

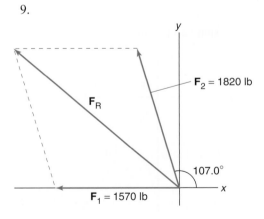

10.

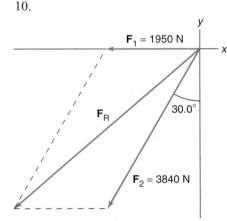

11.

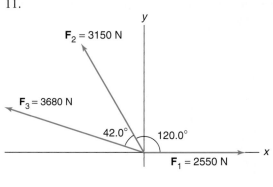

12.

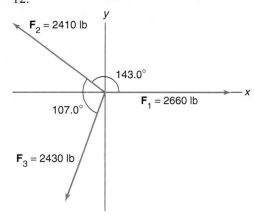

13.   Forces of $F_1 = 1150$ N, $F_2 = 875$ N, and $F_3 = 1450$ N are applied at the same point. The angle between F_1 and F_2 is $90.0°$ and the angle between F_2 and F_3 is $120.0°$. F_2 is between F_1 and F_3. Find the resultant force.

14.   Four forces, each of magnitude 2750 lb, act at the same point. The angle between adjacent forces is $30.0°$. Find the resultant force.

7.2 Concurrent Forces in Equilibrium

Equilibrium in One Dimension

Equilibrium *is the state of a body in which there is no change in its motion.* A body is in equilibrium when the net force acting on it is zero. That is, it is not accelerating; it is either at rest or moving at a constant velocity. The study of objects in equilibrium is called **statics**.

The forces applied to an object in one dimension act in the same direction or in opposite directions. For the net force to be zero, the forces in one direction must equal the forces in the opposite direction. We can write the equation for equilibrium in one dimension as

$$\boxed{F_+ = F_-}$$

where F_+ = the sum of all forces acting in one direction (call it the positive direction).
         F_- = the sum of all the forces acting in the opposite (negative) direction.

Note in Fig. 7.11 that the downward force (weight of the bridge) must equal the sum of the upward forces produced by the two bridge supports for the bridge to be in equilibrium.

Figure 7.11

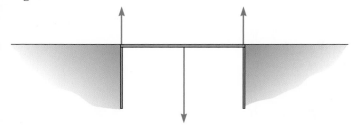

A cable supports a large crate of weight 1250 N (Fig. 7.12). What is the upward force on the crate if it is in equilibrium?

EXAMPLE 1

Figure 7.12

1250 N

Sketch: Draw a force diagram of the crate in equilibrium, and show the forces that act on it. Note that we call the upward direction positive as indicated by the arrow.

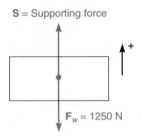

S = Supporting force

+

$\mathbf{F}_w$ = 1250 N

Data:

$$\mathbf{F}_w = 1250 \text{ N}$$
$$\mathbf{S} = ?$$

Basic Equation:

$$\mathbf{F}_+ = \mathbf{F}_-$$

Working Equation:

$$\mathbf{S} = \mathbf{F}_w$$

Substitution:

$$\mathbf{S} = 1250 \text{ N}$$

• • • • • • • • • • • • • • • • •

EXAMPLE 2

Four persons are having a tug-of-war with a rope. Harry and Mary are on the left; Bill and Jill are on the right. Mary pulls with a force of 105 lb, Harry pulls with a force of 255 lb, and Jill pulls with a force of 165 lb. With what force must Bill pull to produce equilibrium?

Sketch:

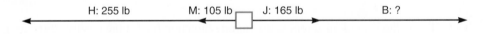

H: 255 lb   M: 105 lb   J: 165 lb   B: ?

Data:

$$M = 105 \text{ lb}$$
$$H = 255 \text{ lb}$$
$$J = 165 \text{ lb}$$
$$B = ?$$

Basic Equation:

$$\mathbf{F}_+ = \mathbf{F}_- \quad \text{or}$$
$$M + H = J + B$$

Working Equation:

$$B = M + H - J$$

Substitution:

$$B = 105 \text{ lb} + 255 \text{ lb} - 165 \text{ lb}$$
$$= 195 \text{ lb}$$

• • • • • • • • • • • • • • • • •

Equilibrium in Two Dimensions

A body is in equilibrium when it is either at rest or moving at a constant speed in a straight line. Figure 7.13(a) shows the resultant force of the sum of two forces from Example 1 in Section 7.1. When two or more forces act at a point, the **equilibrant force** is the force that, when applied at that same point as the resultant force, produces equilibrium. *The equilibrant force is equal in magnitude to that of the resultant force but it acts in the opposite direction* [see Fig. 7.13(b)]. In this case, the equilibrant force is 926 N at 214.5° (180° + 34.5°).

Figure 7.13

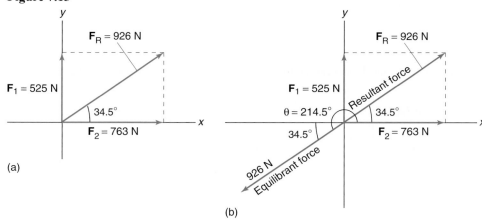

(a)

(b)

If an object is in equilibrium in two dimensions, the net force acting on it must be zero. For the net force to be zero, the sum of the x-components must be zero and the sum of the y-components must be zero. For forces **A**, **B**, and **C** with x-components A_x, B_x, and C_x, respectively, and with y-components A_y, B_y, and C_y, respectively, to be in equilibrium, both of the following conditions must hold:

CONDITIONS FOR EQUILIBRIUM

1. The sum of x-components = 0; that is, $A_x + B_x + C_x = 0$.
2. The sum of y-components = 0; that is, $A_y + B_y + C_y = 0$.

In general, to solve equilibrium problems:

1. Draw a force diagram from the point at which the unknown forces act.
2. Find the x- and y-component of each force.
3. Substitute the components in the equations

$$\text{sum of } x\text{-components} = 0$$
$$\text{sum of } y\text{-components} = 0$$

4. Solve for the unknowns. This may involve two simultaneous equations.

We may need to find the tension or compression in part of a structure, such as in a beam or a cable. **Tension** is a stretching force produced by forces pulling outward on the ends of an object [Fig. 7.14(a)]. **Compression** is a force produced by forces pushing inward on the ends of an object [Fig. 7.14(b)]. A rubber band being stretched is an example of tension [Fig. 7.15(a)]. A valve spring whose ends are pushed together is an example of compression [Fig. 7.15(b)].

Figure 7.14 Tension and compression forces

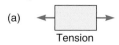

(a) Tension

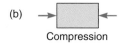

(b) Compression

Figure 7.15

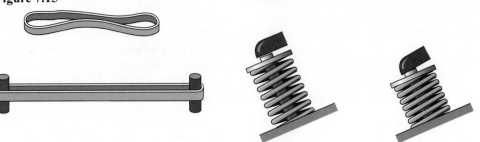

(a) Tension in a rubber band   (b) Compression in a valve spring

EXAMPLE 3

Find the forces **F** and **F**′ necessary to produce equilibrium in the force diagram shown in Fig. 7.16.

1. **Figure 7.16**

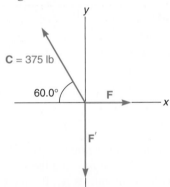

2. *x-components*

$$\mathbf{F}_x = \mathbf{F}$$
$$\mathbf{F}'_x = 0$$
$$\mathbf{C}_x = -(375 \text{ lb})(\cos 60.0°)$$
$$= -188 \text{ lb}$$

y-components

$$\mathbf{F}_y = 0$$
$$\mathbf{F}'_y = -\mathbf{F}'$$
$$\mathbf{C}_y = (375 \text{ lb})(\sin 60.0°)$$
$$= 325 \text{ lb}$$

3. Sum of *x*-components = 0
$$\mathbf{F} + 0 + (-188 \text{ lb}) = 0$$

Sum of *y*-components = 0
$$0 + (-\mathbf{F}') + 325 \text{ lb} = 0$$

4.
$$\mathbf{F} = 188 \text{ lb}$$

$$\mathbf{F}' = 325 \text{ lb}$$

· · · · · · · · · · · · · · · · · ·

EXAMPLE 4

Find the forces **F** and **F**′ necessary to produce equilibrium in the force diagram shown in Fig. 7.17.

1. **Figure 7.17**

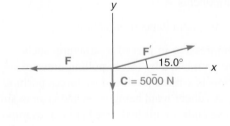

2. *x-components* y-components
   $\mathbf{F}_x = -\mathbf{F}$ $\mathbf{F}_y = 0$
   $\mathbf{F}'_x = \mathbf{F}' \cos 15.0°$ $\mathbf{F}'_y = \mathbf{F}' \sin 15.0°$
   $\mathbf{C}_x = 0$ $\mathbf{C}_y = -50\overline{0}0$ N

3.   Sum of *x*-components = 0   Sum of *y*-components = 0
   $(-\mathbf{F}) + \mathbf{F}' \cos 15.0° + 0 = 0$ $0 + \mathbf{F}' \sin 15.0° + (-50\overline{0}0\text{ N}) = 0$

4. *Note:* Solve for **F**′ in the right-hand equation first. Then substitute this value in the left-hand equation to solve for **F**:

$$\mathbf{F}' = \frac{50\overline{0}0\text{ N}}{\sin 15.0°}$$
$$= 19{,}300\text{ N}$$

$$\mathbf{F} = \mathbf{F}' \cos 15.0°$$
$$= (19{,}300\text{ N})(\cos 15.0°)$$
$$= 18{,}600\text{ N}$$

....

The crane shown in Fig. 7.18 is supporting a beam that weighs 60\overline{0}0 N. Find the tension in the horizontal supporting cable and the compression in the boom. The horizontal cable is attached to the boom at point *A*. The separate vertical cable holding the beam is attached through the pulley at point *A*.

EXAMPLE 5

Figure 7.18

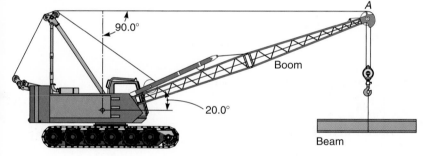

1. Draw the force diagram showing the forces acting at point *A*.

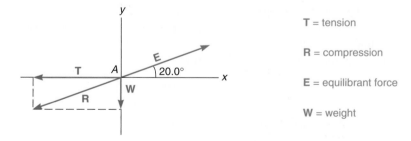

T = tension
R = compression
E = equilibrant force
W = weight

T is the force exerted at *A* by the horizontal supporting cable.
E is the force exerted by the boom at *A*.
W is the force (weight of the beam) pulling straight down at *A*.
R is the sum of forces **W** and **T**, which is equal in magnitude but opposite in direction to force **E**($\mathbf{R} = -\mathbf{E}$).

2. *x-components*

$$\mathbf{E}_x = \mathbf{E} \cos 20.0°$$
$$\mathbf{T}_x = -\mathbf{T}$$
$$\mathbf{W}_x = 0$$

   y-components

$$\mathbf{E}_y = \mathbf{E} \sin 20.0°$$
$$\mathbf{T}_y = 0$$
$$\mathbf{W}_y = -60\overline{0}0 \text{ N}$$

3. Sum of *x*-components = 0

$$\mathbf{E} \cos 20.0° + (-\mathbf{T}) = 0$$

   Sum of *y*-components = 0

$$\mathbf{E} \sin 20.0° + (-60\overline{0}0 \text{ N}) = 0$$

4. $$\mathbf{T} = \mathbf{E} \cos 20.0°$$

$$\mathbf{E} = \frac{60\overline{0}0 \text{ N}}{\sin 20.0°}$$
$$= 17,500 \text{ N}$$

$$\mathbf{T} = (17,500 \text{ N})(\cos 20.0°)$$
$$= 16,400 \text{ N}$$

· · · · · · · · · · · · · · · · ·

EXAMPLE 6

Figure 7.19

A homeowner pushes a 40.0-lb lawn mower at a constant velocity (Fig. 7.19). The frictional force on the mower is 20.0 lb. What force must the person exert on the handle, which makes an angle of 30.0° with the ground? Also, find the normal (perpendicular to ground) force.
   This is an equilibrium problem because the mower is not accelerating and the net force is zero.

1. Draw the force diagram.

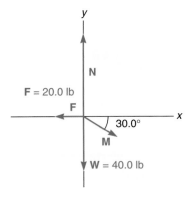

M is the force exerted on the mower by the person; this compression force is directed down along the handle.
W is the weight of the mower directed straight down.
N is the force exerted upward on the mower by the ground, which keeps the mower from falling through the ground.
F is the frictional force that opposes the motion.

2. *x-components*

$$\mathbf{N}_x = 0$$
$$\mathbf{W}_x = 0$$
$$\mathbf{F}_x = -20.0 \text{ lb}$$
$$\mathbf{M}_x = \mathbf{M} \cos 30.0°$$

   y-components

$$\mathbf{N}_y = \mathbf{N}$$
$$\mathbf{W}_y = -40.0 \text{ lb}$$
$$\mathbf{F}_y = 0$$
$$\mathbf{M}_y = -\mathbf{M} \sin 30.0°$$

3.   Sum of *x*-components = 0

$$0 + 0 + (-20.0 \text{ lb}) + \mathbf{M} \cos 30.0° = 0$$

   Sum of *y*-components = 0

$$\mathbf{N} + (-40.0 \text{ lb}) + 0$$
$$+ (-\mathbf{M} \sin 30.0°) = 0$$
$$\mathbf{N} = \mathbf{M} \sin 30.0 + 40.0 \text{ lb}$$

4. $M = \dfrac{20.0 \text{ lb}}{\cos 30.0°}$

   $= 23.1 \text{ lb}$

$N = (23.1 \text{ lb})(\sin 30.0°) + 40.0 \text{ lb}$
$= 51.6 \text{ lb}$

· · · · · · · · · · · · · · · · ·

The crane shown in Fig. 7.20 is supporting a beam that weighs $60\overline{0}0$ N. Find the tension in the supporting cable and the compression in the boom.

EXAMPLE 7

1.   Draw the force diagram showing the forces acting at point A.

Figure 7.20

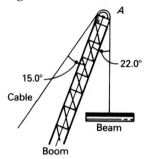

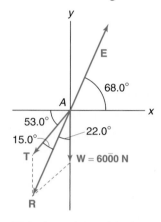

W is the weight of the beam, which pulls straight down.
T is the force exerted at A by the supporting cable.
E is the force exerted by the boom at A.
R is the sum of forces **W** and **T**, which is equal in magnitude but opposite in direction to force **E**($\mathbf{R} = -\mathbf{E}$).

2.   *x-components*   *y-components*

   $\mathbf{E}_x = \mathbf{E} \cos 68.0°$ $\mathbf{E}_y = \mathbf{E} \sin 68.0°$
   $\mathbf{T}_x = -\mathbf{T} \cos 53.0°$ $\mathbf{T}_y = -\mathbf{T} \sin 53.0°$
   $\mathbf{W}_x = 0$ $\mathbf{W}_y = -60\overline{0}0 \text{ N}$

3.   Sum of *x*-components $= 0$ Sum of *y*-components $= 0$
   $\mathbf{E} \cos 68.0° +$ $\mathbf{E} \sin 68.0° +$
   $(-\mathbf{T} \cos 53.0°) + 0 = 0$ $(-\mathbf{T} \sin 53.0°) + (-60\overline{0}0 \text{ N}) = 0$

4.   *Note:* Solve the left equation for **E**. Then substitute this quantity in the right equation and solve for **T**:

   $\mathbf{E} = \dfrac{\mathbf{T} \cos 53.0°}{\cos 68.0°}$ $\left(\dfrac{\mathbf{T} \cos 53.0°}{\cos 68.0°}\right)(\sin 68.0°) - \mathbf{T} \sin 53.0° = 60\overline{0}0 \text{ N}$

   $1.490\mathbf{T} - 0.799\mathbf{T} = 60\overline{0}0 \text{ N}$

   $0.691\mathbf{T} = 60\overline{0}0 \text{ N}$

   $\mathbf{T} = \dfrac{60\overline{0}0 \text{ N}}{0.691}$

   $= 8680 \text{ N}$

   $\mathbf{E} = \dfrac{(8680 \text{ N})(\cos 53.0°)}{\cos 68.0°}$

   $= 13,900 \text{ N}$

Alternate Method: You can orient a force diagram any way you want on the x–y axes. You should orient it so that as many of the vectors as possible are on an x- or a y-axis. The result will be the same. Let's rework Example 7 as follows:

1. Draw the force diagram showing the forces acting at point A using the same notation as follows:

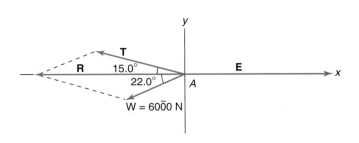

2. *x-components*

$$\mathbf{E}_x = \mathbf{E}$$
$$\mathbf{T}_x = -\mathbf{T}\cos 15.0°$$
$$\mathbf{W}_x = -(60\bar{0}0\text{ N})(\cos 22.0°)$$

   y-components

$$\mathbf{E}_y = 0$$
$$\mathbf{T}_y = \mathbf{T}\sin 15.0°$$
$$\mathbf{W}_y = -(60\bar{0}0\text{ N})(\sin 22.0°)$$

3. Sum of x-components $= 0$

$$\mathbf{E} + (-\mathbf{T}\cos 15.0°) +$$
$$(-60\bar{0}0\text{ N})(\cos 22.0°) = 0$$

   Sum of y-components $= 0$

$$0 + \mathbf{T}\sin 15.0° +$$
$$(-60\bar{0}0\text{ N})(\sin 22.0°) = 0$$

4. Solve the right equation for $\mathbf{T}$ (since it has only one variable). Then solve the left equation for $\mathbf{E}$ and substitute this quantity:

$$\mathbf{T} = \frac{(60\bar{0}0\text{ N})(\sin 22.0°)}{\sin 15.0°}$$

$$= 8680\text{ N}$$

$$\mathbf{E} = \mathbf{T}\cos 15.0° + (60\bar{0}0\text{ N})(\cos 22.0°)$$
$$\mathbf{E} = (8680\text{ N})(\cos 15.0°) + (60\bar{0}0\text{ N})(\cos 22.0°)$$
$$= 13,900\text{ N}$$

....

PROBLEMS 7.2

Find the force $\mathbf{F}$ that will produce equilibrium in each force diagram.

SKETCH

> 12 cm² | w
>
> 4.0 cm

DATA

$A = 12$ cm², $l = 4.0$ cm, $w = ?$

BASIC EQUATION

$A = lw$

WORKING EQUATION

$w = \frac{A}{l}$

SUBSTITUTION

$w = \frac{12 \text{ cm}^2}{4.0 \text{ cm}} = 3.0$ cm

1.

10$\bar{0}$ N | | $\mathbf{F} = ?$

2.

$\mathbf{F} = ?$

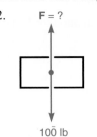

10$\bar{0}$ lb

3.

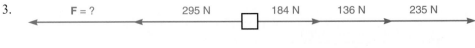

$\mathbf{F} = ?$ 295 N   184 N   136 N   235 N

4.

$\mathbf{F} = ?$ 25$\bar{0}$ N   25$\bar{0}$ N   25$\bar{0}$ N   125$\bar{0}$ N

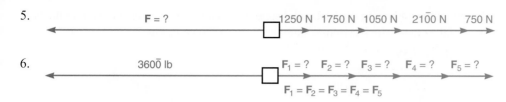

5.

6.

7. Five persons are having a tug-of-war. Kurt and Brian are on the left; Amy, Barbara, and Joyce are on the right. Amy pulls with a force of 225 N, Barbara pulls with a force of 495 N, Joyce pulls with a force of 455 N, and Kurt pulls with a force of 605 N. With what force must Brian pull to produce equilibrium?

8. A certain wire can support 6450 lb before it breaks. Seven 820-lb weights are suspended from the wire. Can the wire support an eighth weight of 820 lb?

9. The frictional force of a loaded pallet in a warehouse is 385 lb. Can three workers, each exerting a force of 135 lb, push it to the side?

10. A bridge has a weight limit of 7.0 tons. How heavy a load can a 2.5-ton truck carry across?

11. A tractor transmission weighing $26\bar{0}$ N and a steering gear box weighing 62.0 N are on a workbench. What upward force must the bench exert to maintain equilibrium?

12. A skid loader lifts a compressor weighing 672 N and a hose weighing 26.0 N. What upward force must the loader exert to maintain equilibrium?

Find the forces F_1 and F_2 that produce equilibrium in each force diagram.

13.

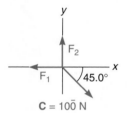

14.

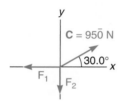

15.

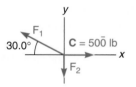

16.

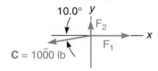

17.

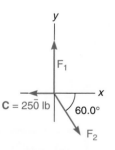

18.

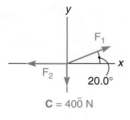

Figure 7.21

19. A rope is attached to two buildings and supports a $50\bar{0}$-lb sign (Fig. 7.21). Find the tensions in the two ropes T_1 and T_2. (*Hint:* Draw the force diagram of the forces acting at the point labeled A.)

20. If the angle between the horizontal and the ropes in Problem 19 is changed to 10.0°, what are the tensions in the two ropes T_1 and T_2?

21. If the angles between the horizontal and the ropes in Problem 19 are changed to 20.0° and 30.0°, find the tension in each rope.

22. Find the tension in the horizontal supporting cable and the compression in the boom of the crane which supports an 8900-N beam shown in Fig. 7.22.

Figure 7.22

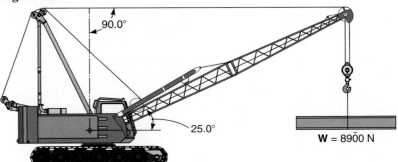

23. Find the tension in the horizontal supporting cable and the compression in the boom of the crane which supports a 1500-lb beam shown in Fig. 7.23.

24. The frictional force of the mower shown in Fig. 7.24 is 20 lb. What force must the man exert along the handle to push it at a constant velocity?

Figure 7.23   **Figure 7.24**

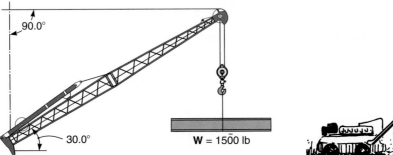

25. A vehicle that weighs 16,200 N is parked on a 20.0° hill (Fig. 7.25). What braking force is necessary to keep it from rolling? Neglect frictional forces. (*Hint:* When you draw the force diagram, tilt the *x*- and *y*-axes as shown. **B** is the braking force directed up the hill and along the *x*-axis.)

26. Find the tension in the cable and the compression in the support of the sign shown in Fig. 7.26.

Figure 7.25   **Figure 7.26**

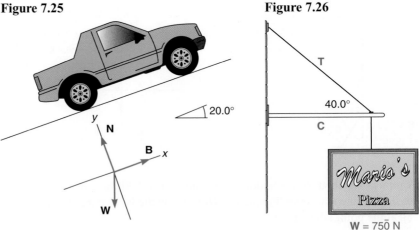

27. The crane shown in Fig. 7.27 is supporting a load of 1850 lb. Find the tension in the supporting cable and the compression in the boom.

28. The crane shown in Fig. 7.28 is supporting a load of 11,500 N. Find the tension in the supporting cable and the compression in the boom.

Figure 7.27

Figure 7.28

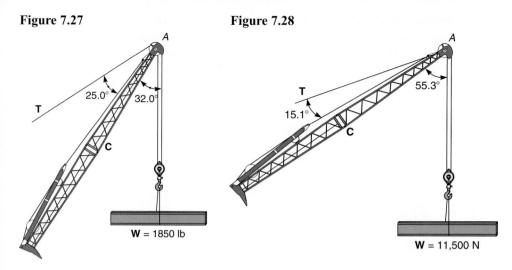

W = 1850 lb

W = 11,500 N

7.3 Torque

A *torque* is produced when a force is applied to produce a rotation, as, for example, when a wrench is used to turn a bolt or a claw hammer is used to pull a nail from wood. **Torque** is the tendency to produce change in rotational motion. The torque developed depends on two factors:

1. The amount of force applied
2. How far from the point of rotation the force is applied

Torque is expressed by the equation

$$\tau = Fs_t$$

where τ = torque (N m or lb ft) (τ is the lowercase Greek letter "tau.")
F = applied force (N or lb)
s_t = length of torque arm (m or ft)

Note that s_t, the length of the torque arm, is different from s in the equation defining work ($W = Fs$). Recall that s in the work equation is the linear distance over which the force acts.

When you use a wrench to turn a bolt, less effort is used (greater torque is produced) as the distance you place your hand from the bolt increases (Fig. 7.29). Plumbers often use a wrench with a long torque arm to loosen or tighten large bolts and fittings.

Figure 7.29   Even though the same force is used, the torque applied to the bolt increases as the distance from your hand to the bolt increases. In (b), you produce more torque by placing your hand on the end of the wrench handle. In (c), you produce even more torque by using an extender sleeve.

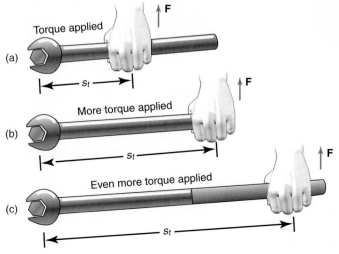

In all torque problems, we are concerned with motion about a point or axis of rotation as in pedaling a bicycle (Fig. 7.30). In pedaling, we apply a force to the pedal, causing the sprocket to rotate. The torque arm is the *perpendicular* distance from the point of rotation to the applied force [Fig. 7.30(a)]. In torque problems, s_t is always perpendicular to the force [Fig. 7.30(a)]. Note that s_t is the distance from the pedal to the axle. The units of torque look similar to those of work, but note the difference between s and s_t.

Figure 7.30   Torque produced in pedaling a bicycle

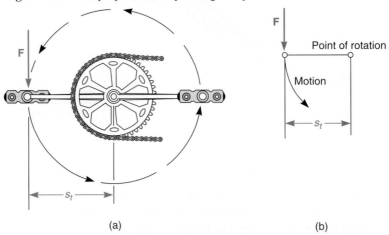

(a)   (b)

Figure 7.31   Maximum torque is only produced when the pedal reaches a position perpendicular to the applied force.

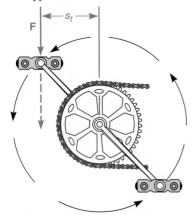

If the force is not exerted tangent to the circle made by the pedal (Fig. 7.31), the length of the torque arm is *not* the length of the pedal arm. The torque arm, s_t, is measured as the perpendicular distance to the force. Since s_t is therefore shorter, the product $F \cdot s_t$ is smaller, and the turning effect, the torque, is less in the pedal position shown in Fig. 7.30. Maximum torque is produced when the pedals are horizontal and the force applied is straight down.

Torque is a vector quantity that acts along the axis of rotation (not along the force) and points in the direction in which a right-handed screw would advance if turned by the torque as in Fig. 7.32(a). The *right-hand rule* is often used to determine the direction of the torque as follows: Grasp the axis of rotation with your right hand so that your fingers circle it in the direction that the torque tends to induce rotation. Your thumb will point in the direction of the torque vector [Fig. 7.32(b)]. Thus, the torque vector in Fig. 7.32(a) is perpendicular to and points out of the page.

Figure 7.32   Torque is a vector quantity that acts along the axis of rotation according to the right-hand rule.

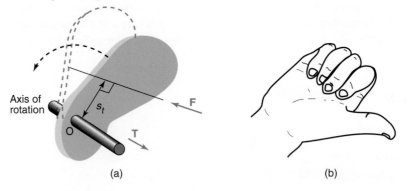

(a)   (b)

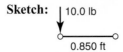

A force of 10.0 lb is applied to a bicycle pedal. If the length of the pedal arm is 0.850 ft, what torque is applied to the shaft?

Sketch: | 10.0 lb

     0.850 ft

Data:

$$F = 10.0 \text{ lb}$$
$$s_t = 0.850 \text{ ft}$$
$$\tau = ?$$

Basic Equation:

$$\tau = Fs_t$$

Working Equation: Same

Substitution:

$$\tau = (10.0 \text{ lb})(0.850 \text{ ft})$$
$$= 8.50 \text{ lb ft}$$

················

TRY THIS ACTIVITY

Hammers and Screwdrivers

Torque is an essential component of most hand tools. Drive a nail into a piece of wood by holding a hammer near its head. Count the number of hits it takes to drive the nail into the wood. Then, drive a like nail into the wood by holding the hammer near the end of the handle. Count the number of hits it takes. Using physics terminology, explain which handle grip is better for driving nails into wood.

Use two screwdrivers with different diameter handles to screw two similar screws into a board. Which screwdriver is able to apply more torque to a screw? If one screwdriver applies more torque to a screw than the other, why would anyone want to use a screwdriver that cannot exert the maximum torque?

PROBLEMS 7.3

Assume that each force is applied perpendicular to the torque arm.

1. Given: $F = 16.0$ lb
   $s_t = 6.00$ ft
   $\tau = ?$

2. Given: $F = 10\overline{0}$ N
   $s_t = 0.420$ m
   $\tau = ?$

3. Given: $\tau = 60.0$ N m
   $F = 30.0$ N
   $s_t = ?$

4. Given: $\tau = 35.7$ lb ft
   $s_t = 0.0240$ ft
   $F = ?$

5. Given: $\tau = 65.4$ N m
   $s_t = 35.0$ cm
   $F = ?$

6. Given: $F = 63\overline{0}$ N
   $s_t = 74.0$ cm
   $\tau = ?$

7. If the torque on a shaft of radius 2.37 cm is 38.0 N m (Fig. 7.33), what force is applied to the shaft?

8. If a force of 56.2 lb is applied to a torque wrench 1.50 ft long (Fig. 7.34), what torque is indicated by the wrench?

Figure 7.33

F = ?

r = 2.37 cm

Figure 7.34

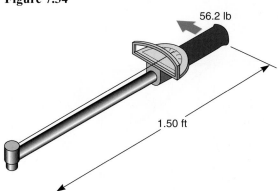

56.2 lb

1.50 ft

SKETCH

$$\boxed{12 \text{ cm}^2} \;\; w$$

4.0 cm

DATA

$A = 12 \text{ cm}^2$, $l = 4.0$ cm, $w = ?$

BASIC EQUATION

$A = lw$

WORKING EQUATION

$w = \frac{A}{l}$

SUBSTITUTION

$w = \frac{12 \text{ cm}^2}{4.0 \text{ cm}} = 3.0$ cm

PROBLEM SOLVING

9. A motorcycle head bolt is torqued to 25.0 N m. What length shaft do we need on a wrench to exert a maximum force of 70.0 N?
10. A force of 112 N is applied to a shaft of radius 3.50 cm. What is the torque on the shaft?
11. A torque of 175 lb ft is needed to free a large rusted-on nut. The length of the wrench is 1.10 ft. What force must be applied to free it?
12. A torque wrench reads 14.5 N m. If its length is 25.0 cm, what force is being applied to the handle?
13. The torque on a shaft of radius 3.00 cm is 12.0 N m. What force is being applied to the shaft?
14. An engine bolt is torqued to 30.0 N m. If the length of the wrench is 29.0 cm, what force is applied to the wrench?
15. A mower bolt is torqued to 65.0 N m. If the length of the wrench is 30.0 cm, what force is applied to the wrench?
16. An automobile bolt is torqued to 27.0 N m. If the length of the wrench is 30.0 cm, what force is applied to the wrench?
17. A torque wrench reads 25 lb ft. (a) If its length is 1.0 ft, what force is being applied to the wrench? (b) What is the force if the length is doubled? Explain the results.
18. If 13 N m of torque is applied to a bolt with an applied force of 28 N, what is the length of the wrench?
19. If the torque required to loosen a nut on the wheel of a pickup truck is 40.0 N m, what minimum force must be applied to the end of a wrench 30.0 cm long to loosen the nut?
20. How is the required force to loosen the nut in Problem 19 affected if the length of the wrench is doubled?
21. A truck mechanic must loosen a rusted lug nut. If the torque required to loosen the nut is 60.0 N m, what force must be applied to a 35.0-cm wrench?
22. An ag mechanic tries to loosen a nut on a tractor wheel with a wrench that is 32.5 cm long. If the torque required to loosen the nut is 55.0 N m, what force must she apply to the wrench?

7.4 Parallel Forces

A painter stands 2.00 ft from one end of a 6.00-ft plank that is supported at each end by a scaffold [Fig. 7.35(a)]. How much of the painter's weight must each end of the scaffold support? Problems of this kind are often faced in the construction industry, particularly in the design of bridges and buildings. Using some things we learned about torques and equilibrium, we can now solve problems of this type.

Figure 7.35 Parallel forces shown by the example of a painter on a scaffold

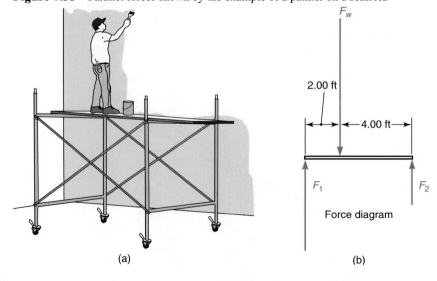

(a)   (b)

Let's look more closely at the painter problem. The force diagram [Fig. 7.35(b)] shows the forces and distances involved. The arrow pointing down represents the weight of the person, F_w. The arrows pointing up represent the forces exerted by each end of the scaffold in supporting the plank and painter. (For now, we will neglect the weight of the plank.) We have a condition of equilibrium. The plank and painter are not moving. The sum of the forces exerted by the ends of the scaffold is equal to the weight of the painter (Fig. 7.36). Since these forces are vectors and are parallel, we can show that their sum is zero. Using engineering notation, we write

$$\Sigma \mathbf{F} = 0$$

where Σ (Greek capital letter sigma) means summation or "the sum of" and $\mathbf{F}$ is force, a vector quantity. So $\Sigma\mathbf{F}$ means "the sum of forces," in this case the sum of parallel forces.

Figure 7.36 In equilibrium, the sum of the forces is zero.

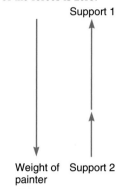

Support 1

Weight of Support 2
painter

FIRST CONDITION OF EQUILIBRIUM
The sum of all parallel forces on a body in equilibrium must be zero.

If the vector sum is not zero (forces up unequal to forces down), we have an unbalanced force tending to cause motion.

Now consider this situation: One end of the scaffold remains firmly in place, supporting the man, and the other is removed. What happens to the painter? The plank, supported only on one end, falls (Fig. 7.37), and the painter has a mess to clean up!

Figure 7.37 The position of the supporting force is important!

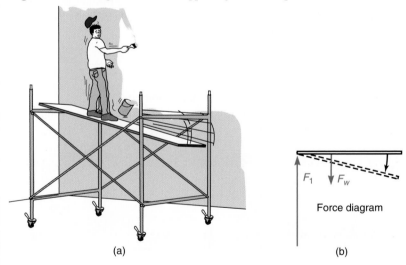

F_1 F_w

Force diagram

(a) (b)

A sign of weight $150\overline{0}$ lb is supported by two cables (Fig. 7.38). If one cable has a tension of $60\overline{0}$ lb, what is the tension in the other cable?

EXAMPLE 1

Sketch: Draw the force diagram.

Figure 7.38

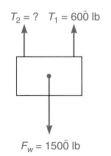

$T_2 = ?$ $T_1 = 60\overline{0}$ lb

$F_w = 150\overline{0}$ lb

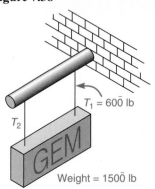

$T_1 = 60\overline{0}$ lb

T_2

GEM

Weight $= 150\overline{0}$ lb

Data:

$$F_w = 150\overline{0} \text{ lb}$$
$$T_1 = 60\overline{0} \text{ lb}$$
$$T_2 = ?$$

Basic Equation:

$$F_+ = F_-$$

Working Equation:

$$T_1 + T_2 = F_w$$
$$T_2 = F_w - T_1$$

Substitution:

$$T_2 = 150\overline{0} \text{ lb} - 60\overline{0} \text{ lb}$$
$$= 90\overline{0} \text{ lb}$$

· · · · · · · · · · · · · · · · · ·

Not only must the forces balance each other (vector sum = 0), but they must also be positioned so that there is no rotation in the system. To avoid rotation, we can have no unbalanced torques.

Sometimes there will be a natural point of rotation, as in our painter problem. We can, however, choose any point as our center of rotation as we consider the torques present. We will soon see that one of any number of points could be selected. What is necessary, though, is that there be no rotation (no unbalanced torques).

Again, using engineering notation, we write

$$\Sigma \tau_{\text{any point}} = 0$$

where $\Sigma \tau_{\text{any point}}$ is the sum of the torques about any chosen point or,

SECOND CONDITION OF EQUILIBRIUM

The sum of the clockwise torques on a body in equilibrium must equal the sum of the counterclockwise torques about any point.

$$\Sigma \tau_{\text{clockwise (cw)}} = \Sigma \tau_{\text{counterclockwise (ccw)}}$$

EXAMPLE 2

To illustrate these principles, we will find how much weight each end of the scaffold must support if our painter weighs $15\overline{0}$ lb.

Sketch:

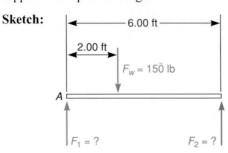

Data:

$$F_w = 15\overline{0}\ \text{lb}$$
$$\text{plank} = 6.00\ \text{ft}$$
$$F_w \text{ is } 2.00\ \text{ft from one end}$$

Basic Equations:

1. $$\Sigma F = 0$$
   sum of forces $= 0$
   $$F_1 + F_2 - F_w = 0$$ (**Note:** F_w is negative because its
   $$\text{or } F_1 + F_2 = F_w$$ direction is opposite F_1 and F_2.)
   $$F_1 + F_2 = 15\overline{0}\ \text{lb}$$

2. $$\Sigma\tau_{\text{clockwise}} = \Sigma\tau_{\text{counterclockwise}}$$

First, select a point of rotation. Choosing an end is usually helpful in simplifying the calculations. Choose the left end (point A) where F_1 acts. What are the clockwise torques about this point?

The force due to the weight of the painter tends to cause clockwise motion. The torque arm is 2.00 ft (Fig. 7.39). Then $\tau = (15\overline{0}\ \text{lb})(2.00\ \text{ft})$. This is the only clockwise torque. The only counterclockwise torque is F_2 times its torque arm, 6.00 ft (Fig. 7.40). $\tau = (F_2)(6.00\ \text{ft})$. There is no torque involving F_1 because its torque arm is zero. Setting $\Sigma\tau_{\text{clockwise}} = \Sigma\tau_{\text{counterclockwise}}$ we have the equation:

Figure 7.39 Torque arm of painter about point A

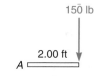

$$(15\overline{0}\ \text{lb})(2.00\ \text{ft}) = (F_2)(6.00\ \text{ft})$$

Note that by selecting an end as the point of rotation, we were able to have an equation with just one variable (F_2). Solving for F_2 gives the working equation:

Figure 7.40 Torque arm of F_2 about point A

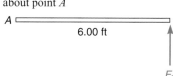

$$F_2 = \frac{(15\overline{0}\ \text{lb})(2.00\ \cancel{\text{ft}})}{6.00\ \cancel{\text{ft}}} = 50.0\ \text{lb}$$

Since $\Sigma F = F_1 + F_2 = F_w$, substitute for F_2 and F_w to find F_1:

$$F_1 + 50.0\ \text{lb} = 15\overline{0}\ \text{lb}$$
$$F_1 = 15\overline{0}\ \text{lb} - 50.0\ \text{lb}$$
$$= 10\overline{0}\ \text{lb}$$

· · · · · · · · · · · · · · · · ·

To solve parallel force problems:

1. Sketch the problem.
2. Write an equation setting the sums of the opposite forces equal to each other.
3. Choose a point of rotation. Eliminate a variable, if possible (by making its torque arm zero).
4. Write the sum of all clockwise torques.
5. Write the sum of all counterclockwise torques.
6. Set $\Sigma\tau_{\text{clockwise}} = \Sigma\tau_{\text{counterclockwise}}$.
7. Solve the equation $\Sigma\tau_{\text{clockwise}} = \Sigma\tau_{\text{counterclockwise}}$ for the unknown quantity.
8. Substitute the value found in step 7 into the equation in step 2 to find the other unknown quantity.

EXAMPLE 3

A bricklayer weighing 175 lb stands on an 8.00-ft scaffold 3.00 ft from one end (Fig. 7.41). He has a pile of bricks, which weighs 40.0 lb, 3.00 ft from the other end. How much weight must each end support?

Figure 7.41

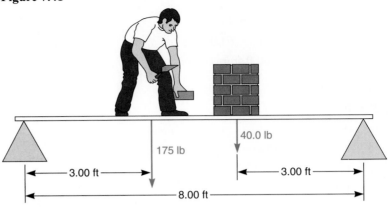

1.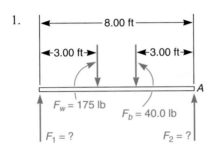

2. $\Sigma F = F_1 + F_2 = 175 \text{ lb} + 40.0 \text{ lb}$

3. Choose a point of rotation. Choose either end to eliminate one of the variables F_1 or F_2. Let us choose the right end and label it A.

4. $\Sigma \tau_{\text{clockwise}} = (F_1)(8.00 \text{ ft})$

5. $\Sigma \tau_{\text{counterclockwise}} = (40.0 \text{ lb})(3.00 \text{ ft}) + (175 \text{ lb})(5.00 \text{ ft})$
   Note that there are two counterclockwise torques.

6. $\Sigma \tau_{\text{clockwise}} = \Sigma \tau_{\text{counterclockwise}}$
   $F_1(8.00 \text{ ft}) = (40.0 \text{ lb})(3.00 \text{ ft}) + (175 \text{ lb})(5.00 \text{ ft})$

7. $F_1 = \dfrac{(40.0 \text{ lb})(3.00 \text{ ft}) + (175 \text{ lb})(5.00 \text{ ft})}{8.00 \text{ ft}}$

   $= \dfrac{12\overline{0} \text{ lb ft} + 875 \text{ lb ft}}{8.00 \text{ ft}} = \dfrac{995 \text{ lb ft}}{8.00 \text{ ft}} = 124 \text{ lb}$

8. $F_1 + F_2 = 175 \text{ lb} + 40.0 \text{ lb}$
   $124 \text{ lb} + F_2 = 215 \text{ lb} \qquad\qquad (F_1 = 124 \text{ lb})$
   $F_2 = 91 \text{ lb}$

. . . .

TRY THIS ACTIVITY

The Physics of Window Washing

Window washers on tall buildings typically stand on a platform that is suspended from the top of the building by ropes or cables. Designers of these devices must make sure that the cables can safely suspend the workers while they are all working on one side of the platform. To simulate this activity, take the two strings, the scales, and the mass from the previous Try This Activity and use a metre stick or a wooden dowel as the platform.

Set up the activity as indicated in Fig. 7.42, making sure both suspending strings are the same length and that the metre stick is horizontal. Place the weight directly in the middle of the metre stick and note the readings in the scales. Then gradually shift the mass over to one side and observe what happens to the readings in the spring scales. What happens to the sum of the tension forces as the mass is shifted to one of the sides?

Figure 7.42 After suspending the mass from the middle of the platform, shift the mass toward one side and observe what happens to the tension in the strings.

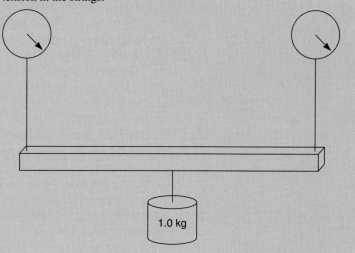

1.0 kg

PROBLEMS 7.4

Find the force F that will produce equilibrium for each force diagram. Use the same procedure as in Example 1.

1.
100 lb $F = ?$

2.
$F = ?$

200 N

3. $F = ?$ 200 N

700 N

SKETCH

12 cm² w

4.0 cm

DATA

A = 12 cm², l = 4.0 cm, w = ?

BASIC EQUATION

A = lw

WORKING EQUATION

$w = \frac{A}{l}$

SUBSTITUTION

$w = \frac{12 \text{ cm}^2}{4.0 \text{ cm}} = 3.0 \text{ cm}$

4.
$F = ?$

200 N   150 N

5.
900 N   450 N

$F = ?$

6.
650 lb   100 lb
          250 lb
          $F = ?$

7.
$F = ?$ 750 N
           1500 N
2100 N   250 N

8.
50.0 N   10.0 N

35.0 N $F = ?$

15.0 N   75.0 N

9. A 90.0-kg painter stands 3.00 m from one end of an 8.00-m scaffold. If the scaffold is supported at each end by a stepladder, how much of the weight of the painter must each ladder support?

10. A 5000-lb truck is 20.0 ft from one end of a 50.0-ft bridge. A 4000-lb car is 40.0 ft from the same end. How much weight must each end of the bridge support? (Neglect the weight of the bridge.)

11. A 2400-kg truck is 6.00 m from one end of a 27.0-m-long bridge. A 1500-kg car is 10.0 m from the same end. How much weight must each end of the bridge support?

12. An auto transmission of mass 165 kg is located 1.00 m from one end of a 2.50-m bench. What weight must each end of the bench support?

13. A bar 8.00 m long supports masses of 20.0 kg on the left end and 40.0 kg on the right end. At what distance from the 40.0-kg mass must the bar be supported for the bar to balance?

14. Two painters, each of mass 75.0 kg, stand on a 12.0 m scaffold, 6.00 m apart and 3.00 m from each end. They share a paint container of mass 21.0 kg in the middle of the scaffold. What weight must be supported by each of the ropes secured to the ends of the scaffold?

15. Two painters, one of mass 75.0 kg and the other 90.0 kg, stand on a 12.00-m scaffold, 6.00 m apart and 3.00 m from each end. They share a paint container of mass 21.0 kg in the middle of the scaffold. What weight must be supported by each of the ropes secured at the end of the scaffold?

16. Two painters stand on a 10.00-m scaffold. One, of mass 65.0 kg, stands 2.00 m from one end. The other, of mass 95.0 kg, stands 4.00 m from the other end. They share a paint container of mass 18.0 kg located between the two and 2.50 m from the larger person. What weight must be supported by each of the ropes secured at the ends of the scaffold?

17. An auto differential with a mass of 76.0 kg is 1.00 m from the end of a 2.22-m workbench. What mass must each end of the workbench support?

18. A chop saw with mass of 12.60 kg is 0.75 m from one end of a worktable that is 2.00 m long. What mass must each end of the table support?

7.5 Center of Gravity

In Section 7.4 we neglected the weight of the plank in the painter example. In practice, the weight of the plank or bridge is extremely important. The weight of a bridge being designed must be known in order to use materials of sufficient strength to support the bridge and the traffic and not collapse. An important concept in this kind of problem is center of gravity. *The center of gravity of any body is that point at which all of its weight can be considered to be concentrated*. A body such as a brick or a uniform rod has its center of gravity at its middle or center. The center of gravity of something like an automobile, however, is not at its center or middle because its weight is not evenly distributed throughout. Its center of gravity is located nearer the heavy engine.

Figure 7.43 The center of gravity of a uniform thin plate can also be found by suspending it from a point and using a vertical chalkline with a suspended weight as shown in (b). The center of gravity is the point of intersection of any two or more such chalklines as in (c).

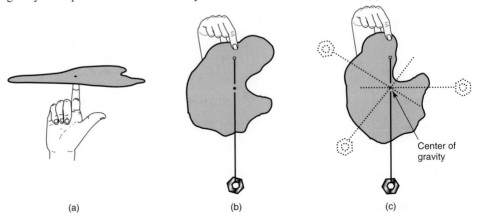

(a) (b) (c)

The center of gravity of an irregularly shaped uniform thin plate is the point at which it can be supported as in Fig. 7.43(a). The center of gravity of a uniform thin plate can also be found by suspending it from a point and using a vertical chalkline with a suspended weight as shown in Fig. 7.43(b). The center of gravity is the point of intersection of any two or more such chalklines as in Fig. 7.43(c).

You have probably had the experience of carrying a long board by yourself. If the board was not too heavy, you could carry it yourself by balancing it at its middle (Fig. 7.44). You didn't have to hold up both ends. You applied the principle of center of gravity and balanced the board at that point.

Figure 7.44   Support of the board at its center of gravity

We shall represent the weight of a body by a vector through its center of gravity. We use a vector to show the weight (force due to gravity) of the body (Fig. 7.45). It is placed through the center of gravity to show that all the weight may be considered concentrated at that point. If the center of gravity is not at the middle of the body, its location will be given. In solving problems, the weight of the plank or bridge is represented like the other forces by a vector, which in the case of weight is through the center of gravity of the object.

Figure 7.45   Weight can be represented by a vector through the center of gravity.

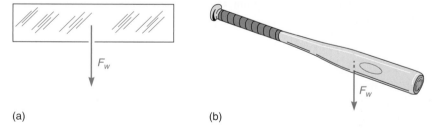

(a)   (b)

A carpenter stands 2.00 ft from one end of a 6.00-ft scaffold that is uniform and weighs 20.0 lb. If the carpenter weighs 165 lb, how much weight must each end support?

EXAMPLE 1

1. **Sketch:**

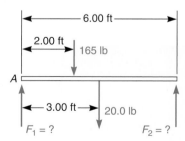

Since the plank is uniform, its center of gravity is at the middle.

2. $\Sigma F = F_1 + F_2 = 165 \text{ lb} + 20.0 \text{ lb}$

3.   Choose the left end as the point of rotation and label it A.

4. $\Sigma \tau_{\text{clockwise}} = (165 \text{ lb})(2.00 \text{ ft}) + (20.0 \text{ lb})(3.00 \text{ ft})$

5. $\Sigma \tau_{\text{counterclockwise}} = (F_2)(6.00 \text{ ft})$

6. $(165 \text{ lb})(2.00 \text{ ft}) + (20.0 \text{ lb})(3.00 \text{ ft}) = (F_2)(6.00 \text{ ft})$

7. $F_2 = \dfrac{330 \text{ lb ft} + 60.0 \text{ lb ft}}{6.00 \text{ ft}} = \dfrac{390 \text{ lb ft}}{6.00 \text{ ft}} = 65.0 \text{ lb}$

8. $F_1 + 65.0 \text{ lb} = 165 \text{ lb} + 20.0 \text{ lb}$
$$F_1 = 165 \text{ lb} + 20.0 \text{ lb} - 65.0 \text{ lb}$$
$$= 120 \text{ lb}$$

....

We can also use this method to find the magnitude and position of a parallel force vector that produces equilibrium.

EXAMPLE 2

Find the magnitude, direction, and placement (from point A) of a parallel vector F_6 that will produce equilibrium in the parallel force diagram in Fig. 7.46.

Figure 7.46

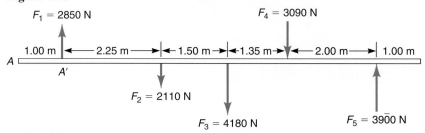

1. $\Sigma F = F_1 + F_5 + F_6 = F_2 + F_3 + F_4$
$$2850 \text{ N} + 3900 \text{ N} + F_6 = 2110 \text{ N} + 4180 \text{ N} + 3090 \text{ N}$$
$$F_6 = 2630 \text{ N (up)}$$

2.   Choose A' instead of A as the point of rotation to make the torque arm zero for F_1. Also, let x be the distance of F_6 from point A'.

3. $\Sigma \tau_{\text{clockwise}} = (2110 \text{ N})(2.25 \text{ m}) + (4180 \text{ N})(3.75 \text{ m}) + (3090 \text{ N})(5.10 \text{ m})$

4. $\Sigma \tau_{\text{counterclockwise}} = (3900 \text{ N})(7.10 \text{ m}) + (2630 \text{ N})(x)$

5. $\Sigma \tau_{\text{clockwise}} = \Sigma \tau_{\text{counterclockwise}}$

6. $(2110 \text{ N})(2.25 \text{ m}) + (4180 \text{ N})(3.75 \text{ m}) + (3090 \text{ N})(5.10 \text{ m}) = (3900 \text{ N})(7.10 \text{ m})$
$$+ (2630 \text{ N})(x)$$
$$3.23 \text{ m} = x \text{ (from } A')$$
$$\text{or } 4.23 \text{ m} = x \text{ (from } A)$$

Thus, the equilibrium vector is 2630 N (up) placed at 4.23 m from point A.

....

TRY THIS ACTIVITY

Center of Mass

Stand with your back and heels touching a wall. Without moving your feet, bend over and touch your legs below your knees. Using the concept of center of gravity, explain what happened.

PROBLEMS 7.5

Solve each problem using the methods outlined in this chapter.

1. Solve for F_1: $30.0F_1 = (14.0)(18.0) + (25.0)(17.0)$
2. Solve for F_w: $(12.0)(15.0) + 45.0F_w = (21.0)(65.0) + (22.0)(32.0)$
3. Two workers carry a uniform 15.0-ft plank that weighs 22.0 lb (Fig. 7.47). A load of blocks weighing 165 lb is located 7.00 ft from the first worker. What force must each worker exert to hold up the plank and load?

Figure 7.47

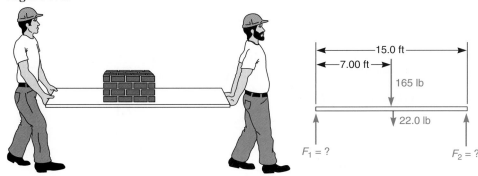

4. Juan and Pablo carry a load weighing 720 N on a pole between them. (a) If the pole is 2.0 m long and the load is 0.50 m from Pablo, what force does each person support? Neglect the weight of the pole. (b) If the weight of the 120-N pole is considered, what force does each person support?
5. A wooden beam is 3.30 m long and has its center of gravity 1.30 m from one end. If the beam weighs 1500 N, what force is needed to support each end?
6. An auto engine weighs 650 lb and is located 4.00 ft from one end of a 10.0-ft workbench. If the bench is uniform and weighs 75.0 lb, what weight must each end of the bench support?
7. A bridge across a country stream weighs 89,200 N. A large truck stalls 4.00 m from one end of the 9.00-m bridge. What weight must each of the piers support if the truck weighs 98,000 N?
8. A window washer's scaffold 12.0 ft long and weighing 75.0 lb is suspended from each end. One washer weighs 155 lb and is 3.00 ft from one end. The other washer is 4.00 ft from the other end. If the force supported by the end near the first washer is 200 lb, how much does the second washer weigh?
9. A porch swing weighs 29.0 lb. It is 4.40 ft long and has a dog weighing 14.0 lb sleeping on it 1.90 ft from one end and a 125-lb person sitting 1.00 ft from the other end. What weight must the support ropes on each end hold up?
10. A wooden plank is 5.00 m long and supports a 75.0-kg block 2.00 m from one end. If the plank is uniform with mass 30.0 kg, how much force is needed to support each end?
11. A bridge has a mass of 1.60×10^4 kg, is 21.0 m long, and has a 3500-kg truck 7.00 m from one end. What force must each end of the bridge support?
12. A uniform steel beam is 5.00 m long and weighs 360 N. What force is needed to lift one end?
13. A wooden pole is 4.00 m long, weighs 315 N, and has its center of gravity 1.50 m from one end. What force is needed to lift each end?
14. A bridge has a mass of 2.60×10^4 kg, is 32.0 m long, and has a 3500-kg truck 15.0 m from one end. What force must each end of the bridge support?
15. An auto engine of mass 295 kg is located 1.00 m from one end of a 4.00-m workbench. If the uniform bench has a mass of 45.0 kg, what weight must each end of the bench support?

16. A 125-kg horizontal beam is supported at each end. A 325-kg mass rests one-fourth of the way from one end. What weight must be supported at each end?

17. The sign shown in Fig. 7.48 is 4.00 m long, weighs $155\bar{0}$ N, and is made of uniform material. A weight of 245 N hangs 1.00 m from the end. Find the tension in each support cable.

18. The uniform bar in Fig. 7.49 is 5.00 m long and weighs 975 N. A weight of 255 N is attached to one end while a weight of 375 N is attached 1.50 m from the other end. (a) Find the tension in the cable. (b) Where should the cable be tied to lift the bar and its weights so that the bar hangs in a horizontal equilibrium position?

Figure 7.48

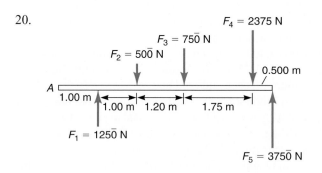

Figure 7.49

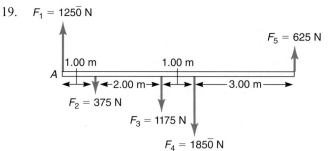

Find the magnitude, direction, and placement (from point A) of a parallel vector F_6 that will produce equilibrium in each force diagram.

19. $F_1 = 125\bar{0}$ N

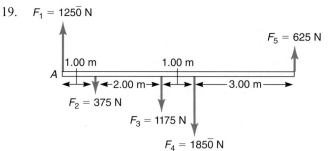

20.

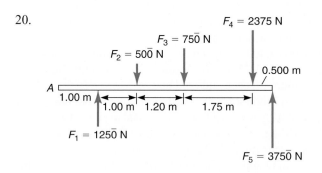

Glossary

Center of Gravity The point of any body at which all of its weight can be considered to be concentrated. (p. 194)

Compression A force produced by forces pushing inward on the ends of an object (p. 177)

Concurrent Forces Two or more forces applied to, or acting at, the same point. (p. 169)

Equilibrant Force The force that, when applied at the same point as the resultant force, produces equilibrium. (p. 177)

Equilibrium An object is said to be in equilibrium when the net force acting on it is zero. A body that is in equilibrium is either at rest or moving at a constant velocity. (p. 175)

First Condition of Equilibrium The sum of all parallel forces on a body in equilibrium must be zero. (p. 189)

Resultant Force The sum of the forces applied at the same point. The single force that has the same effect as two or more forces acting together. (p. 169)

Second Condition of Equilibrium The sum of the clockwise torques on a body in equilibrium must be equal to the sum of the counterclockwise torques about any point. (p. 190)

Statics The study of objects that are in equilibrium. (p. 175)

Tension A stretching force produced by forces pulling outward on the ends of an object. (p. 177)

Torque The tendency to produce change in rotational motion. Equal to the applied force times the length of the torque arm. (p. 185)

Formulas

7.1 To find the resultant vector $\mathbf{F}_R$ of two or more vectors:

(a) find the x- and y-components of each vector and add the components.

(b) find angle A as follows:

$$\tan A = \frac{|\text{sum of } y\text{-components}|}{|\text{sum of } x\text{-components}|} = \frac{|\mathbf{F}_{Ry}|}{|\mathbf{F}_{Rx}|}$$

Determine the quadrant of the angle from the signs of the sum of the x- and y-components.

(c) find the magnitude of $\mathbf{F}_R$ using the Pythagorean theorem:

$$|\mathbf{F}_R| = \sqrt{|\mathbf{F}_{Rx}|^2 + |\mathbf{F}_{Ry}|^2}$$

7.2 Condition for equilibrium in one dimension:

$$\mathbf{F}_+ = \mathbf{F}_-$$

where $\mathbf{F}_+$ is the sum of the forces acting in one direction (call it the positive direction) and $\mathbf{F}_-$ is the sum of the forces acting in the opposite (negative) direction.

Conditions for equilibrium in two dimensions:

(a) The sum of x-components = 0; that is, $\mathbf{A}_x + \mathbf{B}_x + \mathbf{C}_x = 0$; and

(b) The sum of y-components = 0; that is, $\mathbf{A}_y + \mathbf{B}_y + \mathbf{C}_y = 0$.

To solve equilibrium problems:

1. Draw a force diagram from the point at which the unknown forces act.
2. Find the x- and y-components of each force.
3. Substitute the components in the equations

$$\text{sum of } x\text{-components} = 0$$
$$\text{sum of } y\text{-components} = 0$$

4. Solve for the unknowns. This may involve two simultaneous equations.

7.3 $\tau = Fs_t$

7.4   *First condition of equilibrium:* The sum of all parallel forces on an object must be zero.

$$\Sigma F = 0$$

Second condition of equilibrium: The sum of the clockwise torques on an object must equal the sum of the counterclockwise torques.

$$\Sigma \tau_{\text{clockwise}} = \Sigma \tau_{\text{counterclockwise}}$$

Review Questions

1. Concurrent forces act at
    (a) two or more different points.   (b) the same point.   (c) the origin.
2. The resultant force is
    (a) the last force applied.
    (b) the single force that has the same effect as two or more forces acting together.
    (c) equal to either diagonal when using the parallelogram method to add vectors.
3. A moving object
    (a) can be in equilibrium.   (b) is never in equilibrium.
    (c) has no force being applied.
4. The study of an object in equilibrium is called
    (a) dynamics.   (b) astronomy.   (c) statics.   (d) biology.
5. Torque is
    (a) applied force in rotational motion.
    (b) the length of the torque arm.
    (c) applied force times the length of the torque arm.
    (d) none of the above.
6. The first condition of equilibrium states that
    (a) all parallel forces must be zero.
    (b) all perpendicular forces must be zero.
    (c) all frictional forces must be zero.
7. In the second condition of equilibrium,
    (a) clockwise and counterclockwise torques are unequal.
    (b) clockwise and counterclockwise torques are equal.
    (c) there are no torques.
8. The center of gravity of an object
    (a) is always at its geometric center.
    (b) does not have to be at the geometric center.
    (c) exists only in symmetrical objects.
9. Is motion produced every time a force is applied to an object?
10. What is the relationship between opposing forces on a body that is in equilibrium?
11. Define *equilibrium*.
12. In what direction does the force due to gravity always act?
13. What may be said about concurrent forces whose sum of x-components equals zero and whose sum of y-components equals zero?
14. What is a force diagram?
15. Is the length of the pedal necessarily the true length of the torque arm in pedaling a bicycle?
16. In your own words, explain the second condition of equilibrium.
17. What is the primary consideration in the selection of a point of rotation in an equilibrium problem?
18. List three examples from daily life in which you use the concept of center of gravity.
19. Is the center of gravity of an object always at its geometric center?
20. On a 3.00-m scaffold of uniform mass, with supports at each end, there is a pile of bricks 0.500 m from one end. Which support will exert a greater force: the one closer to the bricks or the one farther away?

Review Problems

1. Find the sum of the following forces acting at the same point in a straight line: 345 N (right); 108 N (right); 481 N (left); 238 N (left); 303 N (left).
2. Forces of 275 lb and 225 lb act at the same point.
   (a) What is the magnitude of the maximum net force the two forces can exert together?
   (b) What is the magnitude of the minimum net force the two forces can exert together?

Find the sum of each set of vectors. Give angles in standard position.

3.

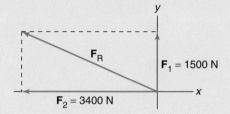

$F_1 = 1500$ N
$F_2 = 3400$ N

4.

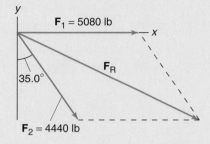

$F_1 = 5080$ lb
35.0°
F_R
$F_2 = 4440$ lb

SKETCH

| 12 cm² | w |

4.0 cm

DATA

$A = 12$ cm², $l = 4.0$ cm, w = ?

BASIC EQUATION

$A = lw$

WORKING EQUATION

$w = \frac{A}{l}$

SUBSTITUTION

$w = \frac{12 \text{ cm}^2}{4.0 \text{ cm}} = 3.0$ cm

5.

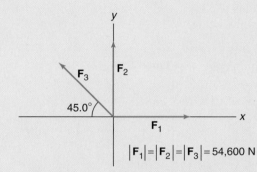

F_3 F_2
45.0°
F_1

$|F_1| = |F_2| = |F_3| = 54{,}600$ N

6. Forces of $F_1 = 1250$ N, $F_2 = 625$ N, and $F_3 = 1850$ N are applied at the same point. The angle between F_1 and F_2 is 120.0° and the angle between F_2 and F_3 is 30.0°. F_2 is between F_1 and F_3. Find the resultant force.
7. Eight people are involved in a tug-of-war. The blue team members pull with forces of 220 N, 340 N, 180 N, and 560 N. Three members of the red team pull with forces of 250 N, 160 N, and 420 N. With what force must the fourth person pull to maintain equilibrium?
8. A bridge has a weight limit of 14.0 tons. What is the maximum weight an 8.0-ton truck can carry across and still maintain equilibrium?
9. The x-components of three vectors are F_x, 375 units, and 150 units. If their sum is equal to zero, what is F_x?
10. If $W_y = 600$ N and $W_x = 900$ N, what are the magnitude and direction of the resultant W?

Find forces F_1 and F_2 that produce equilibrium in each force diagram.

11.

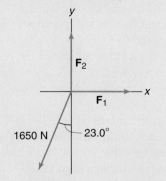

F_2
F_1
1650 N 23.0°

12.

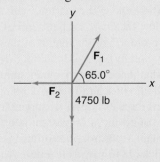

F_1
65.0°
F_2
4750 lb

13. Find the tension in the cable and the compression in the support of the sign shown in Fig. 7.50.
14. Find the tension in each cable in Fig. 7.51.

Figure 7.50

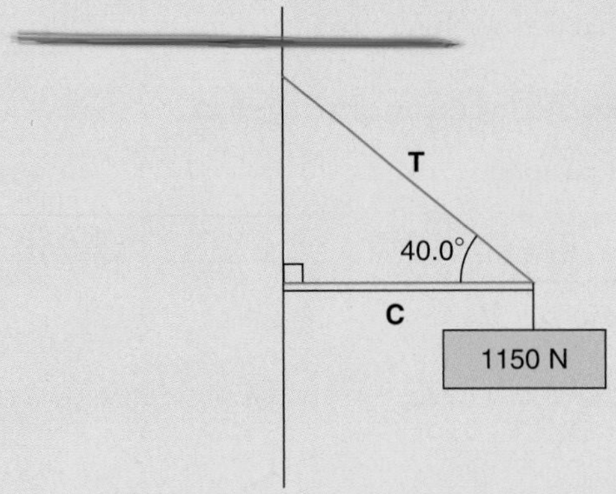

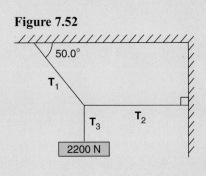

1150 N

Figure 7.51

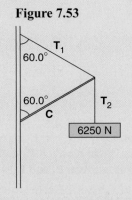

30.0°   45.0°

T_1 T_2

T_3

475 lb

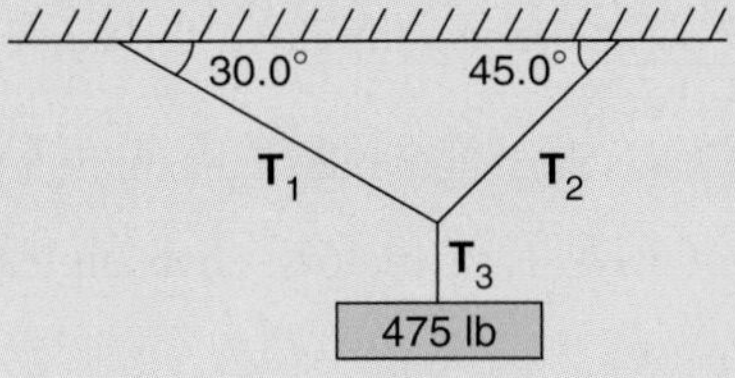

15. Find the tension in each cable in Fig. 7.52.
16. Find the tension and the compression in Fig. 7.53.

Figure 7.52

50.0°

T_1

T_3 T_2

2200 N

Figure 7.53

T_1

60.0°

60.0° T_2

C

6250 N

17. A man is changing a flat tire using a tire iron that is 50.0 cm long. If he exerts a force of 53.0 N, how much torque (in N m) does he produce?
18. A torque of 81.0 lb ft is produced by a torque arm of 3.00 ft. What force is being applied?
19. A hanging sign has mass $20\overline{0}$ kg. If the tension in one support cable is 1080 N, what is the tension in the other support cable?
20. A scaffold supports a bricklayer and bricks weighing 450 lb. If the force in one end support is 290 lb, what is the supporting force in the other?
21. Two ladders at the ends of a scaffold support a mass of 90.0 kg each. An 80.0-kg worker is on the scaffold with a pile of bricks. Find the mass of the bricks.
22. How far from the light end of a 68.0-cm bat would its center of gravity be if it is one-fourth of the length of the bat from the heavy end?
23. A bridge has mass $800\overline{0}$ kg. If a 3200-kg truck stops in the middle of the bridge, what mass must each pier support?
24. If the truck in Problem 23 stops 7.00 m from one end of the 26.0-m bridge, what weight must each end support?
25. A uniform 2.20-kg steel bar with length 2.70 m is suspended on each end by a chain. A 40.0-kg person hangs 70.0 cm from one end while a 55.0-kg person hangs 50.0 cm from the other end. Another person pushes up halfway between the two persons with a force of 127 N. How much weight does each chain support?

26. Find the vertical force needed to support the 4.00-m-long uniform beam in Fig. 7.54, which weighs 3475 N.

Figure 7.54

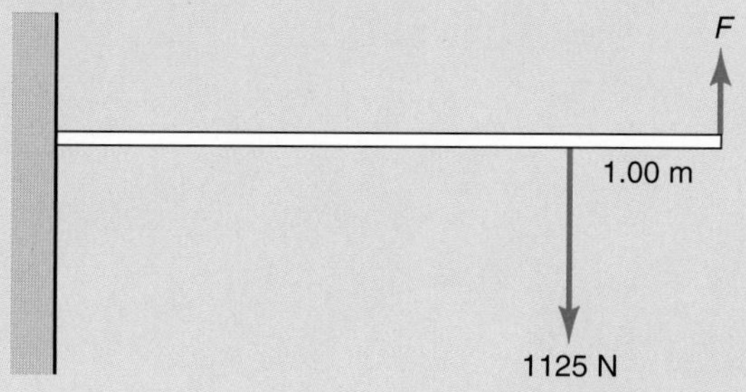

F

1.00 m

1125 N

APPLIED CONCEPTS

1. Archeologists in Egypt are attempting to open a 2.57-m-wide door in the tomb of Tutankhamen. Miles, one of the rookie archeologists, pushes perpendicularly on the door with a force of 894 N. (a) How much torque does Miles exert on the door? (b) As the door opens, Miles continues to push with the same force, but is at an angle of 30.0° to the face of the door. How much torque does Miles apply to the door? (c) What could Miles do to continually exert the same amount of torque on the door?

2. Sean and Greg are on a job site standing on two beams 11.0 ft apart. They need to lift their crate of tools midway between them with ropes up 33.5 ft to where they are working. (a) What is the angle between the ropes when the crate is on the ground? (b) How much force do Sean and Greg need to exert on the ropes when lifting the 115-lb crate off the ground? (c) How much force do both Sean and Greg need to exert when the crate is 5.75 ft below them? (d) Explain why the force to lift the crate changes as it moves closer to them.

3. Maria has severe arthritis and can only apply a maximum force of 25.5 N when opening her front door. (a) How much more torque would Maria be able to apply if she purchased a lever-style door opener with a handle 12.7 cm long compared to her conventional doorknob with a radius of 3.74 cm? (b) How much less force would she need to apply to the new door handle in order to maintain the original amount of torque she had with her old doorknob?

4. Krista's flagpole bracket is mounted at an angle of 45.0° to the wall and is designed to support a maximum torque of 40.0 N m. (a) If the new flag and pole that Krista bought have a mass of 8.75 kg and their center of mass is located 0.750 m from the bracket, will the bracket support the flag and pole? (b) What could Krista do to the angle of the bracket to reduce the torque?

5. Luisa, whose mass is 45.0 kg, is standing at the end of a 5.50-m diving board, which has a mass of 35.7 kg (Fig. 7.55). (a) What force must the bracket and fulcrum exert on the diving board? (b) Where would Luisa stand to have both the fulcrum and the bracket apply an upward force?

Figure 7.55

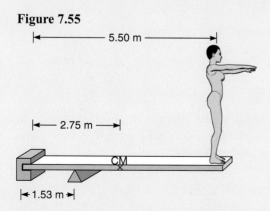

5.50 m

2.75 m

CM

1.53 m

$$E_{TOTAL} = PE_{TOP} = KE_{BOTTOM} = mgh_{TOP} = mv^2_{BOTTOM}$$

The Conservation of Energy

Work, power, and energy are common terms used to describe changes in physical activity. In science each of these terms has a limited definition. Work, for example, is accomplished only where there is movement of the object on which the applied force acts. Effort alone is insufficient.

We will now study how the scientist and engineer use work, power, and energy; how they are related; and how they differ from their everyday meanings.

Objectives

The major goals of this chapter are to enable you to:

1. Distinguish the common and technical definitions of work.
2. Analyze how power is used and described in technical applications.
3. Relate kinetic and potential energy to the law of conservation of mechanical energy.

8.1 Work

What is work? The common idea of the definition of work is quite different from the technical definition. We often associate work with physical or mental effort that leads to fatigue. The technical definition of work is more limited. If we try to lift a heavy crate that doesn't budge [Fig. 8.1(a)], we would probably say that we have done work because we strained our muscles and feel tired, but in a technical sense, no work was done, because the crate did not move. Work would be done *on* the crate if we were to push it across the floor [Fig. 8.1(b)]. In this case, work was done *by* us, and work was done *on* the crate.

Figure 8.1 Work is done only in the case shown in part (b).

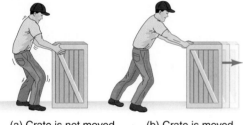

   (a) Crate is not moved.   (b) Crate is moved.

    The technical meaning of work requires that work must be done *by* one object *on* another object. When a stake is driven into the ground (Fig. 8.2), work is done *by* the moving sledgehammer and work is done *on* the stake. When a bulldozer pushes dirt (Fig. 8.3), work is done *by* the bulldozer and work is done *on* the dirt.

Figure 8.2 Work is done by one object on another.

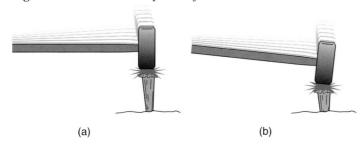

    (a)   (b)

Figure 8.3 Work is done *by* the bulldozer *on* the dirt.

The previous examples show a limited meaning of work: that work is done when a force acts through a distance. The physical definition of **work** is even narrower: *Work is the product of the force in the direction of the motion and the displacement.*

$$W = Fs$$

where W = work
F = force applied *in the direction of the motion*
s = displacement

Now, let us apply our technical definition of work to our unsuccessful effort to lift the crate. We applied a force by lifting on the crate but were unable to move it. Therefore, the displacement was zero, and the product of the force and the displacement must also be zero. So, no work was done.

From the equation for work, we can determine the units for work. In the metric system, force is expressed in newtons and displacement in metres:

$$\text{work} = \text{force} \times \text{displacement} = \text{newton} \times \text{metre} = \text{N m}$$

This unit (N m) has a special name in honor of **James P. Joule**. It is the joule (J) [pronounced j$\overline{oo}$l]:

$$1 \text{ N m} = 1 \text{ joule} = 1 \text{ J}$$

In the U.S. system, force is expressed in pounds (lb) and displacement in feet (ft):

$$\text{work} = \text{force} \times \text{displacement} = \text{pounds} \times \text{feet} = \text{ft lb}$$

The U.S. unit of work is called the foot-pound.

Work is not a vector quantity because it has no particular direction. It is a scalar and has only magnitude.

EXAMPLE 1

Find the amount of work done by a worker lifting 225 N of bricks to a height of 1.75 m as shown in Fig. 8.4.

Data:

$$F = 225 \text{ N}$$
$$s = 1.75 \text{ m}$$
$$W = ?$$

Figure 8.4

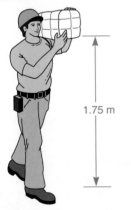

1.75 m

Basic Equation:

$$W = Fs$$

Working Equation: Same

Substitution:

$$W = (225 \text{ N})(1.75 \text{ m})$$
$$= 394 \text{ N m} \quad \text{or} \quad 394 \text{ J}$$

. . . .

EXAMPLE 2

A worker pushes a 350-lb cart a distance of $3\overline{0}$ ft by exerting a constant force of $4\overline{0}$ lb as shown in Fig. 8.5. How much work does the person do?

Figure 8.5

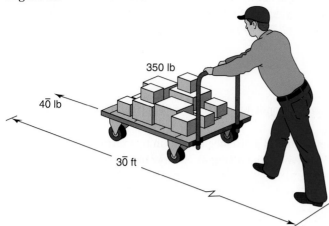

Data:

$$F = 4\overline{0}\ \text{lb}$$
$$s = 3\overline{0}\ \text{ft}$$
$$W = ?$$

Basic Equation:

$$W = Fs$$

Working Equation: Same

Substitution:

$$W = (4\overline{0}\ \text{lb})(3\overline{0}\ \text{ft})$$
$$= 1200\ \text{ft lb}$$

. . . .

Note: In Example 2 the cart weighs 350 lb but $F = 4\overline{0}$ lb. (Recall that the weight of an object is the measure of its gravitational attraction to the earth and is represented by a vertical vector pointing down to the center of the earth.) There is no vertical motion in the direction of the gravitational force. Therefore, the weight of the box is not the force used to determine the amount of work being done.

Work is being done by the worker pushing the pallet. Exerting a force of $4\overline{0}$ lb results in a displacement in the direction of the applied force. The work done is the product of this force ($4\overline{0}$ lb) and the displacement ($3\overline{0}$ ft) in the direction the force is applied.

Recall that the definition of work states that work is the product of the *force in the direction of the motion* and the displacement. To determine the work when the force is not applied in the direction of the motion, consider a block being pulled by a rope with a force **F** that makes an angle θ with level ground as shown in Fig. 8.6. First, draw the horizontal component $\mathbf{F}_x$ and complete the right triangle. Note that $\mathbf{F}_x$ is the force in the direction of the motion. From the right triangle we have

$$\cos \theta = \frac{\text{side adjacent to } \theta}{\text{hypotenuse}} = \frac{|\mathbf{F}_x|}{|\mathbf{F}|}$$

Or,

$$|\mathbf{F}_x| = |\mathbf{F}|\cos \theta$$

Figure 8.6

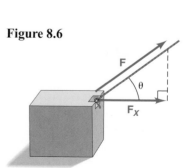

That is, when the applied force is not in the direction of the motion, the work done is

$$W = Fs \cos \theta$$

where $W =$ the work done
$F =$ the applied force
$s =$ the displacement
$\theta =$ the angle between the applied force and the direction of the motion

EXAMPLE 3

A person pulls a sled along level ground a distance of 15.0 m by exerting a constant force of 215 N at an angle of 30.0° with the ground (Fig. 8.7). How much work does she do?

Figure 8.7

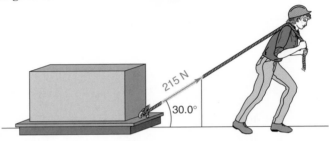

Data:

$$F = 215 \text{ N}$$
$$s = 15.0 \text{ m}$$
$$\theta = 30.0°$$
$$W = ?$$

Basic Equation:

$$W = Fs \cos \theta$$

Working Equation: Same

Substitution:

$$W = (215 \text{ N})(15.0 \text{ m}) \cos 30.0°$$
$$= 2790 \text{ N m}$$
$$= 2790 \text{ J} \quad (1 \text{ N m} = 1 \text{ J})$$

· · · · · · · · · · · · · · · ·

EXAMPLE 4

Juan and Sonja use a push mower to mow a lawn. Juan, who is taller, pushes at a constant force of 33.1 N on the handle at an angle of 55.0° with the ground. Sonja, who is shorter, pushes at a constant force of 23.2 N on the handle at an angle of 35.0° with the ground. Assume they each push the mower 3000 m. Who does more work and by how much?

Sketch:

Data:

$F = 33.1$ N	$F = 23.2$ N
$s = 30\overline{0}0$ m	$s = 30\overline{0}0$ m
$\theta = 55.0°$	$\theta = 35.0°$
$W = ?$	$W = ?$

Basic Equation:

$W = Fs \cos\theta$ $\qquad\qquad W = Fs \cos\theta$

Working Equation: Same $\qquad$ Same

Substitution:

$W = (33.1 \text{ N})(30\overline{0}0 \text{ m}) \cos 55.0°$ $\qquad W = (23.2 \text{ N})(30\overline{0}0 \text{ m}) \cos 35.0°$
$\quad = 57,\overline{0}00$ N m $\qquad\qquad\qquad\qquad\quad = 57,\overline{0}00$ N m
$\quad = 57,\overline{0}00$ J $\quad$ (1 N m = 1 J) $\qquad\quad = 57,\overline{0}00$ J

They do the same amount of work. However, Juan must exert more energy because he pushes into the ground more than Sonja, who pushes more in the direction of the motion.

. . . .

Find the amount of work done in vertically lifting a steel beam with mass 750 kg at uniform speed a distance of 45 m.
$\quad$ Here the force is the weight of the beam.

EXAMPLE 5

Data:

$F = mg$
$m = 750$ kg
$g = 9.80$ m/s^2
$s = 45$ m
$W = ?$

Basic Equation:

$W = Fs = mgs$

Working Equation: Same

Substitution:

$W = (750 \text{ kg})(9.80 \text{ m/s}^2)(45 \text{ m})$
$\quad = 3.3 \times 10^5 \text{ (kg m/s}^2)(\text{m})$
$\quad = 3.3 \times 10^5$ N m $\quad$ (1 N = 1 kg m/s^2)
$\quad = 3.3 \times 10^5$ J $\quad$ (1 J = 1 N m)

Do you see that 330 kJ would also be an acceptable answer?

. . . .

PROBLEMS 8.1

1. Given: $F = 10.0$ N
   $s = 3.43$ m
   $W = ?$

2. Given: $F = 125$ N
   $s = 4875$ m
   $W = ?$

SKETCH

12 cm^2 | w

4.0 cm

DATA

$A = 12 \text{ cm}^2$, $l = 4.0$ cm, $w = ?$

BASIC EQUATION

$A = lw$

WORKING EQUATION

$w = \frac{A}{l}$

SUBSTITUTION

$w = \frac{12 \text{ cm}^2}{4.0 \text{ cm}} = 3.0$ cm

3. Given: $F = 1850$ N
    $s = 625$ m
    $\theta = 37.5°$
    $W = ?$

4. Given: $W = 697$ ft lb
    $s = 976$ ft
    $F = ?$

5. Given: $F = 25,700$ N
    $s = 238$ m
    $W = 5.57 \times 10^6$ J
    $\theta = ?$

6. Given: $F = ma$
    $m = 16.0$ kg
    $a = 9.80 \text{ m/s}^2$
    $s = 13.0$ m
    $W = ?$

7. How much work is required for a mechanical hoist to lift a 9000-N automobile to a height of 1.80 m for repairs?

8. A hay wagon is used to move bales from the field to the barn. The tractor pulling the wagon exerts a constant force of 350 lb. The distance from field to barn is $\frac{1}{2}$ mi. How much work (ft lb) is done in moving one load of hay to the barn?

9. A worker lifts 75 concrete blocks a distance of 1.50 m to the bed of a truck. Each block has a mass of 4.00 kg. How much work is done to lift all the blocks to the truck bed?

10. The work required to lift eleven 94.0-lb bags of cement from the ground to the back of a truck is 4340 ft lb. What is the distance from the ground to the bed of the truck?

11. How much work is done in lifting 450 lb of cement 75 ft above the ground?

12. How much work is done lifting a 200-kg wrecking ball 6.50 m above the ground?

13. A gardener pushes a mower a distance of 900 m in mowing a yard. The handle of the mower makes an angle of 40.0° with the ground. The gardener exerts a force of 35.0 N along the handle of the mower (Fig. 8.8). How much work does the gardener do in mowing the lawn?

Figure 8.8

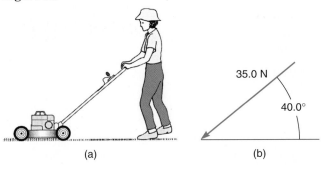

35.0 N

40.0°

(a)   (b)

14. The handle of a vegetable wagon makes an angle of 25.0° with the horizontal (Fig. 8.9). If the peddler exerts a force of 35.0 lb along the handle, how much work does the peddler do in pulling the cart 1.00 mi?

Figure 8.9

35.0 lb

25.0°

(a)   (b)

15. A crate is pulled 675 ft across a warehouse floor by a worker using a rope that makes an angle of 50.0° with the floor. If 375 lb is exerted on the rope, how much work is done in pulling the crate across the floor?

16. A man pulls a sled a distance of 231 m. The rope attached to the sled makes an angle of 30.0° with the ground. The man exerts a force of 775 N on the rope. How much work does the man do in pulling the sled?

17. A tractor tows a barge through a canal with a towrope that makes an angle of 21° with the bank of the canal. If the tension in the rope is 12,000 N, how much work is done in moving the barge 550 m?

18. Two tractors tow a barge through a canal; each tractor uses a towrope that makes an angle of 21° with the bank of the canal. If the tension in each rope is 12,000 N, how much work is done in moving the barge 550 m?

19. Two students push a dune buggy 35.0 m across a lot. The force required is 825 N. How much work is done?

20. After a rain, the force necessary to push the dune buggy in Problem 19 through the mud is doubled. How does the amount of work done by the students change?

21. A delivery person carries a 215-N box up stairs 4.20 m vertically and 6.80 m horizontally.
    (a) How much work does the delivery person do?
    (b) How much work does the delivery person do in carrying the box down the stairs?

22. A crate is pulled by a force of 628 N across the floor by a worker using a rope making an angle of 46.0° with the floor. If the crate is pulled 15.0 m, how much work does the force on the rope do?

23. A laborer pushes a wheelbarrow weighing $20\overline{0}$ N at 25.0° above the horizontal. If he pushes it a distance of 25.0 m, how much work is done?

24. An end loader lifts a $100\overline{0}$-N bucket of gravel 1.75 m above the ground. How much work is done?

8.2 Power

Power is the rate of doing work; that is,

$$P = \frac{W}{t}$$

where P = power
W = work
t = time

The units of power are familiar to most of us. In the metric system, the unit of power is the *watt:*

$$P = \frac{W}{t} = \frac{Fs}{t} = \frac{N\,m}{s} = \frac{J}{s} = watt$$

Power is often expressed in kilowatts and megawatts:

$$1000 \text{ watts (W)} = 1 \text{ kilowatt (kW)}$$

$$1,000,000 \text{ watts} = 1 \text{ megawatt (MW)}$$

In the U.S. system, the unit of power is either ft lb/s or horsepower:

$$P = \frac{W}{t} = \frac{Fs}{t} = \frac{ft\,lb}{s}$$

Horsepower (hp) is a unit defined by **James Watt**:

$$1 \text{ horsepower (hp)} = 550 \text{ ft lb/s} = 33,000 \text{ ft lb/min}$$

One horsepower is equivalent to moving a force of 550 lb a distance of 1 ft in 1 s or moving 1 lb a distance of 550 ft in 1 s.

Note: Since the above is a definition, treat any conversion factor as an exact number, which does not affect the number of significant digits in any calculation.

James Watt (1736–1819),

engineer and inventor, was born in Scotland. He made fundamental improvements to steam engines and is credited for several related inventions. The term horsepower was first used by him; the SI unit of power, the watt, is named after him.

TRY THIS ACTIVITY

Human Horsepower

How much equivalent horsepower do you possess? Using a tape measure, a stopwatch, and a flight of stairs, determine the horsepower in your legs when climbing a flight of stairs. First, measure the vertical height of the stairs. Use this distance and your weight to determine the work required to move your body's weight up the stairs. Clock the time it takes to walk and to run up the stairs. Then, find and compare the power. Convert your power to horsepower. How does your running horsepower compare to the horsepower of a lawnmower or a car?

EXAMPLE 1

A freight elevator with operator weighs $50\overline{0}0$ N. If it is raised to a height of 15.0 m in 10.0 s, how much power is developed?

Data:

$$F = 50\overline{0}0 \text{ N}$$
$$s = 15.0 \text{ m}$$
$$t = 10.0 \text{ s}$$
$$P = ?$$

Basic Equations:

$$P = \frac{W}{t} \quad \text{and} \quad W = Fs$$

Working Equation:

$$P = \frac{Fs}{t}$$

Substitution:

$$P = \frac{(50\overline{0}0 \text{ N})(15.0 \text{ m})}{10.0 \text{ s}}$$
$$= 75\overline{0}0 \text{ N m/s}$$

· · · · · · · · · · · · · · · · ·

EXAMPLE 2

The power expended in lifting an 825-lb girder to the top of a building $10\overline{0}$ ft high is 10.0 hp. How much time is required to raise the girder?

Data:

$$F = 825 \text{ lb}$$
$$s = 10\overline{0} \text{ ft}$$
$$P = 10.0 \text{ hp}$$
$$t = ?$$

Basic Equations:

$$P = \frac{W}{t} \quad \text{and} \quad W = Fs$$

Working Equation:

$$t = \frac{W}{P} = \frac{Fs}{P}$$

Substitution:

$$t = \frac{(825 \text{ lb})(100 \text{ ft})}{10.0 \text{ hp}}$$

$$= \frac{(825 \text{ lb})(100 \text{ ft})}{10.0 \text{ hp}} \times \frac{1 \text{ hp}}{550 \dfrac{\text{ft lb}}{\text{s}}}$$

$$= 15.0 \text{ s}$$

$$\frac{\text{lb ft}}{\text{hp}} \times \frac{\text{hp}}{\frac{\text{ft lb}}{\text{s}}} = \frac{\text{lb ft}}{\text{hp}} \times \left(\text{hp} \div \frac{\text{ft lb}}{\text{s}} \right) = \frac{\text{lb ft}}{\text{hp}} \times \left(\text{hp} \times \frac{\text{s}}{\text{ft lb}} \right) = \text{s}$$

Note: We use a conversion factor to obtain time units.

EXAMPLE 3

The mass of a large steel wrecking ball is $200\overline{0}$ kg. What power is used to raise it to a height of 40.0 m if the work is done in 20.0 s?

Data:

$$m = 200\overline{0} \text{ kg}$$
$$s = 40.0 \text{ m}$$
$$t = 20.0 \text{ s}$$
$$P = ?$$

Basic Equations:

$$P = \frac{W}{t} \quad \text{and} \quad W = Fs$$

Working Equation:

$$P = \frac{Fs}{t}$$

Substitution: Note that we cannot directly substitute into the working equation because our data are given in terms of *mass* and we must find *force* to substitute in $P = Fs/t$. The force is the weight of the ball:

$$F = mg = (200\overline{0} \text{ kg})(9.80 \text{ m/s}^2) = 19{,}600 \text{ kg m/s}^2 = 19{,}600 \text{ N}$$

Then

$$P = \frac{Fs}{t} = \frac{(19{,}600 \text{ N})(40.0 \text{ m})}{20.0 \text{ s}}$$

$$= 39{,}200 \text{ N m/s}$$

$$= 39{,}200 \text{ W} \quad \text{or} \quad 39.2 \text{ kW}$$

EXAMPLE 4

A machine is designed to perform a given amount of work in a given amount of time. A second machine does the same amount of work in half the time. Find the power of the second machine compared with the first.

Data (for the second machine given in terms of the first):

$$W = W$$

$$t = \tfrac{1}{2}t = \frac{t}{2}$$

$$P = ?$$

Basic Equation:

$$P = \frac{W}{t}$$

Working Equation: Same

Substitution:

$$P = \frac{W}{\dfrac{t}{2}} = W \div \frac{t}{2} = W \times \frac{2}{t} = 2\left(\frac{W}{t}\right) = 2P$$

Thus, the power is doubled when the time is halved.

. . . .

EXAMPLE 5

A motor is capable of developing 10.0 kW of power. How large a mass can it lift 75.0 m in 20.0 s?

Data:

$$P = 10.0 \text{ kW} = 10{,}\bar{0}00 \text{ W}$$

$$s = 75.0 \text{ m}$$

$$t = 20.0 \text{ s}$$

$$F = ?$$

Basic Equations:

$$P = \frac{W}{t} \quad \text{and} \quad W = Fs \quad \text{or} \quad P = \frac{Fs}{t}$$

Working Equation:

$$F = \frac{Pt}{s}$$

Substitution:

$$F = \frac{(10{,}\bar{0}00 \text{ W})(20.0 \text{ s})}{75.0 \text{ m}}$$

$$= 2670 \frac{\cancel{W} \cancel{s}}{\cancel{m}} \times \frac{1 \text{ N } \cancel{m}/\cancel{s}}{1 \cancel{W}} \qquad (1 \text{ W} = 1 \text{ J/s} = 1 \text{ N m/s})$$

$$= 2670 \text{ N}$$

Next, change the weight to mass as follows:

Data:

$$F = 2670 \text{ N}$$
$$g = 9.80 \text{ m/s}^2$$
$$m = ?$$

Basic Equation:

$$F = mg$$

Working Equation:

$$m = \frac{F}{g}$$

Substitution:

$$m = \frac{2670 \text{ N̶}}{9.80 \text{ m̶/s}^2} \times \frac{1 \text{ kg m̶/s}^2}{1 \text{ N̶}} \qquad (1 \text{ N} = 1 \text{ kg m/s}^2)$$
$$= 272 \text{ kg}$$

· · · · · · · · · · · · · · · · · ·

A pump is needed to lift $15\overline{0}0$ L of water per minute a distance of 45.0 m. What power, in kW, must the pump be able to deliver? (1 L of water has a mass of 1 kg.)

EXAMPLE 6

Data:

$$m = 15\overline{0}0 \text{ L} \times \frac{1 \text{ kg}}{1 \text{ L}} = 15\overline{0}0 \text{ kg}$$

$$s = 45.0 \text{ m}$$
$$t = 1 \text{ min} = 60.0 \text{ s}$$
$$g = 9.80 \text{ m/s}^2$$
$$P = ?$$

Basic Equations:

$$P = \frac{W}{t}, \quad W = Fs, \quad \text{and} \quad F = mg, \quad \text{or} \quad P = \frac{mgs}{t}$$

Working Equation:

$$P = \frac{mgs}{t}$$

Substitution:

$$P = \frac{(15\overline{0}0 \text{ kg})(9.80 \text{ m/s}^2)(45.0 \text{ m})}{60.0 \text{ s}}$$

$$= 1.10 \times 10^4 \text{ kg m}^2/\text{s} \qquad \left(1 \text{ W} = \frac{1 \text{ J}}{\text{s}} = \frac{1 \text{ N m}}{\text{s}} = \frac{1 \text{ (kg m/s}^2)(\text{m})}{\text{s}} = 1 \text{ kg m}^2/\text{s} \right)$$

$$= 1.10 \times 10^4 \text{ W̶} \times \frac{1 \text{ kW}}{10^3 \text{ W̶}}$$

$$= 11.0 \text{ kW}$$

· · · · · · · · · · · · · · · · · ·

SKETCH

$$12\ cm^2 \quad w$$

4.0 cm

DATA

$A = 12\ cm^2$, $l = 4.0\ cm$, $w = ?$

BASIC EQUATION

$A = lw$

WORKING EQUATION

$w = \frac{A}{l}$

SUBSTITUTION

$w = \frac{12\ cm^2}{4.0\ cm} = 3.0\ cm$

PROBLEMS 8.2

1. Given: $W = 132$ J
    $t = 7.00$ s
    $P = ?$

2. Given: $P = 231$ ft lb/s
    $t = 14.3$ s
    $W = ?$

3. Given: $P = 75.0$ W
    $W = 40.0$ J
    $t = ?$

4. Given: $W = 55.0$ J
    $t = 11.0$ s
    $P = ?$

5. The work required to lift a crate is $31\overline{0}$ J. If the crate is lifted in 25.0 s, what power is developed?

6. When a 3600-lb automobile runs out of gas, it is pushed by its unhappy driver and a friend a quarter of a mile (0.250 mi). To keep the car rolling, they must exert a constant force of 175 lb.
    (a) How much work do they do?
    (b) If it takes them 15.0 min, how much power do they develop?
    (c) Expressed in horsepower, how much power do they develop?

7. An electric golf cart develops 1.25 kW of power while moving at a constant speed.
    (a) Express its power in horsepower.
    (b) If the cart travels $20\overline{0}$ m in 35.0 s, what force is exerted by the cart?

8. How many seconds would it take a 7.00-hp motor to raise a 475-lb boiler to a platform 38.0 ft high?

9. How long would it take a $95\overline{0}$-W motor to raise a $36\overline{0}$-kg mass to a height of 16.0 m?

10. A $150\overline{0}$-lb casting is raised 22.0 ft in 2.50 min. Find the required horsepower.

11. What is the rating in kW of a 2.00-hp motor?

12. A wattmeter shows that a motor is drawing $220\overline{0}$ W. What horsepower is being delivered?

13. A 525-kg steel beam is raised 30.0 m in 25.0 s. How many kilowatts of power are needed?

14. How long would it take a 4.50-kW motor to raise a 175-kg boiler to a platform 15.0 m above the floor?

15. A 475-kg prestressed concrete beam is to be raised 10.0 m in 24.0 s. How many kilowatts of power are needed for the job?

16. A 50.0-kg welder is to be raised 15.0 m in 12.0 s. How many kilowatts of power are needed for the job?

17. An escalator is needed to carry 75 passengers per minute a vertical distance of 8.0 m. Assume that the mass of each passenger is $7\overline{0}$ kg.
    (a) What is the power (in kW) of the motor needed?
    (b) Express this power in horsepower.
    (c) What is the power (in kW) of the motor needed if 35% of the power is lost to friction and other losses?

18. A pump is needed to lift $75\overline{0}$ L of water per minute a distance of 25.0 m. What power (in kW) must the pump be able to deliver? (1 L of water has a mass of 1 kg.)

19. A machine is designed to perform a given amount of work in a given amount of time. A second machine does twice the same amount of work in half the time. Find the power of the second machine compared with the first.

20. A certain machine is designed to perform a given amount of work in a given amount of time. A second machine does 2.5 times the same amount of work in one-third the time. Find the power of the second machine compared with the first.

21. A motor on an escalator is capable of developing 12 kW of power.
    (a) How many passengers of mass 75 kg each can it lift a vertical distance of 9.0 m per min, assuming no power loss?
    (b) What power, in kW, motor is needed to move the same number of passengers at the same rate if 45% of the actual power developed by the motor is lost to friction and heat loss?

22. A pump is capable of developing 4.00 kW of power. How many litres of water per minute can be lifted a distance of 35.0 m? (1 L of water has a mass of 1 kg.)

23. A pallet weighing 575 N is lifted a distance of 20.0 m vertically in 10.0 s. What power is developed in kilowatts?
24. A pallet is loaded with bags of cement; the total weight of 875 N is lifted 21.0 m vertically in 11.0 s. What power in kilowatts is required to lift the cement?
25. A bundle of steel reinforcing rods weighing 175 N is lifted 32.0 m in 16.0 s. What power in kilowatts is required to lift the steel?
26. An ironworker carries a 7.50-kg toolbag up a vertical ladder on a high-rise building under construction.
    (a) After 30.0 s, he is 8.20 m above his starting point. How much work does the worker do on the toolbag?
    (b) If the worker weighs 645 N, how much work does he do in lifting himself and the toolbag?
    (c) What is the average power developed by the worker?

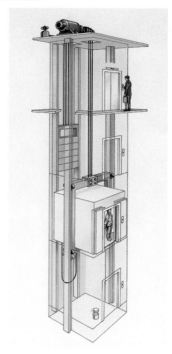

Figure 8.10   Here the counterweight working with the electric motor balances the load in the elevator.

8.3 Energy

Energy is defined as the ability to do work. There are many forms of energy, such as mechanical, electrical, thermal, fluid, chemical, atomic, and sound.

The mechanical energy of a body or a system is due to its position, its motion, or its internal structure. There are two kinds of mechanical energy: potential energy and kinetic energy. **Potential energy** is the stored energy of a body due to its internal characteristics or its position. **Kinetic energy** is the energy due to the mass and the velocity of a moving object.

Internal potential energy is determined by the nature or condition of the substance; for example, gasoline, a compressed spring, or a stretched rubber band has internal potential energy due to its internal characteristics. **Gravitational potential energy** is determined by the position of an object relative to a particular reference level; for example, a rock lying on the edge of a cliff, the raised counterweight on an elevator (Fig. 8.10), or a raised pile driver has potential energy due to its position. Each weight has the ability to do work because of the pull of gravity on it. The unit of energy is the joule (J) in the metric system and the foot-pound (ft lb) in the U.S. system.

The formula for gravitational potential energy is

$$PE = mgh$$

where   PE = potential energy
    m = mass
    g = 9.80 m/s² or 32.2 ft/s²
    h = height above reference level

In position 1 in Fig. 8.11, the crate is at rest on the floor. It has no ability to do work because it is in its lowest position. To raise the crate to position 2, work must be done to lift it. In the raised position, however, it now has stored ability to do work (by falling to the floor). Its PE (potential energy) can be calculated by multiplying the mass of the crate times acceleration of gravity (g) times height above reference level (h). Note that we can calculate the potential energy of the crate with respect to any level we choose. Here we have chosen the floor as the zero or lowest reference level.

Figure 8.11   Work done in raising the crate gives it potential energy.

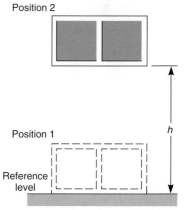

A wrecking ball of mass $200\overline{0}$ kg is poised 4.00 m above a concrete platform whose top is 2.00 m above the ground.

EXAMPLE 1

(a) With respect to the platform, what is the potential energy of the ball?
(b) With respect to the ground, what is the potential energy of the ball?

Sketch:

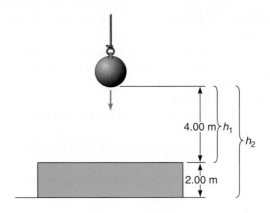

Data:

$$m = 20\overline{0} \text{ kg}$$
$$h_1 = 4.00 \text{ m}$$
$$h_2 = 6.00 \text{ m}$$
$$\text{PE} = ?$$

Basic Equation:

$$\text{PE} = mgh$$

Working Equation: Same

(a) Substitution:

$$\text{PE} = (20\overline{0} \text{ kg})(9.80 \text{ m/s}^2)(4.00 \text{ m})$$
$$= 7840 \frac{\text{kg m}^2}{\text{s}^2} \times \frac{1 \text{ J}}{\text{kg m}^2/\text{s}^2} \qquad [1 \text{ J} = 1 \text{ N m} = 1 \text{ (kg m/s}^2)(\text{m}) = 1 \text{ kg m}^2/\text{s}^2]$$
$$= 7840 \text{ J}$$

(b) Substitution:

$$\text{PE} = (20\overline{0} \text{ kg})(9.80 \text{ m/s}^2)(6.00 \text{ m})$$
$$= 11,800 \frac{\text{kg m}^2}{\text{s}^2} \times \frac{1 \text{ J}}{\text{kg m}^2/\text{s}^2}$$
$$= 11,800 \text{ J}$$

· · · · · · · · · · · · · · · · ·

Kinetic energy is due to the mass and the velocity of a moving object and is given by the formula

$$\boxed{\text{KE} = \tfrac{1}{2}mv^2}$$

where   KE = kinetic energy
        m = mass of moving object
        v = velocity of moving object

A pile driver (Fig. 8.12) shows the relation of energy of motion to useful work. The energy of the driver is its kinetic energy as it hits. When the driver strikes the pile, work is done on the pile, and it is forced into the ground. The depth it goes into the ground is determined by the force applied to it. The force applied is determined by the energy of the driver. If all the kinetic energy of the driver is converted to useful work, then

$$\boxed{\tfrac{1}{2}mv^2 = Fs}$$

Figure 8.12   Energy of motion becomes useful work in the pile driver.

A pile driver with mass 10,000 kg strikes a pile with velocity 10.0 m/s.

EXAMPLE 2

(a)   What is the kinetic energy of the driver as it strikes the pile?
(b)   If the pile is driven 20.0 cm into the ground, what force is applied to the pile by the driver as it strikes the pile? Assume that all the kinetic energy of the driver is converted to work.

Sketch:

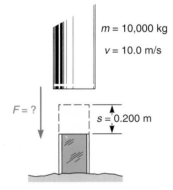

$m = 10,000$ kg
$v = 10.0$ m/s
$F = ?$
$s = 0.200$ m

Data:

$$m = 1.00 \times 10^4 \text{ kg}$$
$$v = 10.0 \text{ m/s}$$
$$s = 20.0 \text{ cm} = 0.200 \text{ m}$$
$$F = ?$$

(a) Basic Equation:

$$\text{KE} = \tfrac{1}{2}mv^2$$

Working Equation: Same

Substitution:

$$\text{KE} = \tfrac{1}{2}(1.00 \times 10^4 \text{ kg})(10.0 \text{ m/s})^2$$

$$= 5.00 \times 10^5 \, \frac{\text{kg m}^2}{\text{s}^2} \times \frac{1 \text{ J}}{\text{kg m}^2/\text{s}^2} \qquad [1 \text{ J} = 1 \text{ N m} = 1 \, (\text{kg m/s}^2)(\text{m}) = 1 \text{ kg m}^2/\text{s}^2]$$

$$= 5.00 \times 10^5 \text{ J} \quad \text{or} \quad 5\overline{0}0 \text{ kJ}$$

(b) Basic Equation:

$$KE = W = Fs$$

Working Equation:

$$F = \frac{KE}{s} \qquad \text{[Use KE from part (a).]}$$

Substitution:

$$F = \frac{5.00 \times 10^5 \, \cancel{J}}{0.200 \, \cancel{m}} \times \frac{1 \, N \, \cancel{m}}{1 \, \cancel{J}} \qquad (1 \, J = 1 \, N \, m)$$

$$= 2.50 \times 10^6 \, N$$

. . . .

EXAMPLE 3

A 60.0-g bullet is fired from a gun with 3150 J of kinetic energy. Find its velocity.

Data:

$$KE = 3150 \, J$$
$$m = 60.0 \, g = 0.0600 \, kg$$
$$v = \, ?$$

Basic Equation:

$$KE = \tfrac{1}{2}mv^2$$

Working Equation:

$$v = \sqrt{\frac{2(KE)}{m}}$$

Substitution:

$$v = \sqrt{\frac{2(3150 \, \cancel{J})}{0.0600 \, \cancel{kg}} \times \frac{1 \, kg \, m^2/s^2}{1 \, \cancel{J}}} \qquad [1 \, J = 1 \, N \, m = 1 \, (kg \, m/s^2)(m) = 1 \, kg \, m^2/s^2]$$

$$= 324 \, m/s$$

. . . .

We have discussed only two types of energy—kinetic and potential. Keep in mind that energy exists in many other forms—chemical, atomic, electrical, sound, and heat. These forms and the conversion of energy from one form to another will be studied later.

PROBLEMS 8.3

1. Given: $m = 11.4 \, kg$
   $g = 9.80 \, m/s^2$
   $h = 22.0 \, m$
   $PE = \, ?$

2. Given: $m = 3.50 \, kg$
   $g = 9.80 \, m/s^2$
   $h = 15.0 \, m$
   $PE = \, ?$

3. Given: $m = 4.70 \, kg$
   $v = 9.60 \, m/s$
   $KE = \, ?$

SKETCH

12 cm² | w

4.0 cm

DATA

$A = 12 \, cm^2, l = 4.0 \, cm, w = \, ?$

BASIC EQUATION

$A = lw$

WORKING EQUATION

$w = \frac{A}{l}$

SUBSTITUTION

$w = \frac{12 \, cm^2}{4.0 \, cm} = 3.0 \, cm$

4. Given: PE = 93.6 J
   $g = 9.80$ m/s^2
   $m = 2.30$ kg
   $h = ?$

5. A truck with mass $95\bar{0}$ slugs is driven 55.0 mi/h.
   (a) What is its velocity in ft/s?
   (b) What is its kinetic energy?

6. A bullet with mass 12.0 g travels 415 m/s. Find its kinetic energy. (*Hint:* Convert 12.0 g to kg.)

7. A bicycle and rider together have a mass of 7.40 slugs. If the kinetic energy is 742 ft lb, find the velocity.

8. A crate of mass 475 kg is raised to a height 17.0 m above the floor. What potential energy has it acquired with respect to the floor?

9. A tank of water containing $250\bar{0}$ L of water is stored on the roof of a building.
   (a) Find its potential energy with respect to the floor, which is 12.0 m below the roof.
   (b) Find its potential energy with respect to the basement, which is 4.0 m below the first floor.

10. The potential energy of a girder, after being lifted to the top of a building, is 5.17×10^5 ft lb. If its mass is 173 slugs, how high is the girder?

11. A 30.0-g bullet is fired from a gun and possesses 1750 J of kinetic energy. Find its velocity.

12. The Hoover Dam is 726 ft high. Find the potential energy of 1.00 million ft^3 of water at the top of the dam. (1 ft^3 of water weighs 62.4 lb.)

13. A 250-kg part falls from a plane and hits the ground at 150 km/h. Find its kinetic energy.

14. A meteorite is a solid composed of stone and/or metal material from outer space that passes through the atmosphere and hits the earth's surface. Find the kinetic energy of a meteorite with mass $25\bar{0}$ kg that hits the earth at 25 km/s.

15. Water is pumped at $25\bar{0}$ m^3/min from a lake into a tank 65.0 m above the lake.
    (a) What power, in kW, must be delivered by the pump?
    (b) What horsepower rating does this pump motor have?
    (c) What is the increase in potential energy of the water each minute?

16. Oil is pumped at 25.0 m^3/min into a tank 10.0 m above the ground. (1 L of oil has a mass of 0.68 kg.)
    (a) What power, in kW, must be delivered by the pump?
    (b) What is the increase in potential energy of the oil after 10.0 min?
    (c) Find the increase in potential energy of the oil after 10.0 min if the tank is 5.00 m above the ground.

17. If the velocity of an object is doubled, by what factor is its kinetic energy increased?
18. If the kinetic energy of an object is doubled, by what factor is its velocity increased?
19. A 4.20-g slug is shot from a rifle at 965 m/s.
    (a) What is the kinetic energy of the slug?
    (b) How much work is done on the slug if it starts from rest?
    (c) Find the average force on the slug if the work is done over a distance of 0.750 m.
    (d) If the slug comes to rest after penetrating 1.50 cm into metal, what is the magnitude of the average force it exerts?

20. A window washer with mass 90.0 kg first climbs 45.0 m upward to the top of a building, then from the top goes down 85.0 m to the ground.
    (a) What is the potential energy of the window washer at the top of the building, using his initial position as the reference level?
    (b) Find the potential energy of the window washer at ground level with respect to his initial position.

21. A painter weighing $63\bar{0}$ N climbs to a height of 5.00 m on a ladder.
    (a) How much work does she do in climbing the ladder?
    (b) What is the increase in gravitational potential energy of the painter?
    (c) Where does the energy come from to cause this increase in potential energy?

8.4   Conservation of Mechanical Energy

Kinetic and potential energy are related by the **law of conservation of mechanical energy**.

LAW OF CONSERVATION OF MECHANICAL ENERGY

The sum of the kinetic energy and the potential energy in a system is constant if no resistant forces do work.

A pile driver shows this energy conservation. When the driver is at its highest position, the potential energy is maximum and the kinetic energy is zero [Fig. 8.13(a)]. Its potential energy is

$$PE = mgh$$

and its kinetic energy is

$$KE = \tfrac{1}{2}mv^2 = \tfrac{1}{2}m(0)^2 = 0$$

Figure 8.13

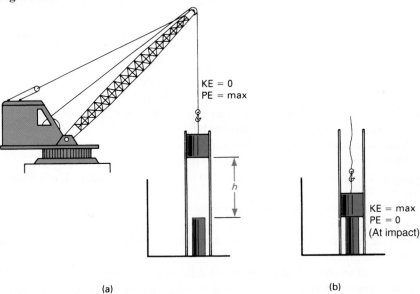

(a)   (b)

When the driver hits the top of the pile [Fig. 8.13(b)], it has its maximum kinetic energy; its potential energy is

$$PE = mgh = mg(0) = 0$$

Since the total energy in the system must remain constant, the maximum potential energy must equal the maximum kinetic energy:

$$PE_{max} = KE_{max}$$
$$mgh = \tfrac{1}{2}mv^2$$

Solving for the velocity of the driver as it hits the pile when the initial velocity of the driver is zero gives

$$v = \sqrt{2gh}$$

where v = velocity
        g = 9.80 m/s^2 or 32.2 ft/s^2
        h = height above the reference level

A pile driver falls freely from a height of 3.50 m above a pile. What is its velocity as it hits the pile?

EXAMPLE 1

Data:

$$h = 3.50 \text{ m}$$
$$g = 9.80 \text{ m/s}^2$$
$$v = ?$$

Basic Equation:

$$v = \sqrt{2gh}$$

Working Equation: Same

Substitution:

$$v = \sqrt{2(9.80 \text{ m/s}^2)(3.50 \text{ m})}$$
$$= 8.28 \text{ m/s} \qquad \boxed{\sqrt{\text{m}^2/\text{s}^2} = \text{m/s}}$$

. . . .

The conservation of mechanical energy can also be illustrated by considering a swinging pendulum bob where there is no resistance involved. Pull the bob over to the right side so that the string makes an angle of 65° with the vertical [Fig. 8.14(a)]. At this point, the bob contains its maximum potential energy and its minimum kinetic energy (zero). Note that a larger maximum potential energy is possible when an initial deflection of greater than 65° is made.

Figure 8.14   Kinetic and potential energy changes in a pendulum

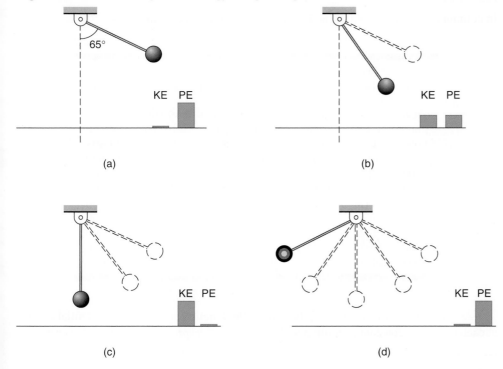

An instant later, the bob has lost some of its potential or stored energy, but it has gained in kinetic energy due to its motion [Fig. 8.14(b)]. At the bottom of its arc of swing [Fig. 8.14(c)], its potential energy is zero and its kinetic energy is maximum (its velocity is maximum). The kinetic energy of the bob then causes the bob to swing upward to the left. As it completes its swing [Fig. 8.14(d)], its kinetic energy is decreasing and its potential energy is increasing. That is, its kinetic energy is changing to potential energy.

According to the law of conservation of mechanical energy, the sum of the kinetic energy and the potential energy of the bob at any instant is a constant. Assuming no resistant forces, such as friction or air resistance, the bob would swing uniformly "forever."

EXAMPLE 2

Drop a 5.000-kg mass from a hot air balloon 400.0 m above the ground. Find its kinetic energy, its potential energy, and the sum of the kinetic energy and the potential energy in 1-s intervals until the mass hits the ground. (Assume no air resistance.)

Data:

$$m = 5.000 \text{ kg}$$
$$g = 9.80 \text{ m/s}^2$$

In the accompanying table, fill in each column as follows:

In column (1), list the times, t, in 1.000-s increments until the mass hits the ground.

In column (2), use $s = \frac{1}{2}gt^2$ to find the distance, s, the mass has fallen from the balloon at each time, t, rounded to the nearest 0.1 m.

In column (3), use $v = \sqrt{2gh} = \sqrt{2gs}$ to find its velocity at each time, t, rounded to the nearest 0.01 m/s.

In column (4), use $KE = \frac{1}{2}mv^2$ to find the kinetic energy at each time, t, rounded to the nearest 10 J.

In column (5), use $h = 400.0 \text{ m} - s$ to find the height above the ground at each time, t, rounded to the nearest 0.1 m.

In column (6), use $PE = mgh$ to find the potential energy at each time, t, rounded to the nearest 10 J.

In column (7), find the sum of the KE and PE columns at each time, t.

(1) t (s)	(2) s (m)	(3) v (m/s)	(4) KE (J)	(5) h (m)	(6) PE (J)	(7) Total (J)
0.000	0.0	0.00	0	400.0	19,600	19,600
1.000	4.9	9.80	240	395.1	19,360	19,600
2.000	19.6	19.60	960	380.4	18,640	19,600
3.000	44.1	29.40	2,160	355.9	17,440	19,600
4.000	78.4	39.20	3,840	321.6	15,760	19,600
5.000	122.5	49.00	6,000	277.5	13,600	19,600
6.000	176.4	58.80	8,640	223.6	10,960	19,600
7.000	240.1	68.60	11,760	159.9	7,840	19,600
8.000	313.6	78.40	15,370	86.4	4,230	19,600
9.000	396.9	88.20	19,450	3.1	150	19,600
9.035	400.0	88.54	19,600	0.0	0	19,600

As you can see from the table, the sum of the kinetic energy and the potential energy at each time, t, is constant according to the *law of conservation of mechanical energy*.

Figure 8.15 Work is done to take the roller coaster car from the beginning of the ride to the top of the structure to give it potential energy. After it leaves the peak of the ride, the sum of its potential energy and its kinetic energy is equal at each point of the ride.

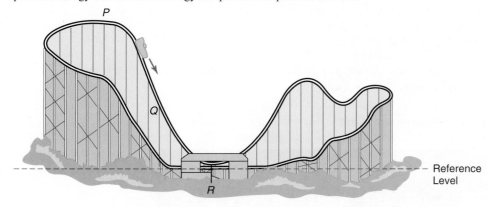

A roller coaster is an excellent example of the law of conservation of mechanical energy. Figure 8.15 shows a roller coaster with various points marked for discussion. First, work is done to take the roller coaster car from the beginning of the ride to the top of the structure (point P) to give it potential energy. (Assume $v = 0$ at P for this discussion.) After it reaches the peak of the ride, the sum of its potential energy and its kinetic energy is equal at each point of the ride. That is,

Point P		Point Q		Point R	
Kinetic	Potential	Kinetic	Potential	Kinetic	Potential
0 $+$	mgh_p	$= \frac{1}{2}mv_Q^2 +$	mgh_Q	$= \frac{1}{2}mv_R^2 +$	0

In studying collisions (Chapter 6), we learned that whenever objects collide in the absence of any external forces, the total momentum of the objects before the collision equals the total momentum after the collision. This was an example of the law of conservation of momentum.

In an *elastic* collision, the total kinetic energy in the system *before* the collision equals the total kinetic energy in the system *after* the collision.

That is,

$$\text{total kinetic energy}_{\text{before collision}} = \text{total kinetic energy}_{\text{after collision}}$$

Let's check this principle in Example 1 in Section 6.2.
Kinetic energy before collision:

$$\frac{1}{2}m_1v_1^2 + \frac{1}{2}m_2v_2^2 = \frac{1}{2}(0.600 \text{ kg})(9.00 \text{ m/s})^2 + \frac{1}{2}(0.300 \text{ kg})(-8.00 \text{ m/s})^2$$
$$= 33.9 \text{ kg m}^2/\text{s}^2 = 33.9 \text{ N m} = 33.9 \text{ J}$$

Kinetic energy after collision:

$$\frac{1}{2}m_1(v_1')^2 + \frac{1}{2}m_2(v_2')^2 = \frac{1}{2}(0.600 \text{ kg})(-2.33 \text{ m/s})^2 + \frac{1}{2}(0.300 \text{ kg})(14.66 \text{ m/s})^2$$
$$= 33.9 \text{ kg m}^2/\text{s}^2 = 33.9 \text{ N m} = 33.9 \text{ J}$$

TRY THIS ACTIVITY

Backyard Physics

Croquet players use the conservation of energy when their opponent's ball is touching their own ball and they want to knock their opponent's ball away. To do so, a player will place his foot on his ball and strike his ball with the mallet. Since the stepped-on ball remains stationary, the kinetic energy from the mallet gets transferred to the opponent's ball, causing it to travel.

Figure 8.16   Step firmly on the red ball so that it will not move when struck with the croquet mallet. Observe what happens to the green ball.

PHYSICS CONNECTIONS

Landing on an Aircraft Carrier

Landing any airplane is a complicated procedure. Furthermore, placing a fast-moving jet on the deck of a ship in the middle of the ocean is one of the most complicated and dangerous tasks for a Navy pilot. Although the length of an aircraft carrier is over 300 m (approximately three football fields in length), its landing strip for the jets is only half that length. Even if the pilot can place the jet on the landing strip, he or she is not able to stop the jet in such a short distance without applying an external force on it.

Upon approaching the carrier, the pilot extends a mechanism called a tail-hook from the rear of the jet. This tail-hook is used to catch one of the four hydraulically controlled arresting cables on the deck of the aircraft carrier. Once the tail-hook catches one of the cables, the hydraulic cabling system extends and applies a force to slow the aircraft (Fig. 8.17). The force from the cable, performed over the distance that the cable extends, works to bring the aircraft to a quick, safe stop. The hydraulic cabling system absorbs the kinetic energy of the moving plane. If the pilot misses all four arresting cables, he or she must increase the throttle to remain safely airborne after leaving the deck of the aircraft carrier and try again.

Figure 8.17 The cable must absorb the kinetic energy of the landing jet.

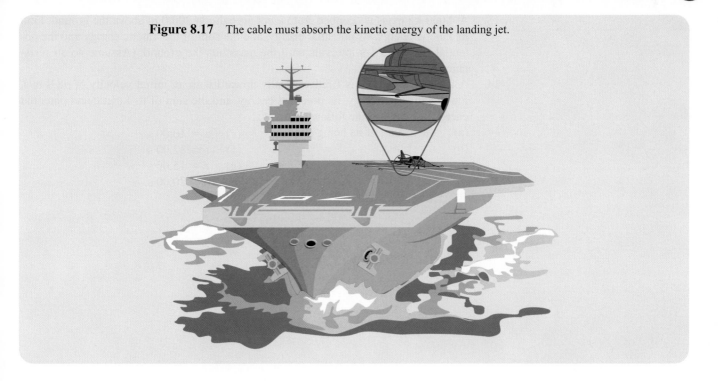

PROBLEMS 8.4

1. A pile driver falls a distance of 2.50 m before hitting a pile. Find its velocity as it hits the pile.
2. A sky diver jumps out of a plane at a height of $50\overline{0}0$ ft. If her parachute does not open until she reaches $100\overline{0}$ ft, what is her velocity at that point if air resistance is neglected?
3. A piece of shattered glass falls from the 82nd floor of a building, $27\overline{0}$ m above the ground. What is the velocity of the glass when it hits the ground, if air resistance is neglected?
4. A 10.0-kg mass is dropped from a hot air balloon at a height of 325 m above the ground. Find its speed at points $30\overline{0}$ m, $20\overline{0}$ m, and $10\overline{0}$ m above the ground and as it hits the ground.
5. A 0.175-lb ball is thrown upward with an initial velocity of 75.0 ft/s. What is the maximum height reached by the ball?
6. A pile driver falls a distance of 1.75 m before hitting a pile. Find its velocity as it hits the pile.
7. A sandbag is dropped from a hot air balloon at a height of 125 m above the ground. Find its velocity as it hits the ground. Ignore air resistance.
8. An ironworker drops a hammer 5.25 m to the ground. What is its speed as it hits the ground?
9. A box is dropped 3.60 m to the ground. What is its speed as it hits the ground?
10. A piece of broken glass with mass 15.0 kg falls from the side of a building 8.00 m above the street.
    (a) What is the kinetic energy of the glass as it hits the street?
    (b) What is the speed of the glass as it hits the street?
11. A ball is thrown downward from the top of a building at a speed of 75 ft/s. Find its velocity as it hits the ground 475 ft below. Ignore air resistance.
12. Find the maximum height reached by a ball thrown upward at a velocity of 95 ft/s.

SKETCH

12 cm² | w

4.0 cm

DATA

$A = 12$ cm², $l = 4.0$ cm, w = ?

BASIC EQUATION

$A = lw$

WORKING EQUATION

$w = \frac{A}{l}$

SUBSTITUTION

$w = \frac{12 \text{ cm}^2}{4.0 \text{ cm}} = 3.0$ cm

PROBLEM SOLVING

13. A 4.000-kg mass is dropped from a hot air balloon 300.0 m above the ground. Find its kinetic energy, its potential energy, and the sum of the kinetic energy and the potential energy in 1-s intervals until the mass hits the ground. (Assume no air resistance.)

14. A 2.00-kg projectile is fired vertically upward with an initial velocity of 98.0 m/s. Find its kinetic energy, its potential energy, and the sum of its kinetic and potential energies at each of the following times:

(a)   the instant of its being fired   (e) $t = 10.00$ s
(b) $t = 1.00$ s   (f) $t = 12.00$ s
(c) $t = 2.00$ s   (g) $t = 15.00$ s
(d) $t = 5.00$ s   (h) $t = 20.00$ s

Glossary

Energy The ability to do work. There are many forms of energy, such as mechanical, electrical, thermal, fluid, chemical, atomic, and sound. (p. 217)

Gravitational Potential Energy The energy determined by the position of an object relative to a particular reference level. (p. 217)

Internal Potential Energy The energy determined by the nature or condition of a substance. (p. 217)

Kinetic Energy The energy due to the mass and the velocity of a moving object. (p. 217)

Law of Conservation of Mechanical Energy The sum of the kinetic energy and the potential energy in a system is constant if no resistant forces do work. (p. 222)

Potential Energy The stored energy of a body due to its internal characteristics or its position. (p. 217)

Power The rate of doing work (work divided by time). (p. 211)

Work The product of the force in the direction of motion and the displacement. (p. 206)

Formulas

8.1 $W = Fs$

$W = Fs \cos \theta$

8.2 $P = \dfrac{W}{t}$

8.3 $PE = mgh$

$KE = \frac{1}{2}mv^2$

8.4 $v = \sqrt{2gh}$

Review Questions

1. Work is done when
   (a) a force is applied.
   (b) a person tries unsuccessfully to move a crate.
   (c) force is applied and an object is moved.
2. Power
   (a) is work divided by time.
   (b) is measured in newtons.
   (c) is time divided by work.
   (d) none of the above.
3. A large boulder at rest possesses
   (a) potential energy.
   (b) kinetic energy.
   (c) no energy.
4. A large boulder rolling down a hill possesses
   (a) potential energy.
   (b) kinetic energy.
   (c) no energy.
   (d) both kinetic and potential energy.
5. With no air resistance and no friction, a pendulum would
   (a) not swing.
   (b) swing for a short time.
   (c) swing forever.

6. Can work be done by a moving object on itself?
7. Has a man swinging a sledgehammer done work if he misses the stake at which he is swinging?
8. Develop the units associated with work from the components of the definition: work = force × displacement.
9. Is work a vector quantity?
10. Is work being done on a boulder by gravity?
11. Is work being done by the weight of a grandfather clock?
12. How could the power developed by a man pushing a stalled car be measured?
13. How does water above a waterfall possess potential energy?
14. What are two devices possessing gravitational potential energy?
15. Is kinetic energy dependent on time?
16. At what point is the kinetic energy of a swinging pendulum bob at a maximum?
17. At what point is the potential energy of a swinging pendulum bob at a maximum?
18. Is either kinetic or potential energy a vector quantity?
19. Can an object possess both kinetic and potential energy at the same time?
20. Why is a person more likely to be severely injured by a bolt falling from the fourth floor of a job site than by one falling from the second floor?

Review Problems

PROBLEM SOLVING

SKETCH

12 cm² | w

4.0 cm

DATA

$A = 12$ cm², $l = 4.0$ cm, $w = ?$

BASIC EQUATION

$A = lw$

WORKING EQUATION

$w = \frac{A}{l}$

SUBSTITUTION

$w = \frac{12 \text{ cm}^2}{4.0 \text{ cm}} = 3.0$ cm

1. How many joules are in one kilowatt-hour?
2. An endloader holds 1500 kg of sand 2.00 m off the ground for 3.00 min. How much work does it do?
3. How high can a 10.0-kg mass be lifted by 1000 J of work?
4. A 40.0-kg pack is carried up a 2500-m-high mountain in 10.0 h. How much work is done?
5. Find the average power output in Problem 4 in (a) watts; (b) horsepower.
6. A 10.0-kg mass has a potential energy of 10.0 J when it is at what height?
7. A 10.0-lb weight has a potential energy of 20.0 ft lb at what height?
8. At what speed does a 1.00-kg mass have a kinetic energy of 1.00 J?
9. At what speed does a 10.0-N weight have a kinetic energy of 1.00 J?
10. What is the kinetic energy of a 3000-lb automobile moving at 55.0 mi/h?
11. What is the potential energy of an 80.0-kg diver standing 3.00 m above the water?
12. What is the kinetic energy of a 0.020-kg bullet having a velocity of 550 m/s?
13. What is the potential energy of an 85.0-kg high jumper clearing a 2.00-m bar?
14. A worker pulls a crate 10.0 m by exerting a force of 300 N.
    (a) How much work does the worker do?
    (b) How much work does the worker do pulling the crate a distance of 10.0 m by exerting the same force at an angle of 20.0° with the horizontal?
15. A hammer falls from a scaffold on a building 50.0 m above the ground. Find its speed as it hits the ground.

APPLIED CONCEPTS

1. Rosita needs to purchase a sump pump for her basement. (a) If the pump must carry 10.0 kg of water to a height of 2.75 m each minute, what minimum wattage pump is needed? (b) What three main factors determine power for a sump pump?

2. A roller coaster designer must carefully balance the desire for excitement and the need for safety. The most recent design is shown in Fig. 8.18. (a) If a 355-kg roller coaster car has zero velocity on the top of the first hill, determine its potential energy. (b) What is the velocity of the roller coaster car at the specified locations in the design? (c) Explain the relationship between velocity and the position on the track throughout the ride. (Consider the track to be frictionless.)

Figure 8.18

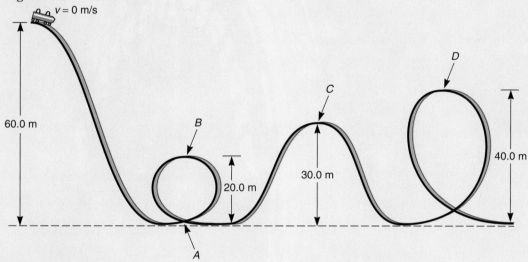

3. A 22,500-kg Navy fighter jet flying 235 km/h must catch an arresting cable to land safely on the runway strip of an aircraft carrier. (a) How much energy must the cable absorb to stop the fighter jet? (b) If the cable allows the jet to move 115 m before coming to rest, what is the average force that the cable exerts on the jet? (c) If the jet were given more than 115 m to stop, how would the force applied by the cable change?

4. The hydroelectric plant at the Itaipu Dam, located on the Parana River between Paraguay and Brazil, uses the transfer of potential to kinetic energy of water to generate electricity. (a) If 1.00×10^6 gallons of water (3.79×10^6 kg) flows down 142 m into the turbines each second, how much power does the hydroelectric power plant generate? (For comparison purposes, the Hoover Dam generates 1.57×10^6 W of power.) (b) How much power could the plant produce if the Itaipu Dam were twice its actual height? (c) Explain why the height of a dam is important for hydroelectric power plants.

5. A 1250-kg wrecking ball is lifted to a height of 12.7 m above its resting point. When the wrecking ball is released, it swings toward an abandoned building and makes an indentation of 43.7 cm in the wall. (a) What is the potential energy of the wrecking ball at a height of 12.7 m? (b) What is its kinetic energy as it strikes the wall? (c) If the wrecking ball transfers all of its kinetic energy to the wall, how much force does the wrecking ball apply to the wall? (d) Why should a wrecking ball strike a wall at the lowest point in its swing?

CHAPTER 9

ROTATIONAL MOTION

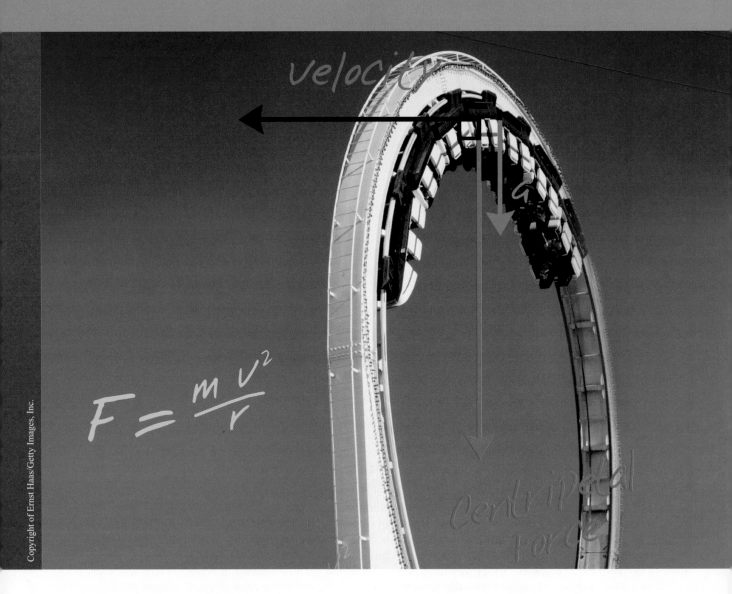

velocity

a

$$F = \frac{m\,v^2}{r}$$

centripetal force

T he concepts of displacement, velocity, acceleration, vectors, and forces in a straight line also apply to motion in a curved path and rotational motion.

Objectives

The major goals of this chapter are to enable you to:

1. Distinguish between rectilinear, curvilinear, and rotational motion.
2. Find angular displacement, velocity, and acceleration.
3. Use conservation of angular momentum to describe rotational motion.
4. Find centripetal force.
5. Find power in rotational systems.
6. Analyze how gears, gear trains, and pulleys are used to transfer rotational motion.

9.1 Measurement of Rotational Motion

Until now we have considered only motion in a straight line, called **rectilinear motion**. Technicians are often faced with many problems with motion along a curved path or with objects rotating about an axis. Although these kinds of motion are similar, we must distinguish between them.

Motion along a curved path is called **curvilinear motion**. A satellite in orbit around the earth is an example of curvilinear motion [Fig. 9.1(a)].

Figure 9.1

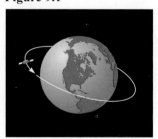 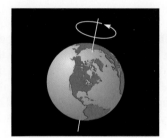 

(a) Curvilinear motion of an orbiting satellite

(b) Rotational motion of earth spinning on its axis

(c) Rotational motion of a wheel spinning on its axle

Rotational motion occurs when the body itself is spinning. Examples of rotational motion are the earth spinning on its axis, a turning wheel, a turning driveshaft, and the turning shaft of an electric motor [Fig. 9.1(b) and (c)].

We can see a wheel turn, but to gather useful information about its motion, we need a system of measurement. There are three basic systems of defining angle measurement. The **revolution** is one complete rotation of a body. This unit of measurement of rotational motion is the number of rotations—how many times the object goes around. The unit of rotation (most often used in industry) is the revolution (rev). A second system of angular measurement divides the circle of rotation into 360 degrees ($360° = 1$ rev). One **degree** is 1/360 of a complete revolution.

The **radian** (rad), which is approximately 57.3° or exactly $\left(\dfrac{360}{2\pi}\right)^{\circ}$, is a third angular

Figure 9.2

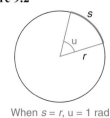

When $s = r$, u = 1 rad

unit of measurement. A radian is defined as that angle with its vertex at the center of a circle whose sides cut off an arc on the circle equal to its radius (Fig. 9.2), where $s = r$ and $\theta = 1$ rad.

Stated as a formula,

$$\theta = \frac{s}{r}$$

where θ = angle determined by s and r
          s = length of the arc of the circle
          r = radius of the circle

Technically, angle θ measured in radians is defined as the ratio of two lengths: the lengths of the arc and the radius of a circle. Since the length units in the ratio cancel, the radian is a dimensionless unit. As a matter of convenience, "rad" is often used to show radian measurement. A useful relationship is 2π rad equals one revolution. Therefore,

$$1 \text{ rev} = 360° = 2\pi \text{ rad}$$

You may need to use this conversion between systems of measurement.

EXAMPLE 1

Convert the angle 10π rad (a) to rev and (b) to degrees.
    Using 1 rev = 360° = 2π rad, form conversion factors so that the old units are in the denominator and the new units are in the numerator.

(a) $\theta = (10\pi \text{ rad})\left(\dfrac{1 \text{ rev}}{2\pi \text{ rad}}\right)$ (b) $\theta = (10\pi \text{ rad})\left(\dfrac{360°}{2\pi \text{ rad}}\right)$

          $= 5 \text{ rev}$ $= 1800°$

. . . .

Figure 9.3 The angular displacements of points A and B on the flywheel are always the same.

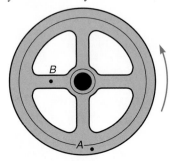

Angular displacement is the angle through which any point on a rotating body moves. Note that on any rotating body, all points on that body move through the same angle in any given amount of time—even though each may travel different linear distances. Point A on the flywheel shown in Fig. 9.3 travels much farther than point B (along a curved line), but during one revolution both travel through the same angle (have equal angular displacements).

In the automobile industry, technicians are concerned with the *rate* of rotational motion. Recall that in the linear system, velocity is the rate of motion (displacement/time). Similarly, **angular velocity** in the rotational system is the rate of angular displacement. Angular velocity (designated ω, the Greek lowercase letter omega) is usually measured in rev/min (rpm) for relatively slow rotations (e.g., automobile engines) and rev/s or rad/s for high-speed instruments. We use the term *angular velocity* when referring to a vector that includes the direction of rotation. We use the term *angular speed* in referring to a magnitude when the direction of rotation is either not known or not important.

$$\omega = \text{angular velocity} = \frac{\text{number of revolutions}}{\text{time}} = \frac{\text{angular displacement}}{\text{time}}$$

Written as a formula,

$$\omega = \frac{\theta}{t}$$

where
     ω = angular velocity or speed (rad/s)   or ω = angular velocity or speed (rev/min)
     θ = angle (in radians) θ = angle (in revolutions)
     t = time (in seconds) t = time (in minutes)

EXAMPLE 2

A motorcycle wheel turns $36\overline{0}0$ times while being ridden for 6.40 min. What is the angular speed in rev/min?

Data:

$$t = 6.40 \text{ min}$$
$$\text{number of revolutions} = 36\overline{0}0 \text{ rev}$$
$$\omega = ?$$

Basic Equation:

$$\omega = \frac{\theta}{t}$$

Working Equation: Same

Substitution:

$$\omega = \frac{36\overline{0}0 \text{ rev}}{6.40 \text{ min}}$$
$$= 563 \text{ rev/min or 563 rpm}$$

. . . .

Formulas for linear speed of a rotating point on a circle and angular speed are related as follows. We know

$$(1) \quad \theta = \frac{s}{r} \qquad (2) \quad v = \frac{s}{t} \qquad (3) \quad \omega = \frac{\theta}{t}$$

Therefore, combining and substituting s/r for θ in (3), we obtain

$$\omega = \frac{s/r}{t}$$

$$\omega(r) = \frac{(s/r)(r)}{t} \qquad \text{Multiply both sides by } r.$$

$$\omega r = \frac{s}{t}$$

$$\omega r = v \qquad \text{Recall that } v = s/t.$$

Thus,

$$\boxed{v = \omega r}$$

where v = linear velocity of a point on the circle
         ω = angular speed
         r = radius

EXAMPLE 3

A wheel of 1.00 m radius turns at $10\overline{0}0$ rpm.

(a) Express the angular speed in rad/s.
(b) Find the angular displacement in 2.00 s.
(c) Find the linear speed of a point on the rim of the wheel.

Sketch:

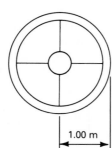

1.00 m

(a) Data:

$$\omega = 10\overline{0}0 \text{ rpm} \qquad \text{(change to rad/s)}$$

$$\omega = 10\overline{0}0 \, \frac{\text{rev}}{\text{min}} \times \frac{2\pi \text{ rad}}{1 \text{ rev}} \times \frac{1 \text{ min}}{60 \text{ s}} = 105 \text{ rad/s}$$

(b) Data:

$$\omega = 105 \text{ rad/s}$$
$$t = 2.00 \text{ s}$$
$$\theta = ?$$

Basic Equation:

$$\omega = \frac{\theta}{t}$$

Working Equation:

$$\theta = \omega t$$

Substitution:

$$\theta = (105 \text{ rad/s})(2.00 \text{ s})$$
$$= 21\overline{0} \text{ rad}$$

(c) Data:

$$\omega = 105 \text{ rad/s}$$
$$r = 1.00 \text{ m}$$
$$v = ?$$

Basic Equation:

$$v = \omega r$$

Working Equation: Same

Substitution:

$$v = (105 \text{ rad/s})(1.00 \text{ m})$$
$$= 105 \text{ m/s}$$

> (rad/s)(m) = m/s because the rad is a dimensionless unit.

· · · · · · · · · · · · · · · · · ·

A device called a *stroboscope* or strobe light may be used to measure or check the speed of rotation of a shaft or other machinery part. Repeating motion is "slowed down" so it can be observed more easily. The light flashes rapidly, and the rate of flash can be adjusted to coincide with the rotation of a point or points on the rotating object. Knowing the rate of flashing will also then reveal the rate of rotation. A slight variation in the rate of rotation and flash will cause the observed point to appear to move either forward or backward as the stagecoach wheels in old western movies sometimes appear to do. Figure 9.4 shows a stroboscopic linear motion time-lapse photo of a woman running.

In linear motion, we found a change in velocity results in an acceleration. Similarly, in rotational motion, changing the rate of rotation involves a change in angular velocity and results in an angular acceleration. For uniformly accelerated rotational motion, **angular acceleration** is the rate of change of angular velocity. That is,

$$\alpha = \frac{\Delta \omega}{t}$$

Figure 9.4

Photo courtesy of Corbis Corporation. Reprinted with permission

where α = angular acceleration
$\Delta\omega$ = change in angular velocity
t = time

The equations for uniformly accelerated linear motion in Section 4.3 may easily be transformed into the corresponding equations for uniformly accelerated rotational motion by substituting θ for s, ω for v, and α for a.

Linear Motion	Rotational Motion
$s = v_{avg}t$	$\theta = \omega_{avg}t$
$s = v_i t + \frac{1}{2}at^2$	$\theta = \omega_i t + \frac{1}{2}\alpha t^2$
$v_{avg} = \dfrac{v_f + v_i}{2}$	$\omega_{avg} = \dfrac{\omega_f + \omega_i}{2}$
$v_f = v_i + at$	$\omega_f = \omega_i + \alpha t$
$a = \dfrac{v_f - v_i}{t}$	$\alpha = \dfrac{\omega_f - \omega_i}{t}$
$s = \frac{1}{2}(v_f + v_i)t$	$\theta = \frac{1}{2}(\omega_f + \omega_i)t$
$2as = v_f^2 - v_i^2$	$2\alpha\theta = \omega_f^2 - \omega_i^2$

where s = linear displacement
v_f = final linear velocity
v_i = initial linear velocity
v_{avg} = average linear velocity
a = linear acceleration
t = time

where θ = angular displacement
ω_f = final angular velocity
ω_i = initial angular velocity
ω_{avg} = average angular velocity
α = angular acceleration
t = time

While these rotational motion equations are somewhat intuitive, their derivations are beyond the scope of this text.

A rotating pulley 24.0 cm in diameter is rotating at an initial angular speed of 30.5 rad/s. The speed is steadily increased to 41.5 rad/s within 6.30 s. (a) Find the pulley's angular acceleration. (b) Find the final linear speed of a point on its rim.

EXAMPLE 4

(a) Data:

$$\omega_i = 30.5 \text{ rad/s}$$
$$\omega_f = 41.5 \text{ rad/s}$$
$$t = 6.30 \text{ s}$$
$$\alpha = ?$$

Basic Equation:

$$\omega_f = \omega_i + \alpha t$$

Working Equation:

$$\alpha = \frac{\omega_f - \omega_i}{t}$$

Substitution:

$$\alpha = \frac{41.5 \text{ rad/s} - 30.5 \text{ rad/s}}{6.30 \text{ s}}$$
$$= 1.75 \text{ rad/s}^2$$

(b) Data:

$$\omega = 41.5 \text{ rad/s}$$
$$r = 12.0 \text{ cm}$$
$$v = ?$$

Basic Equation:

$$v = \omega r$$

Working Equation: Same

Substitution:

$$v = (41.5 \text{ rad/s})(12.0 \text{ cm})$$
$$= 498 \text{ cm/s}$$

TRY THIS ACTIVITY

Global Rotational Physics

On a globe depicting the earth, place a push pin or a small mark on northern Canada, another on Florida, and another on Ecuador. Rotate the globe about its central axis. Of the places that you marked, where would a person experience the greatest linear velocity as the earth is rotating? Where would a person experience the greatest angular velocity?

Finally, what would happen to a person's angular velocity if the rotational speed of the earth changed from one rotation per day to two rotations per day?

PROBLEMS 9.1

1. Convert $6\frac{1}{2}$ revolutions
   (a) to radians.
   (b) to degrees.
2. Convert 2880°
   (a) to revolutions.
   (b) to radians.
3. Convert 25π rad
   (a) to revolutions.
   (b) to degrees.
4. Convert 12.0 revolutions
   (a) to radians.
   (b) to degrees.

Find the angular speed in Problems 5–10.

5. Number of revolutions = 525
   $t = 3.42$ min
   $\omega =$ _____ rpm

6. Number of revolutions = 7360
   $t = 37.0$ s
   $\omega =$ _____ rev/s

7. Number of revolutions = 4.00
   $t = 3.00$ s
   $\omega =$ _____ rad/s

8. Number of revolutions = 325
   $t = 5.00$ min
   $\omega =$ _____ rpm

9. Number of revolutions = 6370
   $t = 18.0$ s
   $\omega =$ _____ rev/s

10. Number of revolutions = 6.25
    $t = 5.05$ s
    $\omega =$ _____ rad/s

11. Convert 675 rad/s to rpm.
12. Convert 285 rpm to rad/s.
13. Convert 136 rpm to rad/s.
14. Convert 88.4 rad/s to rpm.
15. A motor turns at a rate of 11.0 rev/s. Find its angular speed in rpm.
16. A rotor turns at a rate of 180 rpm. Find its angular speed in rev/s.
17. A rotating wheel completes one revolution in 0.150 s. Find its angular speed
    (a) in rev/s.   (b) in rpm.   (c) in rad/s.
18. A rotor completes 50.0 revolutions in 3.25 s. Find its angular speed
    (a) in rev/s.   (b) in rpm.   (c) in rad/s.
19. A flywheel rotates at 1050 rpm.
    (a) How long (in s) does it take to complete one revolution?
    (b) How many revolutions does it complete in 5.00 s?
20. A wheel rotates at 36.0 rad/s.
    (a) How long (in s) does it take to complete one revolution?
    (b) How many revolutions does it complete in 8.00 s?
21. A shaft of radius 8.50 cm rotates 7.00 rad/s. Find its angular displacement (in rad) in 1.20 s.
22. A wheel of radius 0.240 m turns at 4.00 rev/s. Find its angular displacement (in rev) in 13.0 s.
23. A pendulum of length 1.50 m swings through an arc of 5.0°. Find the length of the arc through which the pendulum swings.
24. An airplane circles an airport twice while 5.00 mi from the control tower. Find the length of the arc through which the plane travels.
25. A wheel of radius 27.0 cm has an angular speed of 47.0 rpm. Find the linear speed (in m/s) of a point on its rim.
26. A belt is placed around a pulley that is 30.0 cm in diameter and rotating at 275 rpm. Find the linear speed (in m/s) of the belt. (Assume no belt slippage on the pulley.)
27. A flywheel of radius 25.0 cm is rotating at 655 rpm.
    (a) Express its angular speed in rad/s.
    (b) Find its angular displacement (in rad) in 3.00 min.
    (c) Find the linear distance traveled (in cm) by a point on the rim in one complete revolution.
    (d) Find the linear distance traveled (in m) by a point on the rim in 3.00 min.
    (e) Find the linear speed (in m/s) of a point on the rim.
28. An airplane propeller with blades 2.00 m long is rotating at 1150 rpm.
    (a) Express its angular speed in rad/s.
    (b) Find its angular displacement in 4.00 s.
    (c) Find the linear speed (in m/s) of a point on the end of the blade.
    (d) Find the linear speed (in m/s) of a point 1.00 m from the end of the blade.
29. An automobile is traveling at 60.0 km/h. Its tires have a radius of 33.0 cm.
    (a) Find the angular speed of the tires (in rad/s).
    (b) Find the angular displacement of the tires in 30.0 s.
    (c) Find the linear distance traveled by a point on the tread in 30.0 s.
    (d) Find the linear distance traveled by the automobile in 30.0 s.
30. Find the angular speed (in rad/s) of the following hands on a clock.
    (a) Second hand   (b) Minute hand   (c) Hour hand

SKETCH

12 cm² w

4.0 cm

DATA
$A = 12$ cm², $l = 4.0$ cm, w = ?

BASIC EQUATION
$A = lw$

WORKING EQUATION
$w = \frac{A}{l}$

SUBSTITUTION
$w = \frac{12 \text{ cm}^2}{4.0 \text{ cm}} = 3.0$ cm

31. A bicycle wheel of diameter 30.0 in. rotates twice each second. Find the linear velocity of a point on the wheel.

32. A point on the rim of a flywheel with radius 1.50 ft has a linear velocity of 30.0 ft/s. Find the time for it to complete 4π rad.

33. The earth rotates on its axis at an angular speed of 1 rev/24 h. Find the linear speed (in km/h)
    (a) of Singapore, which is nearly on the equator.
    (b) of Houston, which is approximately 30.0° north latitude.
    (c) of Minneapolis, which is approximately 45.0° north latitude.
    (d) of Anchorage, which is approximately 60.0° north latitude.

34. A truck tire rotates at an initial angular speed of 21.5 rad/s. The driver steadily accelerates, and after 3.50 s the tire's angular speed is 28.0 rad/s. What is the tire's angular acceleration during its linear acceleration?

35. Find the angular acceleration of a radiator fan blade as its angular speed increases from 8.50 rad/s to 15.4 rad/s in 5.20 s.

36. A wheel of radius 20.0 cm starts from rest and makes 6.00 revolutions in 2.50 s. (a) Find its angular velocity in rad/s. (b) Find its angular acceleration. (c) Find the final linear speed of a point on the rim of the wheel. (d) Find the linear acceleration of a point on the rim of the wheel.

37. A circular disk 30.0 cm in diameter is rotating at 275 rpm and then uniformly stopped within 8.00 s. (a) Find its angular acceleration. (b) Find the initial linear speed of a point on its rim. (c) How many revolutions does the disk make before it stops?

38. A rotating flywheel of diameter 40.0 cm uniformly accelerates from rest to $25\overline{0}$ rad/s in 15.0 s. (a) Find its angular acceleration. (b) Find the linear velocity of a point on the rim of the wheel after 15.0 s. (c) How many revolutions does the wheel make during the 15.0 s?

9.2 Angular Momentum

Recall that in Section 5.1 we saw that *inertia* is the property of a body that causes it to remain at rest if it is at rest or to continue moving with a constant velocity unless an unbalanced force acts upon it. Similarly, *rotational inertia,* called the **moment of inertia**, is the property of a rotating body that causes it to continue to turn until a torque causes it to change its rotational motion. A freely spinning wheel on an upside-down bicycle continues to spin after you stop hand cranking the pedals because of its rotational inertia.

In Section 7.3, we saw that a *torque* is produced when a force is applied to produce a rotation ($\tau = Fs_t$). To increase the speed of the spinning bicycle wheel above, additional torque must be applied by increasing the applied force, F. The angular acceleration of a rotating body is found to be directly proportional to the torque applied to it. This applied torque can be expressed as follows:

$$\tau = I\alpha$$

where τ = applied torque
        I = moment of inertia (rotational inertia)
        α = angular acceleration

This is the rotational equivalent of Newton's second law of motion and applies to a rigid body rotating about a fixed axis.

The moment of inertia, I, is a measure of the rotational inertia of a body. The rotational inertia is determined by the mass of the rotating object and how far away that mass is from its axis of rotation. Figure 9.5 shows two cylinders of equal mass, one solid and one hollow. The hollow cylinder has more rotational inertia because its mass is concentrated farther from its axis of rotation. A flywheel is a mechanical device, which is usually a heavy metal rotating wheel attached to a drive shaft with most of its weight concentrated at its circumference. A small motor can slowly increase the speed of a flywheel to store up kinetic en-

Figure 9.5 Even though the two cylinders are of equal mass, the hollow cylinder has more rotational inertia because its mass is concentrated farther from its axis of rotation.

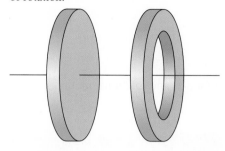

ergy; then, the small motor uses this inertia to perform a task for which it is ordinarily too small. A flywheel is also used to minimize rotational variations due to fluctuations in load and applied torque. Figure 9.6 shows a flywheel that is used to produce a steady rotation where the applied force of the piston is intermittent in this two-cylinder engine.

Figure 9.6 The large flywheel on this 1913 Case 30–60 tractor produces steady rotation of the crankshaft between fuel ignition cycles in its two-cylinder engine.

In Section 6.1 we saw that (linear) *momentum* is a measure of the amount of inertia and motion an object has or of the difficulty in bringing a moving body to rest. The formula for linear momentum is $p = mv$. There we studied applications involving linear motion and found the impulse is the change in linear momentum, $Ft = mv_f - mv_i$. Similarly, **angular momentum** for a rotating body about a fixed axis is defined as

$$L = I\omega$$

where L = angular momentum
        I = moment of inertia (rotational inertia)
        ω = angular velocity

Note the comparison with linear dynamics:

angular momentum = (moment of inertia) × (angular velocity)
linear momentum = (mass, a measure of inertia) × (linear velocity)

Furthermore, the *angular impulse* is the change in angular momentum.

$$\tau t = I\omega_f - I\omega_i$$

where τ = torque
t = time
I = moment of inertia
ω_f = final angular velocity
ω_i = initial angular velocity

Compare the following pairs of equations for linear motion and rotational motion:

Linear Motion	Rotational Motion
$F = ma$	$\tau = I\alpha$
$p = mv$	$L = I\omega$
$Ft = mv_f - mv_i$	$\tau t = I\omega_f - I\omega_i$

where F = applied force
m = mass (inertia)
a = linear acceleration
p = linear momentum
v = linear velocity
t = time
v_f = final linear velocity
v_i = initial linear velocity

where τ = applied torque
I = moment of inertia
α = angular acceleration
L = angular momentum
ω = angular velocity
t = time
ω_f = final angular velocity
ω_i = initial angular velocity

Conservation of Angular Momentum

In Section 6.1 we learned from the law of conservation of momentum that the total linear momentum ($p = mv$) of a system remains unchanged unless an external force acts on it. Similarly, the **law of conservation of angular momentum** states that the total angular momentum ($L = I\omega$) of a system remains unchanged unless an external torque acts on it.

LAW OF CONSERVATION OF ANGULAR MOMENTUM

The angular momentum of a system remains unchanged unless an external torque acts on it.

A spinning ice skater is an interesting example. When the skater's arms are extended, the rotational inertia, I, is relatively large and the angular velocity, ω, is relatively small. Often at the end of a spin, the skater pulls his or her arms tight to the body resulting in a much faster spin (larger angular velocity) because of a much smaller rotational inertia, I. When a rotating body contracts, its angular velocity, ω, increases; and when a rotating body expands, its angular velocity decreases. This phenomenon is the result of the conservation of angular momentum.

Similarly, gymnasts and divers generate their spins (torque) from a solid base or a diving board after which the angular momentum remains unchanged. The usual somersaults and twists result from making variations in their rotational inertia. Astronauts must also learn to control their spins as they maneuver their bodies to work in space.

Spinning Non-Ice Skaters

Ice skaters are able to control their rotational speed by changing their rotational inertia. To do this without a pair of skates, sit in an office chair that rotates freely and hold a couple of weights or heavy books close to your chest. Have someone spin the chair and gradually increase your rotational speed. After reaching your optimum rotational speed, stretch out your arms holding the weights in your hands. What happens to your rotational speed as you move your arms from close to your chest to an out-stretched position? Try this a few times. Explain how you can change your rotational speed like ice skaters do.

9.3 Centripetal Force

Newton's laws of motion apply to motion along a curved path as well as in a straight line. Recall that a moving body tends to continue in a straight line because of inertia. If we are to cause the body to move in a circle, we must constantly apply a force perpendicular to the line of motion of the body. A simple example is a rock on the end of a string being swung in a circle (Fig. 9.7). By Newton's first law, the rock tends to go in a straight line but the string exerts a constant force on the rock perpendicular to this line of travel. The resulting path of the rock is a circle [Fig. 9.8(a)]. The force of the string on the rock is the *centripetal* (toward the center) force. The **centripetal force** acting on a body in circular motion causes it to move in a circular path. This force is exerted toward the center of the circle. If the string should break, however, there would no longer be a centripetal force acting on the rock, which would fly off tangent to the circle [Fig. 9.8(b)].

Figure 9.7 Rock on a string being swung in a circle. The centripetal force is directed toward the center.

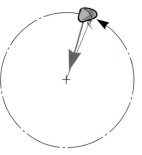

Figure 9.8 Centripetal force on a rock being swung in a circle

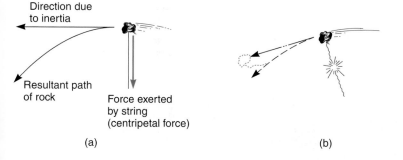

Direction due to inertia

Resultant path of rock

Force exerted by string (centripetal force)

(a)

(b)

The equation for finding the centripetal force on any body moving along a curved path is

$$F = \frac{mv^2}{r}$$

where F = centripetal force
m = mass of the body
v = velocity of the body
r = radius of curvature of the path of the body

TRY THIS ACTIVITY

Whirling a Bucket of Water

Hold a bucket with some water in your hand and quickly swing it vertically in a circular motion. Why does the water not fall out of the bucket when the bucket is upside down? Gradually decrease the speed of the whirling bucket while measuring the approximate rotational speed of the bucket. Measure the radius of the circular arc from your shoulder to the bottom of the bucket, the mass of the bucket and water, and the rotational speed of the bucket to find the minimum centripetal force needed to keep the water in the bucket. Next, double the amount of water in the bucket and repeat the experiment. How does the amount of water influence the rotational speed needed to keep the water in the bucket?

EXAMPLE

An automobile of mass 1640 kg rounds a curve of radius 25.0 m with a velocity of 15.0 m/s (54.0 km/h). What centripetal force is exerted on the automobile while rounding the curve?

Sketch:

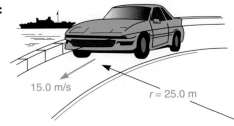

15.0 m/s $r = 25.0$ m

Data:

$$m = 1640 \text{ kg}$$
$$v = 15.0 \text{ m/s}$$
$$r = 25.0 \text{ m}$$
$$F = ?$$

Basic Equation:

$$F = \frac{mv^2}{r}$$

Working Equation: Same

Substitution:

$$F = \frac{(1640 \text{ kg})(15.0 \text{ m/s})^2}{25.0 \text{ m}}$$
$$= 14{,}800 \text{ kg m/s}^2 \qquad (\text{Recall: } 1 \text{ N} = 1 \text{ kg m/s}^2)$$
$$= 14{,}800 \text{ N}$$

PROBLEMS 9.3

1. Given: $m = 64.0$ kg
   $v = 34.0$ m/s
   $r = 17.0$ m
   $F = \underline{\hspace{1cm}}$ N

2. Given: $m = 11.3$ slugs
   $v = 3.00$ ft/s
   $r = 3.24$ ft
   $F = \underline{\hspace{1cm}}$ lb

3. Given: $F = 2500$ lb
   $v = 47.6$ ft/s
   $r = 72.0$ ft
   $m = \underline{\hspace{1cm}}$ slugs

4. Given: $F = 587$ N
   $v = 0.780$ m/s
   $m = 67.0$ kg
   $r = \underline{\hspace{1cm}}$ m

5. Given: $F = 602$ N
$m = 63.0$ kg
$r = 3.20$ m
$v = $ _____ m/s

6. Given: $m = 37.5$ kg
$v = 17.0$ m/s
$r = 3.75$ m
$F = $ _____ N

7. Given: $F = 75.0$ N
$v = 1.20$ m/s
$m = 10\bar{0}$ kg
$r = $ _____ m

8. Given: $F = 80.0$ N
$m = 43.0$ kg
$r = 17.5$ m
$v = $ _____ m/s

9. An automobile of mass 117 slugs follows a curve of radius 79.0 ft with a speed of 49.3 ft/s. What centripetal force is exerted on the automobile while it is rounding the curve?

10. Find the centripetal force exerted on a 7.12-kg mass moving at a speed of 2.98 m/s in a circle of radius 2.72 m.

11. The centripetal force on a car of mass 80$\bar{0}$ kg rounding a curve is 6250 N. If its speed is 15.0 m/s, what is the radius of the curve?

12. The centripetal force on a runner is 17.0 lb. If the runner weighs 175 lb and his speed is 14.0 mi/h, find the radius of the curve.

13. An automobile with mass 1650 kg is driven around a circular curve of radius 15$\bar{0}$ m at 80.0 km/h. Find the centripetal force of the road on the automobile.

14. A cycle of mass 510 kg rounds a curve of radius 4$\bar{0}$ m at 95 km/h. What is the centripetal force on the cycle?

15. What is the centripetal force exerted on a rock with mass 3.2 kg moving at 3.5 m/s in a circle of radius 2.1 m?

16. What is the centripetal force on a 150$\bar{0}$-kg vehicle driven around a curve of radius 35.0 m at 60.0 km/h?

17. What is the centripetal force on a 75$\bar{0}$-kg vehicle rounding a curve of radius 40.0 m at 30.0 km/h?

18. A truck with mass 215 slugs rounds a curve of radius 53.0 ft with a speed of 62.5 ft/s. (a) What centripetal force is exerted on the truck while rounding the curve? (b) How does the centripetal force change when the velocity is doubled? (c) What is the new force?

19. A 225-kg dirt bike is rounding a curve with linear velocity of 35 m/s and an angular speed of 0.25 rad/s. Find the centripetal force exerted on the bike.

20. A 55,0$\bar{0}$0-kg truck rounds a curve at 62.0 km/h. If the radius of the curve is 38.0 m, what is the centripetal force on the truck?

21. The radius of a curve is 27.5 m. What is the centripetal force on a 10,0$\bar{0}$0-kg truck going around it at 35.0 km/h?

9.4 Power in Rotational Systems

One of the most important aspects of rotational motion is the power developed. Recall that torque was discussed in Section 7.3. Power, however, must be considered whenever an engine or motor is used to turn a shaft. Some common examples are winches and drive trains (Fig. 9.9).

Figure 9.9 This driveshaft connects the engine transmission with the axle to supply power to the wheels and other components of this tractor. (Courtesy of Deere & Company)

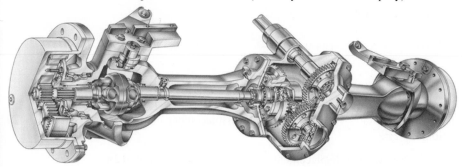

Earlier we learned that

$$power = \frac{force \times displacement}{time} = \frac{work}{time}$$

in the linear system. In the rotational system

$$P = \frac{(torque)(angular\ displacement)}{time}$$
$$= (torque)(angular\ velocity)$$
$$= \tau\omega$$

Recall that angular displacement is the angle through which a shaft is turned. In the metric system, angular displacement must be expressed in radians (1 rev $= 2\pi$ radians). Substituting symbols and units, we have, in watts (W),

$$P = \tau\omega$$
$$= (N\ m)\left(\frac{1}{s}\right) = \frac{N\ m}{s} = \frac{J}{s} = W$$

To find the power in kilowatts (kW), multiply the number of watts by the conversion factor

$$\frac{1\ kW}{1000\ W}$$

Note: In problem solving, the radian unit is a dimensionless unit; ω is expressed with the unit /s.

EXAMPLE 1

How many watts of power are developed by a mechanic tightening bolts using 50.0 N m of torque at a rate of 2.50 rad/s? How many kW?

Data:

$$\tau = 50.0\ N\ m$$
$$\omega = 2.50/s$$
$$P = ?$$

Basic Equation:

$$P = \tau\omega$$

Working Equation: Same

Substitution:

$$P = (50.0\ N\ m)(2.50/s)$$
$$= 125\ N\ m/s$$
$$= 125\ W \qquad (1\ W = 1\ N\ m/s)$$

To find the power in kW:

$$125\ \cancel{W} \times \frac{1\ kW}{1000\ \cancel{W}} = 0.125\ kW$$

In the U.S. system, we measure angular displacement by multiplying the number of revolutions by 2π:

$$angular\ displacement = (number\ of\ revolutions)(2\pi)$$

For the rotational system

$$\text{power} = \frac{(\text{torque})(2\pi \text{ revolutions})}{\text{time}}$$

When time is in minutes

$$\text{power} = \text{torque} \times 2\pi \times \frac{\text{rev}}{\text{min}} \times \frac{1 \text{ min}}{60 \text{ s}}$$

$$\boxed{\text{power in } \frac{\text{ft lb}}{\text{s}} = \text{torque in lb ft} \times \frac{\text{number of revolutions}}{\text{min}} \times 0.105 \frac{\text{min}}{\text{rev s}}}$$

$$\underbrace{\qquad\qquad}$$
$$2\pi \times \frac{1 \text{ min}}{60 \text{ s}}$$

Another common unit of power is the horsepower (hp). The conversion factor between $\frac{\text{ft lb}}{\text{s}}$ and hp is

$$\boxed{\text{power in hp} = \text{power in } \frac{\text{ft lb}}{\text{s}} \times \frac{\text{hp}}{550 \text{ ft lb/s}}}$$

What power (in ft lb/s) is developed by an electric motor with torque 5.70 lb ft and speed 425 rpm?

EXAMPLE 2

Data:

$$\tau = 5.70 \text{ lb ft}$$
$$\omega = 425 \text{ rpm}$$
$$P = ?$$

Basic Equation:

$$P = \text{torque} \times \frac{\text{rev}}{\text{min}} \times 0.105 \frac{\text{min}}{\text{rev s}}$$

Working Equation: Same

Substitution:

$$P = (5.70 \text{ lb ft})\left(425 \frac{\text{rev}}{\text{min}}\right)\left(0.105 \frac{\text{min}}{\text{rev s}}\right)$$
$$= 254 \text{ ft lb/s}$$

....

What horsepower is developed by a racing engine with torque 545 lb ft at $65\overline{0}0$ rpm?
First, find power in ft lb/s and then convert to hp.

EXAMPLE 3

Data:

$$\tau = 545 \text{ lb ft}$$
$$\omega = 65\overline{0}0 \text{ rpm}$$
$$P = ?$$

Basic Equation:

$$P = \text{torque} \times \frac{\text{rev}}{\text{min}} \times 0.105 \frac{\text{min}}{\text{rev s}}$$

Working Equation: Same

Substitution:

$$P = (545 \text{ lb ft})\left(65\overline{0}0 \ \frac{\text{rev}}{\text{min}}\right)\left(0.105 \ \frac{\text{min}}{\text{rev s}}\right)$$

$$= 372{,}000 \ \frac{\text{ft lb}}{\text{s}} \times \frac{1 \text{ hp}}{550 \ \frac{\text{ft lb}}{\text{s}}}$$

$$= 676 \text{ hp}$$

· · · · · · · · · · · · · · · · ·

SKETCH

12 cm² | w

4.0 cm

DATA

A = 12 cm², *l* = 4.0 cm, w = ?

BASIC EQUATION

A = *l*w

WORKING EQUATION

w = $\frac{A}{l}$

SUBSTITUTION

w = $\frac{12 \text{ cm}^2}{4.0 \text{ cm}}$ = 3.0 cm

PROBLEMS 9.4

1. Given: $\tau = 125$ lb ft
   $\omega = 555$ rpm
   $P =$ _____ ft lb/s

2. Given: $\tau = 39.4$ N m
   $\omega = 6.70/s$
   $P =$ _____ W

3. Given: $\tau = 372$ lb ft
   $\omega = 264$ rpm
   $P =$ _____ hp

4. Given: $\tau = 65\overline{0}$ N m
   $\omega = 45.0/s$
   $P =$ _____ kW

5. Given: $P = 8950$ W
   $\omega = 4.80/s$
   $\tau =$ _____

6. Given: $P = 650$ W
   $\tau = 540$ N m
   $\omega =$ _____

7. What horsepower is developed by an engine with torque $40\overline{0}$ lb ft at $45\overline{0}0$ rpm?

8. What torque must be applied to develop 175 ft lb/s of power in a motor if $\omega = 394$ rpm?

9. Find the angular velocity of a motor developing 649 W of power with torque 131 N m.

10. A high-speed industrial drill develops 0.500 hp at $16\overline{0}0$ rpm. What torque is applied to the drill bit?

11. An engine has torque of 550 N m at 8.3 rad/s. What power in watts does it develop?

12. Find the angular velocity of a motor developing 33.0 N m/s of power with a torque of 6.0 N m.

13. What power (in hp) is developed by an engine with torque 524 lb ft
    (a) at $30\overline{0}0$ rpm?   (b) at $60\overline{0}0$ rpm?

14. Find the angular velocity of a motor developing 650 W of power with a torque of 130 N m.

15. A drill develops 0.500 kW of power at $18\overline{0}0$ rpm. What torque is applied to the drill bit?

16. What power is developed by an engine with torque $75\overline{0}$ N m applied at $45\overline{0}0$ rpm?

17. A tangential force of 150 N is applied to a flywheel of diameter 45 cm to maintain a constant angular velocity of 175 rpm. How much work is done per minute?

18. Find the power developed by an engine with a torque of $12\overline{0}0$ N m applied at $20\overline{0}0$ rpm.

19. Find the power developed by an engine with a torque of $16\overline{0}0$ N m applied at $15\overline{0}0$ rpm.

20. Find the power developed by an engine with torque 1250 N m applied at $50\overline{0}0$ rpm.

21. Find the angular velocity of a motor developing $10\overline{0}0$ W of power with a torque of $15\overline{0}$ N m.

22. A motor develops 0.75 kW of power at $2\overline{0}00$ revolutions per $1\overline{0}$ min. What torque is applied to the motor shaft?

23. What power is developed when a tangential force of 175 N is applied to a flywheel of diameter 86 cm, causing it to have an angular velocity of 36 revolutions per 6.0 s?

24. What power is developed when a tangential force of $25\overline{0}$ N is applied to a wheel 57.0 cm in diameter with an angular velocity of 25.0 revolutions in 13.0 s?

25. An engine develops 1.50 kW of power at $10,\overline{0}00$ revolutions per 5.00 min. What torque is applied to the engine's crankshaft?
26. A mechanic tightens engine bolts using 45.5 N m of torque at a rate of 2.75 rad/s. How many watts of power is used to tighten the bolts?
27. An ag mechanic tightens implement bolts using 52.5 N m of torque at a rate of 2.25 rad/s. What power does the mechanic develop in tightening the bolts?

9.5 Transferring Rotational Motion

Suppose that two disks are touching each other as in Fig. 9.10. Disk A is driven by a motor and turns disk B (wheel) by making use of the friction between them. The relationship between the diameters of the two disks and their number of revolutions is

$$D \cdot N = d \cdot n$$

where D = diameter of the driver disk
d = diameter of the driven disk
N = number of revolutions of the driver disk
n = number of revolutions of the driven disk

Figure 9.10 In the self-propelled lawn mower, disk A, driven by the motor, turns disk B, the wheel, which results in the mower moving along the ground.

However, using two disks to transfer rotational motion is not very efficient due to slippage that may occur between them. The most common ways to prevent disk slippage are placing teeth on the edge of the disk and connecting the disks with a belt. Therefore, instead of using disks, we use gears or belt-driven pulleys to transfer this motion. The teeth on the gears eliminate the slippage; the belt connecting the pulleys helps reduce the slippage and provides for distance between rotating centers (Fig. 9.11).

We can change the equation $D \cdot N = d \cdot n$ to the form $D/d = n/N$ by dividing both sides by dN. The left side indicates the ratio of the diameters of the disks. If the ratio is 2, this means that the larger disk must have a diameter two times the diameter of the smaller disk. The same ratio would apply to gears and pulleys. The ratio of the diameters of the gears must be 2 to 1, and the ratio of the diameters of the pulleys must be 2 to 1. In fact, the ratio of the number of teeth on the gears must be 2 to 1.

The right side of the equation indicates the ratio of the number of revolutions of the two disks. If the ratio is 2, this means that the smaller disk makes two revolutions while the larger disk makes one revolution. The same would be true for gears and for pulleys connected by a belt.

Figure 9.11 Gears and pulleys are used to reduce slippage in transferring rotational motion.

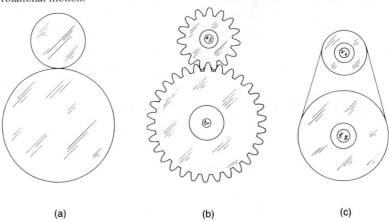

(a)   (b)   (c)

Gears and pulleys are used to increase or reduce the angular velocity of a rotating shaft or wheel. When two gears or pulleys are connected, the speed at which each turns compared to the other is inversely proportional to the diameter of that gear or pulley. The larger the diameter of a pulley or gear, the slower it turns. The smaller the diameter of a pulley or gear, the faster it will turn when connected to a larger one.

9.6 Gears

Gears are used to transfer rotational motion from one gear to another. The gear that causes the motion is called the *driver gear*. The gear to which the motion is transferred is called the *driven gear*.

There are many different sizes, shapes, and types of gears. Some examples are shown in Fig. 9.12. For any type of gear, we use one basic formula:

$$T \cdot N = t \cdot n$$

where T = number of teeth on the driver gear
N = number of revolutions of the driver gear
t = number of teeth on the driven gear
n = number of revolutions of the driven gear

Figure 9.12 Examples of different types of gears.
(Courtesy of Foote-Jones/Illinois Gear, Chicago, IL)

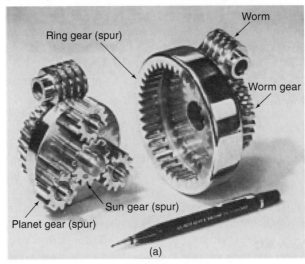

(a)

Figure 9.12 *(Continued)*

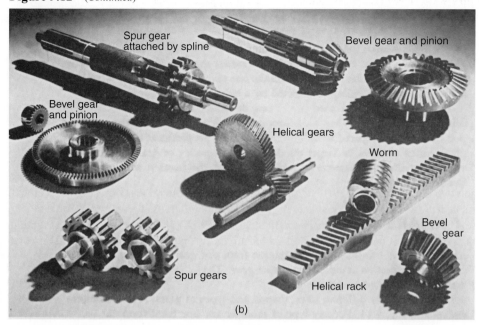

Spur gear attached by spline

Bevel gear and pinion

Bevel gear and pinion

Helical gears

Worm

Bevel gear

Spur gears

Helical rack

(b)

A driver gear has 30 teeth. How many revolutions does the driven gear with 20 teeth make while the driver makes one revolution?

EXAMPLE 1

Data:

$$T = 30 \text{ teeth} \qquad t = 20 \text{ teeth}$$
$$N = 1 \text{ revolution} \qquad n = ?$$

Basic Equation:

$$T \cdot N = t \cdot n$$

Working Equation:

$$n = \frac{T \cdot N}{t}$$

Substitution:

$$n = \frac{(30 \text{ teeth})(1 \text{ rev})}{20 \text{ teeth}}$$
$$= 1.5 \text{ rev}$$

. . . .

A driven gear of 70 teeth makes 63.0 revolutions per minute (rpm). The driver gear makes 90.0 rpm. What is the number of teeth required for the driver gear?

EXAMPLE 2

Data:

$$N = 90.0 \text{ rpm}$$
$$t = 70 \text{ teeth}$$
$$n = 63.0 \text{ rpm}$$
$$T = ?$$

Basic Equation:

$$T \cdot N = t \cdot n$$

Working Equation:

$$T = \frac{t \cdot n}{N}$$

Figure 9.13   Meshed gears shown as cylinders for simplicity

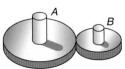

Substitution:

$$T = \frac{(70 \text{ teeth})(63.0 \text{ rpm})}{90.0 \text{ rpm}}$$

$$= 49 \text{ teeth}$$

Figure 9.14   Gear train of three gears

Gear Trains

When two gears mesh (Fig. 9.13),* they turn in opposite directions. If gear *A* turns clockwise, gear *B* turns counterclockwise. If gear *A* turns counterclockwise, gear *B* turns clockwise. If a third gear is inserted between the two (Fig. 9.14), then gears *A* and *B* are rotating in the same direction. This third gear is called an *idler*. A **gear train** is a series of gears that transfers rotational motion from one gear to another.

> When the number of shafts in a gear train is odd (such as 1, 3, 5, . . .), the first gear and the last gear rotate in the same direction. When the number of shafts is even, the gears rotate in opposite directions.

When a complex gear train is considered, the relationship between revolutions and number of teeth is still present. This relationship is: The number of revolutions of the first driver times the product of the number of teeth of all the driver gears equals the number of revolutions of the final driven gear times the product of the number of teeth on all the driven gears. That is,

$$NT_1T_2T_3T_4 \cdots = nt_1t_2t_3t_4 \cdots$$

where N = number of revolutions of first driver gear
         T_1 = teeth on first driver gear
         T_2 = teeth on second driver gear
         T_3 = teeth on third driver gear
         T_4 = teeth on fourth driver gear
         n = number of revolutions of last driven gear
         t_1 = teeth on first driven gear
         t_2 = teeth on second driven gear
         t_3 = teeth on third driven gear
         t_4 = teeth on fourth driven gear

EXAMPLE 3

Determine the relative motion of gears *A* and *B* in Fig. 9.15.

Figure 9.15

(a)

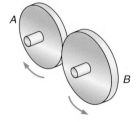

(b)

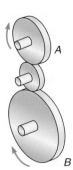

*Although gears have teeth, in technical work they are often shown as cylinders.

Figure 9.15 (*Continued*)

(c)

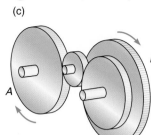

(d)

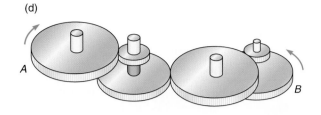

Find the number of revolutions per minute of gear D in Fig. 9.16 if gear A rotates at 20.0 rpm. Gears A and C are drivers and gears B and D are driven.

EXAMPLE 4

Figure 9.16

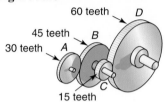

Data:

$$N = 20.0 \text{ rpm} \qquad t_1 = 45 \text{ teeth}$$
$$T_1 = 30 \text{ teeth} \qquad t_2 = 60 \text{ teeth}$$
$$T_2 = 15 \text{ teeth} \qquad n = ?$$

Basic Equation:

$$NT_1T_2 = nt_1t_2$$

Working Equation:

$$n = \frac{NT_1T_2}{t_1t_2}$$

Substitution:

$$n = \frac{(20.0 \text{ rpm})(30 \text{ teeth})(15 \text{ teeth})}{(45 \text{ teeth})(60 \text{ teeth})}$$
$$= 3.33 \text{ rpm}$$

Find the rpm of gear D in the train shown in Fig. 9.17. Gears A and C are drivers and gears B and D are driven.

EXAMPLE 5

Data:

$$N = 16\overline{0}0 \text{ rpm} \qquad t_1 = 30 \text{ teeth}$$
$$T_1 = 60 \text{ teeth} \qquad t_2 = 48 \text{ teeth}$$
$$T_2 = 15 \text{ teeth} \qquad n = ?$$

Figure 9.17

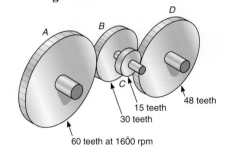

Basic Equation:

$$NT_1T_2 = nt_1t_2$$

Working Equation:

$$n = \frac{NT_1T_2}{t_1t_2}$$

Substitution:

$$n = \frac{(16\overline{0}0 \text{ rpm})(60 \text{ teeth})(15 \text{ teeth})}{(30 \text{ teeth})(48 \text{ teeth})}$$
$$= 10\overline{0}0 \text{ rpm}$$

EXAMPLE 6

In the gear train shown in Fig. 9.18, find the speed in rpm of gear A.

Figure 9.18

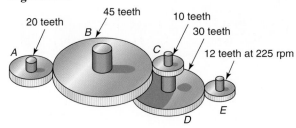

Data:

$$t_1 = 45 \text{ teeth} \qquad T_1 = 20 \text{ teeth}$$
$$t_2 = 10 \text{ teeth} \qquad T_2 = 45 \text{ teeth}$$
$$t_3 = 12 \text{ teeth} \qquad T_3 = 30 \text{ teeth}$$
$$n = 225 \text{ rpm} \qquad N = ?$$

Gear B is both a driver and a driven gear.

Basic Equation:

$$NT_1T_2T_3 = nt_1t_2t_3$$

Working Equation:

$$N = \frac{nt_1t_2t_3}{T_1T_2T_3}$$

Substitution:

$$N = \frac{(225 \text{ rpm})(45 \text{ teeth})(10 \text{ teeth})(12 \text{ teeth})}{(20 \text{ teeth})(45 \text{ teeth})(30 \text{ teeth})}$$
$$= 45.0 \text{ rpm}$$

· · · · · · · · · · · · · · · · · ·

In a gear train, when a gear is both a driver gear and a driven gear, it may be omitted from the computation.

EXAMPLE 7

The problem in Example 6 could have been worked as follows because gear B is both a driver and a driven.

Basic Equation:

$$NT_1T_3 = nt_2t_3$$

Working Equation:

$$N = \frac{nt_2t_3}{T_1T_3}$$

Substitution:

$$N = \frac{(225 \text{ rpm})(10 \text{ teeth})(12 \text{ teeth})}{(20 \text{ teeth})(30 \text{ teeth})}$$
$$= 45.0 \text{ rpm}$$

· · · · · · · · · · · · · · · · · ·

PHYSICS CONNECTIONS

Bicycle Gears

The gearing system on a bicycle allows a cyclist to choose how much force he or she would like to exert when riding a bicycle. What gear ratio should be used when riding uphill, downhill, or on level ground? Prior to the use of gears on bicycles, a rider needed to sit directly above the front wheel in order to pedal. Gears, chains, and other advances have made the modern bicycle much more comfortable and efficient.

To find the gear ratio of a bicycle's gearing system, divide the number of teeth on the rear, driven gear by the number of teeth on the front, driver gear. When the number of teeth on the front gear is larger, the gear ratio is less than one and the rear wheel turns faster than the pedals. This results in high speeds for going down slight inclines or for level ground and allows the cyclist to pedal fewer revolutions while traveling a greater distance. When the number of teeth in the rear gear is larger, the gear ratio is greater than one. Here, the pedals turn faster than the rear wheel. This results in low speeds for going up large hills and allows the cyclist to pedal more revolutions while traveling a shorter distance but exerting a more manageable leg force. The following table illustrates the differences:

Number of Teeth on Front Gear (Driver)	Number of Teeth on Rear Gear (Driven)	Gear Ratio (Driven/ Driver)	Number of Teeth on Front Gear (Driver)	Number of Teeth on Rear Gear (Driven)	Gear Ratio (Driven/ Driver)
44	11	1/4	15	30	2/1
When the front gear turns once, the back gear turns four times (good for traveling at high speeds).			When the front gear turns once, the back gear turns only $\frac{1}{2}$ a rotation (good for reducing the force needed to pedal while going uphill).		

Most beginner bicycles simply connect the chain on the front gear to the rear gear with no option for changing the gear ratios. Children must stand up to pedal with more force. Geared bicycles, including road and mountain bikes, are engineered with a variety of gear ratios to allow a cyclist to travel more easily over many terrains (Fig. 9.19).

Figure 9.19   (a) Beginner bicycle   (b) Mountain bike

SKETCH

12 cm²	w

4.0 cm

DATA

A = 12 cm², l = 4.0 cm, w = ?

BASIC EQUATION

A = lw

WORKING EQUATION

w = $\frac{A}{l}$

SUBSTITUTION

w = $\frac{12 \text{ cm}^2}{4.0 \text{ cm}}$ = 3.0 cm

PROBLEMS 9.6

Fill in the blanks.

	Number of Teeth		rpm	
	Driver	Driven	Driver	Driven
1.	16	48	156	_____
2.	36	24	_____	225
3.	18	_____	72.0	54.0
4.	_____	64	148	55.5
5.	48	36	_____	276
6.	16	12	144	_____

7. A driver gear has 36 teeth and makes 85.0 rpm. Find the rpm of the driven gear with 72 teeth.

8. A motor turning at 1250 rpm is fitted with a gear having 54 teeth. Find the speed of the driven gear if it has 45 teeth.

9. A gear running at $25\overline{0}$ rpm meshes with another revolving at $10\overline{0}$ rpm. If the smaller gear has 30 teeth, how many teeth does the larger gear have?

10. A driver gear with 40 teeth makes 154 rpm. How many teeth must the driven gear have if it makes $22\overline{0}$ rpm?

11. Two gears have a speed ratio of 4.2 to 1. If the smaller gear has 15 teeth, how many teeth does the larger gear have?

12. What size gear should be meshed with a 15-tooth pinion to achieve a speed reduction of 10 to 3?

13. A driver gear has 72 teeth and makes 162 rpm. Find the rpm of the driven gear with 81 teeth.

14. A driver gear with 60 teeth makes 1600 rpm. How many teeth must the driven gear have if it makes 480 rpm?

15. What size gear should be meshed with a 20-tooth pinion to achieve a speed reduction of 3 to 1?

16. A motor turning at $15\overline{0}0$ rpm is fitted with a gear having 60 teeth. Find the speed of the driven gear if it has 40 teeth.

17. The larger of two gears in a clock has 36 teeth and turns at a rate of 0.50 rpm. How many teeth does the smaller gear have if it rotates at 1/30 rev/s?

18. How many revolutions does an 88-tooth gear make in 10.0 min when it is meshed with a 22-tooth pinion rotating at 44 rpm?

If gear A turns in a clockwise motion, determine the motion of gear B in each gear train.

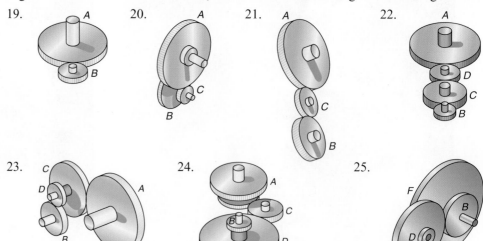

26.

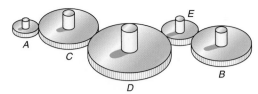

27.

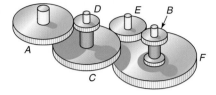

28.

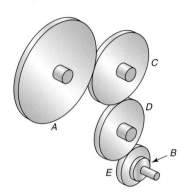

Find the speed in rpm of gear *D* in each gear train.

29.

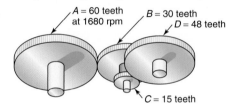

A = 60 teeth at 1680 rpm
B = 30 teeth
D = 48 teeth
C = 15 teeth

30.

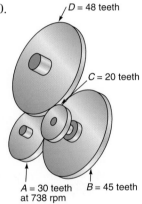

D = 48 teeth
C = 20 teeth
A = 30 teeth at 738 rpm
B = 45 teeth

31.

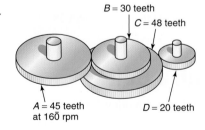

B = 30 teeth
C = 48 teeth
A = 45 teeth at 16̄0 rpm
D = 20 teeth

32.

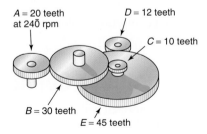

A = 20 teeth at 24̄0 rpm
D = 12 teeth
C = 10 teeth
B = 30 teeth
E = 45 teeth

33.

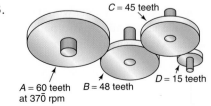

C = 45 teeth
A = 60 teeth at 37̄0 rpm
B = 48 teeth
D = 15 teeth

Find the number of teeth for gear *D* in each gear train.

34. *D:* at 150ō rpm

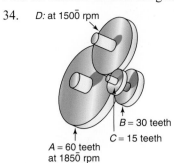

B = 30 teeth
C = 15 teeth
A = 60 teeth
at 185ō rpm

35.

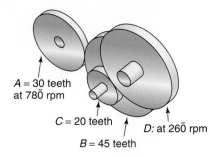

A = 30 teeth
at 78ō rpm
C = 20 teeth
D: at 26ō rpm
B = 45 teeth

36.

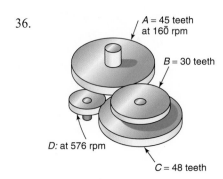

A = 45 teeth
at 16ō rpm
B = 30 teeth
D: at 576 rpm
C = 48 teeth

37.

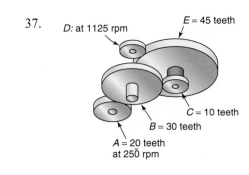

D: at 1125 rpm
E = 45 teeth
C = 10 teeth
B = 30 teeth
A = 20 teeth
at 25ō rpm

38.

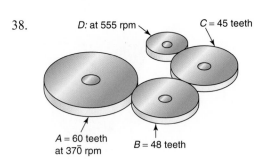

D: at 555 rpm
C = 45 teeth
A = 60 teeth
at 37ō rpm
B = 48 teeth

Figure 9.20 A single belt drives several components from this engine. (Courtesy of Deere & Company)

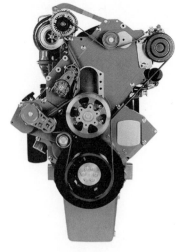

39. Find the direction of rotation of gear *B* if gear *A* is turned counterclockwise in Problems 22 through 28.
40. Find the effect of doubling the number of teeth on gear *A* in Problem 38.

9.7 Pulleys Connected with a Belt

Pulleys connected with a belt are used to transfer rotational motion from one shaft to another (Fig. 9.20). Assuming no slippage, the linear speed of any point on the belt equals the linear speed of any point on the rim of each pulley as the belt travels around each pulley. The larger the pulley, the larger is its circumference: $C = \pi d$. The larger the circumference of the pulley, the longer a point on the belt stays in contact with the pulley. The smaller the circumference of the pulley, the shorter a point on the belt stays in contact with the pulley, which causes the smaller pulley to rotate faster than the larger pulley. Two pulleys connected with a belt have a relationship similar to gears. Assuming no slippage, when two pulleys are connected

$$D \cdot N = d \cdot n$$

where D = diameter of the driver pulley
$\quad\quad N$ = number of revolutions per minute of the driver pulley
$\quad\quad d$ = diameter of the driven pulley
$\quad\quad n$ = number of revolutions per minute of the driven pulley

The preceding equation may be generalized in the same manner as for gear trains as follows:

$$ND_1D_2D_3 \cdots = nd_1d_2d_3 \cdots$$

Find the speed in rpm of pulley A shown in Fig. 9.21.

EXAMPLE

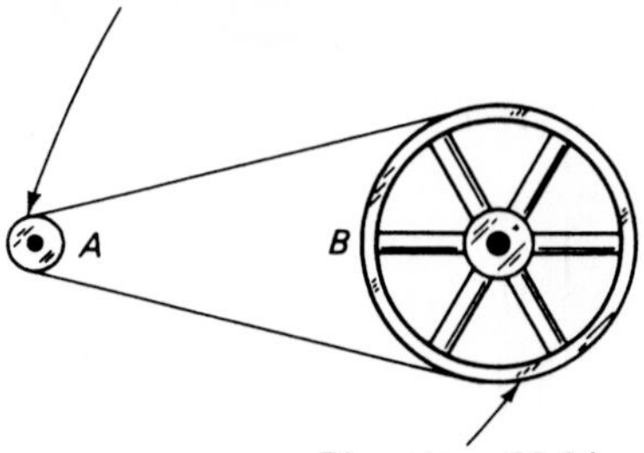

Data:

$$D = 6.00 \text{ in.}$$
$$d = 30.0 \text{ in.}$$
$$n = 35\overline{0} \text{ rpm}$$
$$N = ?$$

Figure 9.21
Driver diameter = 6.00 in.

Diameter = 30.0 in.
at 35$\overline{0}$ rpm

Basic Equation:

$$D \cdot N = d \cdot n$$

Working Equation:

$$N = \frac{dn}{D}$$

Substitution:

$$N = \frac{(30.0 \text{ in.})(35\overline{0} \text{ rpm})}{6.00 \text{ in.}}$$
$$= 1750 \text{ rpm}$$

When two pulleys are connected with an open-type belt, the pulleys turn in the same direction. When two pulleys are connected with a cross-type belt, the pulleys turn in opposite directions. See Fig. 9.22.

Figure 9.22   Crossing a belt reverses direction.

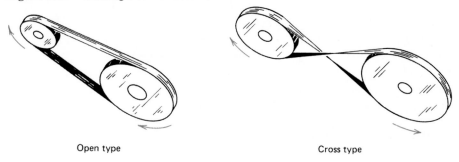

Open type

Cross type

(a) Pulleys rotate in
same direction.

(b) Pulleys rotate in
opposite directions.

SKETCH

```
┌──────────────┐
│  12 cm²      │ w
└──────────────┘
      4.0 cm
```

DATA

A = 12 cm², *l* = 4.0 cm, w = ?

BASIC EQUATION

A = *l*w

WORKING EQUATION

$w = \frac{A}{l}$

SUBSTITUTION

$w = \frac{12 \text{ cm}^2}{4.0 \text{ cm}} = 3.0 \text{ cm}$

PROBLEMS 9.7

Find each missing quantity using $D \cdot N = d \cdot n$.

	D	N	d	n
1.	18.0	$150\bar{0}$	12.0	___
2.	36.0	___	9.00	972
3.	12.0	$180\bar{0}$	6.00	___
4.	___	2250	9.00	1125
5.	49.0	1860	___	$62\bar{0}$

6. A driver pulley of diameter 6.50 in. revolves at 1650 rpm. Find the speed of the driven pulley if its diameter is 26.0 in.
7. A driver pulley of diameter 25.0 cm revolves at $12\bar{0}$ rpm. At what speed will the driven pulley turn if its diameter is 48.0 cm?
8. One pulley of diameter 36.0 cm revolves at $60\bar{0}$ rpm. Find the diameter of the second pulley if it rotates at $36\bar{0}$ rpm.
9. One pulley rotates at $45\bar{0}$ rpm. The diameter of the second pulley is 15.0 in. and rotates at 675 rpm. Find the diameter of the first pulley.
10. A pulley with a radius of 10.0 cm rotates at $12\bar{0}$ rpm. The radius of the second pulley is 15.0 cm; find its rpm.

Determine the direction of pulley *B* in each pulley system.

11.

12.

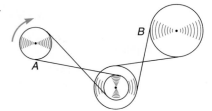

13.

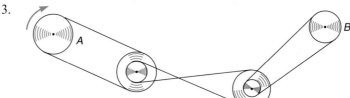

14.

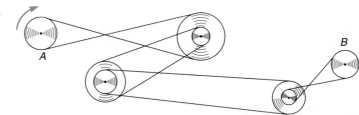

15.

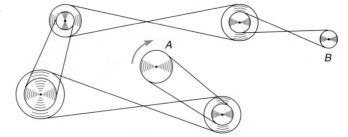

16. What size pulley should be placed on a countershaft turning $15\bar{0}$ rpm to drive a grinder with a 12.0-cm pulley that is to turn at $120\bar{0}$ rpm?

Glossary

Angular Acceleration The rate of change of angular velocity (change in angular velocity/time). (p. 236)

Angular Displacement The angle through which any point on a rotating body moves. (p. 234)

Angular Momentum For a rotating body about a fixed axis, the angular momentum is the product of the moment of inertia and the angular velocity of the body. (p. 241)

Angular Velocity The rate of angular displacement (angular displacement/time). (p. 234)

Centripetal Force The force acting on a body in circular motion that causes it to move in a circular path. This force is exerted toward the center of the circle. (p. 243)

Curvilinear Motion Motion along a curved path. (p. 233)

Degree An angular unit of measure. Defined as 1/360 of one complete revolution. (p. 233)

Gear Train A series of gears that transfers rotational motion from one gear to another. (p. 232)

Law of Conservation of Angular Momentum The angular momentum of a system remains unchanged unless an outside torque acts on it. (p. 242)

Moment of Inertia Rotational inertia; the property of a rotating body that causes it to continue to turn until a torque causes it to change its rotational motion. (p. 240)

Radian An angular unit of measurement. Defined as that angle with its vertex at the center of a circle whose sides cut off an arc on the circle equal to its radius. Equal to $(360°/2\pi)$ or approximately $57.3°$. (p. 233)

Rectilinear Motion Motion in a straight line. (p. 233)

Revolution A unit of measurement in rotational motion. One complete rotation of a body. (p. 233)

Rotational Motion Spinning motion of a body. (p. 233)

Formulas

9.1 $\theta = \dfrac{s}{r}$

$1 \text{ rev} = 360° = 2\pi \text{ rad}$

$\omega = \dfrac{\theta}{t}$

$v = \omega r$

$\alpha = \dfrac{\Delta\omega}{t}$

$\theta = \omega_{\text{avg}}t$

$\theta = \omega_i t + \frac{1}{2}\alpha t^2$

$\omega_{\text{avg}} = \dfrac{\omega_f + \omega_i}{2}$

$\omega_f = \omega_i + \alpha t$

$\alpha = \dfrac{\omega_f - \omega_i}{t}$

$\theta = \frac{1}{2}(\omega_f + \omega_i)t$

$2\alpha\theta = \omega_f^2 - \omega_i^2$

9.2 $\tau = I\alpha$

$L = I\omega$

$\tau t = I\omega_f - I\omega_i$

9.3 $F = \dfrac{mv^2}{r}$

9.4 $P = \tau\omega$

$$\text{power in } \frac{\text{ft lb}}{\text{s}} = \text{torque in lb ft} \times \frac{\text{number of revolutions}}{\text{min}} \times 0.105 \frac{\text{min}}{\text{rev s}}$$

$$\text{power in hp} = \text{power in}\frac{\text{ft lb}}{\text{s}} \times \frac{\text{hp}}{550 \text{ ft lb/s}}$$

9.5 $D \cdot N = d \cdot n$

9.6 $T \cdot N = t \cdot n$

$NT_1T_2T_3T_4 \cdots = nt_1t_2t_3t_4 \cdots$

9.7 $D \cdot N = d \cdot n$

$ND_1D_2D_3 \cdots = nd_1d_2d_3 \cdots$

Review Questions

SKETCH

| 12 cm² | w |

4.0 cm

DATA

$A = 12$ cm², $l = 4.0$ cm, $w = ?$

BASIC EQUATION

$A = lw$

WORKING EQUATION

$w = \dfrac{A}{l}$

SUBSTITUTION

$w = \dfrac{12 \text{ cm}^2}{4.0 \text{ cm}} = 3.0$ cm

1.   Angular velocity is measured in
     (a)   revolutions/minute.
     (b)   radians/second.
     (c)   revolutions/second.
     (d)   all of the above.
2.   Power in the rotational system
     (a)   is found in the same way as in the linear system.
     (b)   is found differently than it is in the linear system.
     (c)   cannot be determined.
     (d)   is always a constant.
3.   A gear train has 13 directly connected gears. The first and last gears will
     (a)   rotate in opposite directions.
     (b)   rotate in the same direction.
     (c)   not rotate.
4.   Distinguish between curvilinear motion and rotational motion.
5.   Name the two types of measurement of rotation.
6.   In your own words, define *radian*.
7.   What is angular displacement? In what units is it measured?
8.   How is linear velocity of a point on a circle related to angular velocity?
9.   How do equations for uniformly accelerated rotational motion compare with those for uniformly accelerated linear motion?
10.   A girl jumping from a high platform into a pool tucks her body into a tight ball to complete two somersaults before extending her body as she enters the water. Her body rotates much more quickly during the somersaults than during her extension into the water. This is an example of what law?
11.   Is the tangent to a circle always perpendicular to the radius?
12.   Will inertia tend to keep a moving body following a curved path?
13.   Explain the relationship between the number of teeth on two interlocking gears and their relative number of revolutions.
14.   How does the presence of an idler gear affect the relationship between a driver gear and a driven gear in a gear train?
15.   When the number of directly connected gears in a gear train is four, do the first and last gears in the train rotate in the same or in opposite directions?
16.   Why can a gear that is both a driver gear and a driven gear be omitted from a computation?
17.   How do pulley combination equations compare to gear train equations?

18. If a large pulley and a small pulley are connected with a belt, which will turn faster?
19. How do we know the belt connecting two pulleys travels at the same rate while in contact with the different-size pulleys?

Review Problems

1. Convert 13 revolutions to (a) radians and (b) degrees.
2. A bicycle wheel turns 25π rad during 45 s. Find the angular velocity of the wheel.
3. A lawn tractor tire turns at 65.0 rpm and has a radius of 13.0 cm. Find the linear speed of the tractor in m/s.
4. A model plane pulls into a tight curve of a radius of 25.0 m. The $30\overline{0}$-g plane is traveling at 90.0 km/h. What is the plane's centripetal force?
5. A 0.950-kg mass is spun in a circle on a string of radius 60.0 cm. If its centripetal force is 12.0 N, at what velocity does it travel?
6. A girl riding her bike creates a torque of 1.20 lb ft with an angular speed of 45.0 rpm. How much power does she produce?
7. A motor generates $30\overline{0}$ W of power. The torque necessary is 50.0 N m. Find the angular velocity.
8. Two rollers are side by side, with the large one turning the small one. The diameter of the small one is 2.00 cm and it turns at 15.0 rpm. The large roller has a diameter of 5.00 cm. How many revolutions does it make in one minute?
9. A clock is driven by a series of gears. The first gear has 30 teeth and rotates 60.0 times a minute. The second gear rotates at 90.0 rpm. How many teeth does it have?
10. Two gears have 13 and 26 teeth, respectively. The first gear turns at 115 rpm. How many times per minute does the second gear rotate?
11. A gear train has 17 directly connected gears. Do the first and last gears rotate in the same direction?
12. A pulley of diameter 14.0 cm is driven by an electric motor to revolve 75.0 rpm. The pulley drives a second one of diameter 10.0 cm. How many revolutions does the second pulley make in 1.00 min?
13. A pulley of diameter 5.00 cm is driven at $10\overline{0}$ rpm. Find the diameter of a second pulley if it is driven by the first at $25\overline{0}$ rpm.
14. If gear C turns counterclockwise, in what direction does gear F turn?

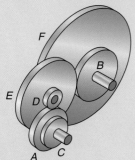

15. Find the speed in rpm of gear D.

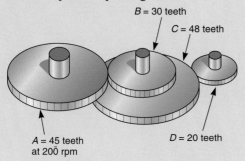

$B = 30$ teeth
$C = 48$ teeth
$A = 45$ teeth at $20\overline{0}$ rpm
$D = 20$ teeth

SKETCH

12 cm² | w
4.0 cm

DATA

$A = 12$ cm², $l = 4.0$ cm, $w = ?$

BASIC EQUATION

$A = lw$

WORKING EQUATION

$w = \frac{A}{l}$

SUBSTITUTION

$w = \frac{12 \text{ cm}^2}{4.0 \text{ cm}} = 3.0$ cm

PROBLEM SOLVING

16.   Find the number of teeth in gear D.

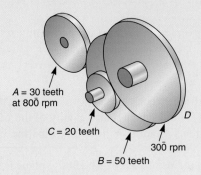

A = 30 teeth
at 80$\bar{0}$ rpm

C = 20 teeth

B = 50 teeth

D

30$\bar{0}$ rpm

APPLIED CONCEPTS

1. As part of their training, NASA astronauts are placed in large rotating machines to see how well their bodies can withstand various "g" forces. (One g equals the gravitational force of gravity at the earth's surface.) (a) What rotational speed is needed in a device with radius 6.25 m to allow a 75.8-kg astronaut to experience a force that is twice his normal weight or "2 g"? (b) What rotational speed is needed to achieve a "4 g" effect? (c) Would the rotational speeds found in (a) and (b) change if the astronaut had a different mass?

2. Waterwheels are used to convert kinetic energy from falling water into useful mechanical energy. (a) If an average of 10.0 kg of water flows onto a waterwheel every second, how much torque does the water exert on a waterwheel of radius 2.45 m? (b) The torque exerted by the water causes the wheel to move with an angular acceleration of 0.593 rad/s^2. Using this information, find the rotational inertia of the water wheel. (c) If you were the designer of this waterwheel, what are two things you could do to increase the rotational inertia of the waterwheel?

3. In Chapter 8 (Fig. 8.17), you were asked to calculate the velocity of a frictionless roller coaster car at various locations around the track. To make sure the loops are safe, you must make sure the track can support between two and five times the normal weight (that is, between 2 g and 5 g) of a car. (a) How many g's does the 355-kg roller coaster car experience in each loop? (b) Are the loops safe? If not, explain what can be done to make the loops safe.

4. A hairpin turn on a concrete racetrack has a radius of 117 ft. (a) Since the frictional force between the road and the tires acts as the centripetal force, find the vehicle's maximum possible speed around the turn. (The coefficient of starting friction between rubber and concrete is 2.00.) (b) What would be the maximum velocity around the next turn if it has double the radius of the first turn? (c) Explain how the radius of a turn influences the centripetal force and the maximum velocity for a vehicle.

5. (a) How much power does a motorcycle need to produce 72.0 lb ft of torque while the engine crankshaft rotates at 3000 rpm? (b) When shifted into a higher gear, the same amount of power rotates the engine crankshaft at 5000 rpm. How much torque does the engine produce in this higher gear? (c) Using your knowledge of power, torque, and angular speed, explain why a motorcycle should be in a low gear when climbing a steep hill.

CHAPTER 10

SIMPLE MACHINES

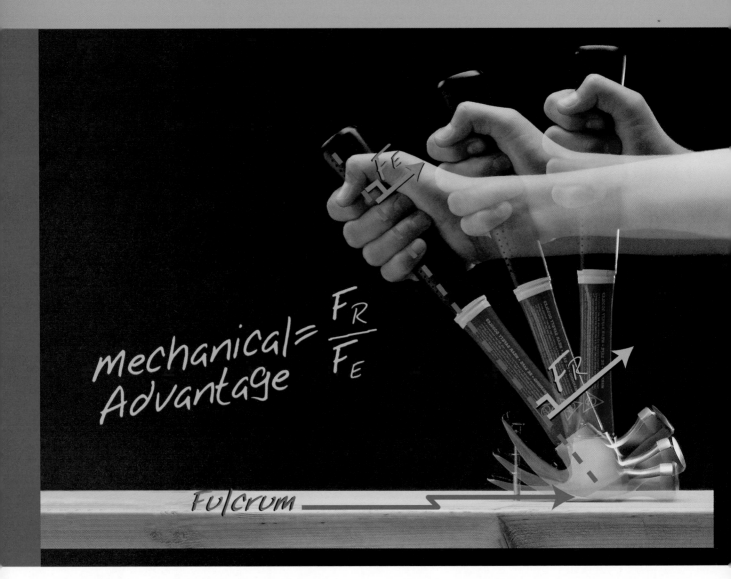

$$\text{mechanical Advantage} = \frac{F_R}{F_E}$$

Fulcrum

Machines may be used to transfer energy, multiply force, or multiply speed. We use them to obtain a mechanical advantage—to do something more efficiently that would be difficult or impossible without mechanical help. In this chapter we examine simple machines and their usefulness in technology.

Objectives

The major goals of this chapter are to enable you to:

1. Determine how energy is transferred using simple machines.
2. Analyze the efficiency and mechanical advantages of simple machines.
3. Distinguish the three types of levers and the mechanical advantage of each.
4. Analyze the mechanical advantage of the wheel-and-axle, the pulley, the inclined plane, and the screw.

10.1 Machines and Energy Transfer

A **machine** is used to transfer energy from one place to another and allows work to be done that could not otherwise be done or could not be done as easily. By using a pulley system [Fig. 10.1(a)], one person can easily lift an engine from an automobile. Pliers [Fig. 10.1(b)] allow a person to cut a wire or turn a nut with the strength of his or her hand.

Machines are sometimes used to multiply force. By applying a small force, we can use a machine to jack up an automobile [Fig. 10.2(a)]. Machines are sometimes used to multi-

Figure 10.1   Simple machines used to transfer energy

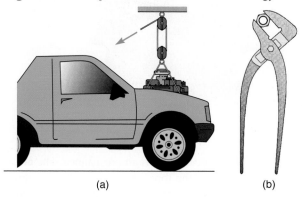

(a)

(b)

Figure 10.2   Simple machines may be used to multiply force or speed or to change direction.

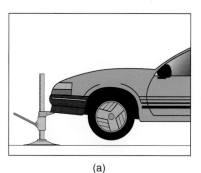

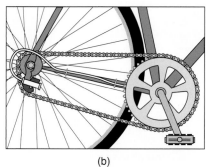

(a)

A car jack is used to multiply force.

(b)

Gears are used to multiply speed.

(c)

A pulley is used to change direction.

ply speed, as with the gears on a bicycle [Fig. 10.2(b)]. Machines are used to change direction. When we use a single fixed pulley on a flag pole to raise a flag [Fig. 10.2(c)], the only advantage we get is the change in direction. (We pull the rope down, and the flag goes up.)

A **simple machine** is any one of six mechanical devices in which an applied force results in useful work (Fig. 10.3). All other machines—no matter how complex—are combinations of two or more of these simple machines.

Figure 10.3 Six simple machines

1. Lever

2. Wheel and axle

3. Pulley

4. Inclined plane

5. Screw

6. Wedge

In every machine we are concerned with two forces—effort and resistance. The **effort** is the force applied *to* the machine. The **resistance** is the force overcome *by* the machine. A person applies 30 lb on the jack handle in Fig. 10.4 to produce a lifting force of 600 lb on the car. The effort force is 30 lb. The resistance force is 600 lb.

Figure 10.4 This lever multiplies force.

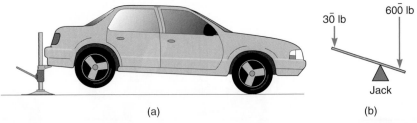

30 lb

600 lb

Jack

(a)

(b)

LAW OF SIMPLE MACHINES
resistance force × resistance distance = effort force × effort distance

Mechanical Advantage and Efficiency

The **mechanical advantage** (MA) is the ratio of the resistance force to the effort force. By formula,

$$MA = \frac{\text{resistance force}}{\text{effort force}}$$

The MA of the jack in Fig. 10.4 is found as follows:

$$MA = \frac{\text{resistance force}}{\text{effort force}} = \frac{600 \, \text{lb}}{30 \, \text{lb}} = \frac{20}{1}$$

This MA means that, for each pound applied by the person, he or she lifts $\overline{20}$ pounds. Note that MA has no units. Why?

Each time a machine is used, part of the energy or effort applied to the machine is lost due to friction (Fig. 10.5). The **efficiency** of a machine is the ratio of the work output to the work input. By formula,

$$\text{efficiency} = \frac{\text{work output}}{\text{work input}} \times 100\% = \frac{F_{\text{output}} \times s_{\text{output}}}{F_{\text{input}} \times s_{\text{input}}} \times 100\%$$

Figure 10.5   Some work is always lost to friction.

10.2 The Lever

A **lever** consists of a rigid bar free to turn on a pivot called a **fulcrum** (Fig. 10.6). The mechanical advantage (MA) is the ratio of the effort arm (s_E) to the resistance arm (s_R):

$$MA_{\text{lever}} = \frac{\text{effort arm}}{\text{resistance arm}} = \frac{s_E}{s_R}$$

Figure 10.6   Mechanical advantage of the lever: $MA = \dfrac{s_E}{s_R}$.

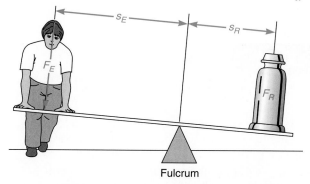

The **effort arm** is the distance from the effort force to the fulcrum. The **resistance arm** is the distance from the fulcrum to the resistance force. The three types or classes of levers are shown in Fig. 10.7. The law of simple machines as applied to levers (basic equation) is

$$F_R \cdot s_R = F_E \cdot s_E$$

where F_R = resistance force
         s_R = length of resistance arm
         F_E = effort force
         s_E = length of effort arm

Figure 10.7   Three classes of levers

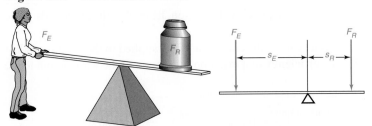

First class: The fulcrum is between the resistance force
(F_R) and the effort force (F_E).

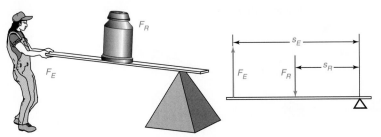

Second class: The resistance force (F_R) is between the
fulcrum and the effort force (F_E).

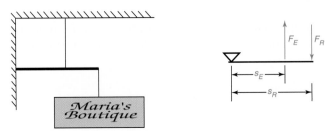

Third class: The effort force (F_E) is between the fulcrum
and the resistance force (F_R).

TRY THIS ACTIVITY

Pulling Nails

Hammer two identical nails into a piece of wood so that the heads are slightly above the wood. Wedge the jaws of the hammer beneath the head of the first nail and hold the handle close to the head of the hammer. Before removing the nail, note the resistance distance, the position of the fulcrum, and the effort distance. Note the amount of effort force necessary to remove the first nail. Next, hold the end of the handle as you remove the second nail. Explain why simple machines, such as hammers pulling nails, are able to reduce the effort force.

A bar is used to raise a $12\overline{0}0$-N stone. The pivot is placed 30.0 cm from the stone. The worker pushes 2.50 m from the pivot. What is the mechanical advantage? What force is exerted?

EXAMPLE 1

Sketch:

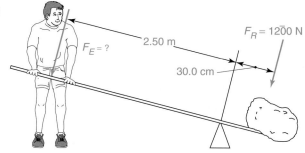

First, find MA:

$$MA_{lever} = \frac{s_E}{s_R} = \frac{2.50 \text{ m}}{0.300 \text{ m}} = \frac{8.33}{1}$$

To find the force:

Data:

$$s_E = 2.50 \text{ m}$$
$$s_R = 30.0 \text{ cm} = 0.300 \text{ m}$$
$$F_R = 12\overline{0}0 \text{ N}$$
$$F_E = ?$$

Basic Equation:

$$F_R \cdot s_R = F_E \cdot s_E$$

Working Equation:

$$F_E = \frac{F_R \cdot s_R}{s_E}$$

Substitution:

$$F_E = \frac{(12\overline{0}0 \text{ N})(0.300 \text{ m})}{2.50 \text{ m}}$$
$$= 144 \text{ N}$$

· · · · · · · · · · · · · · · ·

A wheelbarrow 1.20 m long has a $90\overline{0}$-N load 40.0 cm from the axle. What is the MA? What force is needed to lift the wheelbarrow?

EXAMPLE 2

Sketch:

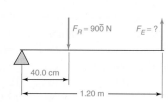

First, find MA:

$$MA = \frac{s_E}{s_R} = \frac{1.20 \text{ m}}{0.400 \text{ m}} = \frac{3.00}{1}$$

To find the force:

Data:

$$s_E = 1.20 \text{ m}$$
$$s_R = 40.0 \text{ cm} = 0.400 \text{ m}$$
$$F_R = 90\overline{0} \text{ N}$$
$$F_E = ?$$

Basic Equation:

$$F_R \cdot s_R = F_E \cdot s_E$$

Working Equation:

$$F_E = \frac{F_R \cdot s_R}{s_E}$$

Substitution:

$$F_E = \frac{(90\overline{0} \text{ N})(0.400 \text{ m})}{1.20 \text{ m}}$$
$$= 30\overline{0} \text{ N}$$

· · · · · · · · · · · · · · · · ·

EXAMPLE 3

The MA of a pair of pliers is 6.0/1. A force of 8.0 lb is exerted on the handle. What force is exerted on a wire in the pliers?

MA = 6.0/1 means that for each pound of force applied on the handle, 6.0 lb is exerted on the wire. Therefore, if a force of 8.0 lb is applied on the handle, a force of (6.0)(8.0 lb) or 48 lb is exerted on the wire.

· · · · · · · · · · · · · · · · ·

SKETCH

12 cm² | w

4.0 cm

DATA

$A = 12$ cm², $l = 4.0$ cm, $w = ?$

BASIC EQUATION

$A = lw$

WORKING EQUATION

$w = \frac{A}{l}$

SUBSTITUTION

$w = \frac{12 \text{ cm}^2}{4.0 \text{ cm}} = 3.0$ cm

PROBLEMS 10.2

Given $F_R \cdot s_R = F_E \cdot s_E$, find each missing quantity.

	F_R	F_E	s_R	s_E
1.	20.0 N	5.00 N	3.70 cm	____ cm
2.	____ N	176 N	49.2 cm	76.3 cm
3.	37.0 N	12.0 N	____ cm	112 cm
4.	23.4 lb	9.80 lb	____ in.	53.9 in.
5.	119 N	____ N	29.7 cm	67.4 cm

Given $MA_{lever} = \dfrac{F_R}{F_E}$, find each missing quantity.

	MA	F_R	F_E
6.	____	20.0 N	5.00 N
7.	____	23.4 lb	9.80 lb
8.	7.00	119 N	____ N
9.	4.00	____ lb	12.2 lb
10.	____	37.0 N	12.0 N

PHYSICS CONNECTIONS

The Human Body—A Complex Machine

The human arm is a classic example of a human simple machine. Figure 10.8(a) illustrates the forces and lever arms that are in place while lifting a weight. The elbow's hinge joint acts as a relatively low-friction fulcrum. The bicep is the muscle that exerts the effort force, and the barbell is the resistance force. According to the equation for mechanical advantage, when the resistance force is farther from the fulcrum than the effort force, the mechanical advantage is less than one. Instead of reducing the force needed to lift the object, the bicep actually exerts more force than the weight of the barbell.

Machines with mechanical advantages less than one, such as the human arm, are useful because the effort force does not have to move far in order for the weight to move large distances. The bicep muscle contracts a relatively small distance, whereas the barbell moves a larger distance. When the arm is used to throw a ball, the muscles exert a large force over a small distance, whereas the end of the forearm moves a relatively large distance with a high velocity. As seen in Fig. 10.8(b), the arm acts like several levers when throwing a ball. Although the force needed to throw the ball is greater than the weight of the ball, the great distance covered by the ball in a short period of time translates into a high velocity of the ball.

Figure 10.8 (a) The bicep moves very little while exerting a large force to lift the heavy barbell.
(b) The parts of the arm act as several simple machines to throw a ball with a high velocity.

(a)   (b)

Given $MA_{lever} = \dfrac{s_E}{s_R}$, find each missing quantity.

	MA	s_R	s_E
11.	___	49.2 cm	76.3 cm
12.	7.00	29.7 in.	___ in.
13.	___	29.7 cm	67.4 cm
14.	4.00	___ cm	67.4 cm

15. A pole is used to lift a car that fell off a jack (Fig. 10.9). The pivot is 2.00 ft from the car. Two people together exert 275 lb of force 8.00 ft from the pivot. (a) What force is applied to the car? (Ignore the weight of the pole.) (b) Find the MA.

Figure 10.9

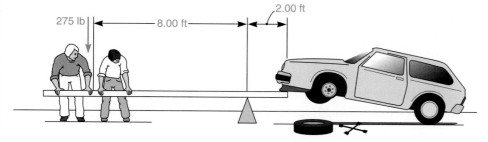

Figure 10.10

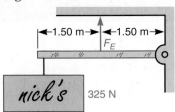

16. A bar is used to lift a 10$\overline{0}$-kg block of concrete. The pivot is 1.00 m from the block. (a) If the worker pushes down on the other end of the bar a distance of 2.50 m from the pivot, what force (in N) must the worker apply? (b) Find the MA.
17. A wheelbarrow 6.00 ft long is used to haul a 180-lb load. (a) How far from the wheel is the load placed so that a person can lift the load with a force of 45.0 lb? (b) Find the MA.
18. (a) Find the force, F_E, pulling up on the beam holding the sign shown in Fig. 10.10. (b) Find the MA.

10.3 The Wheel-and-Axle

The **wheel-and-axle** consists of a large wheel attached to an axle so that both turn together (Fig. 10.11). Other examples include a doorknob and a screwdriver with a thick handle.

The law of simple machines as applied to the wheel-and-axle (basic equation) is

$$F_R \cdot r_R = F_E \cdot r_E$$

where F_R = resistance force
r_R = radius of resistance force
F_E = effort force
r_E = radius of effort force

Figure 10.11   Examples of the wheel-and-axle

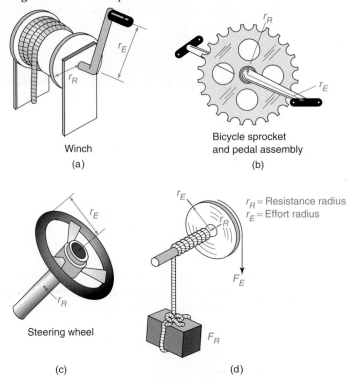

Winch
(a)

Bicycle sprocket
and pedal assembly
(b)

r_R= Resistance radius
r_E= Effort radius

Steering wheel

(c)

(d)

EXAMPLE 1

A winch has a handle that turns in a radius of 30.0 cm. The radius of the drum or axle is 10.0 cm. Find the force required to lift a bucket weighing 50$\overline{0}$ N (Fig. 10.12).

Data:

$$F_R = 50\bar{0}\ N$$
$$r_E = 30.0\ cm$$
$$r_R = 10.0\ cm$$
$$F_E = ?$$

Figure 10.12

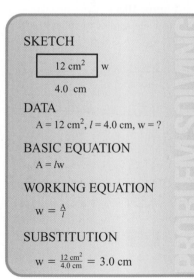

$r_E = 30.0$ cm
$r_R = 10.0$ cm

$50\bar{0}$ N

Basic Equation:

$$F_R \cdot r_R = F_E \cdot r_E$$

Working Equation:

$$F_E = \frac{F_R \cdot r_R}{r_E}$$

Substitution:

$$F_E = \frac{(50\bar{0}\ N)(10.0\ cm)}{30.0\ cm}$$
$$= 167\ N$$

The mechanical advantage (MA) of the wheel-and-axle is the ratio of the radius of the effort force to the radius of the resistance force.

$$MA_{wheel-and-axle} = \frac{\text{radius of effort force}}{\text{radius of resistance force}} = \frac{r_E}{r_R}$$

Calculate the MA of the winch in Example 1.

EXAMPLE 2

$$MA_{wheel-and-axle} = \frac{r_E}{r_R} = \frac{30.0\ cm}{10.0\ cm} = \frac{3.00}{1}$$

PROBLEMS 10.3

Given $F_R \cdot r_R = F_E \cdot r_E$, find each missing quantity.

	F_R	F_E	r_R	r_E
1.	20.0 N	5.30 N	3.70 cm	____ cm
2.	$37\bar{0}$ N	$12\bar{0}$ N	____ m	1.12 m
3.	____ N	175 N	49.2 cm	76.3 cm
4.	23.4 lb	9.80 lb	____ in.	53.9 in.
5.	1190 N	____ N	29.7 cm	67.4 cm

Given $MA_{wheel-and-axle} = \dfrac{r_E}{r_R}$, find each missing quantity.

	MA	r_E	r_R
6.	7.00	119 mm	____ mm
7.	4.00	____ in.	12.2 in.
8.	____	49.2 cm	31.7 cm
9.	3.00	61.3 cm	____ cm
10.	____	67.4 mm	29.7 mm

11. A wheel with radius 75.0 cm is attached to an axle of radius 13.6 cm. What force must be applied to the rim of the wheel to raise a 1000-N weight?

12. An axle of radius 12.0 cm is used with a wheel of radius 62.0 cm. What force must be applied to the rim of the wheel to lift a weight of 975 N?

13. The radius of the axle of a winch is 3.00 in. The length of the handle (radius of wheel) is 1.50 ft. (a) What weight will be lifted by an effort of 73.0 lb? (b) Find the MA.

14. A wheel of radius of 70.0 cm is attached to an axle of radius 20.0 cm. (a) What force must be applied to the rim of the wheel to raise a weight of $15\overline{0}0$ N? (b) Find the MA. (c) What weight can be lifted if a force of 575 N is applied?

15. The diameter of the wheel of a wheel-and-axle is 10.0 cm. (a) If a force of 475 N is raised by applying a force of 142 N, find the diameter of the axle. (b) Find the MA.

16. Two persons use a large winch to raise a mass of 470 kg. The radius of the wheel is 48 cm and the radius of the axle is 4.0 cm. (a) What force is required to lift the load? (b) Find the MA of the windlass. (c) If the efficiency of the windlass is 60% and each person exerts the same force, how much force must each apply?

10.4 The Pulley

A **pulley** is a grooved wheel that turns readily on an axle and is supported in a frame. It can be fastened to a fixed object or to the resistance that is to be moved. A **fixed pulley** is a pulley fastened to a fixed object [Fig. 10.13(a)]. A **movable pulley** is fastened to the object to be moved [Fig. 10.13(b)]. A pulley system consists of combinations of fixed and movable pulleys [Fig. 10.13(c)–(e)].

Figure 10.13 Pulleys and pulley systems

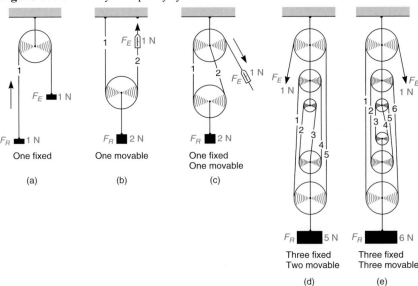

One fixed
(a)

One movable
(b)

One fixed
One movable
(c)

Three fixed
Two movable
(d)

Three fixed
Three movable
(e)

Figure 10.14 Law of simple machines applied to pulleys:
$F_R \cdot s_R = F_E \cdot s_E$

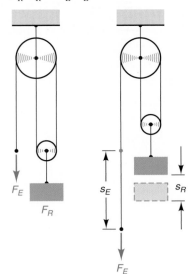

The law of simple machines as applied to pulleys (Fig. 10.14) is

$$F_R \cdot s_R = F_E \cdot s_E$$

Here, s refers to the distance moved. From the preceding equation,

$$\frac{F_R}{F_E} = \frac{s_E}{s_R} = \text{MA}_{\text{pulley}}$$

However, when one continuous cord is used, this ratio reduces to the number of strands holding the resistance in the pulley system. Therefore,

$$\text{MA}_{\text{pulley}} = \text{number of strands holding the resistance}$$

This result may be explained as follows: When a weight is supported by two strands, each individual strand supports one-half of the total weight. Thus, the MA = 2. If a weight is supported by three strands, each individual strand supports one-third of the total weight. Thus, the MA = 3. If a weight is supported by four strands, each individual strand supports one-fourth of the total weight. In general, when a weight is supported by n strands, each individual strand supports $\frac{1}{n}$ of the total weight. Thus, the MA = n.

Stated another way, the resistance force, F_R, is spread equally among the supporting strands. Thus, $F_R = nT$, where n is the number of strands holding the resistance and T is the tension in each supporting strand.

The effort force, F_E, equals the tension, T, in each supporting strand. The equation may then be written

$$\text{MA}_{\text{pulley}} = \frac{F_R}{F_E} = \frac{nT}{T} = n$$

Note: The mechanical advantage of the pulley does not depend on the diameter of the pulley.

A number of examples are shown in Fig. 10.15.

Figure 10.15   Mechanical advantage of pulleys and pulley systems

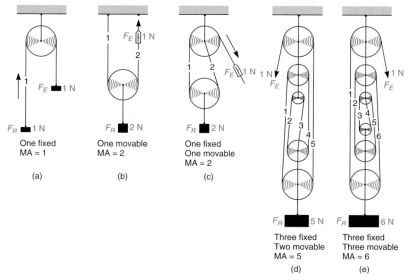

Draw two different sets of pulleys, each with an MA of 4.

EXAMPLE 1

Sketch:

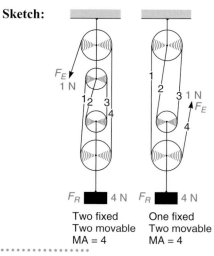

EXAMPLE 2

What effort will lift a resistance of 480 N in the pulley systems in Example 1?

Data:

$$MA_{pulley} = 4$$
$$F_R = 480 \text{ N}$$
$$F_E = \text{?}$$

Basic Equation:

$$MA_{pulley} = \frac{F_R}{F_E}$$

Working Equation:

$$F_E = \frac{F_R}{MA_{pulley}}$$

Substitution:

$$F_E = \frac{480 \text{ N}}{4}$$
$$= 120 \text{ N}$$

. . . .

EXAMPLE 3

If the resistance moves 7.00 ft, what is the effort distance of the pulley system in Example 1?

Data:

$$MA_{pulley} = 4$$
$$s_R = 7.00 \text{ ft}$$
$$s_E = \text{?}$$

Basic Equation:

$$MA_{pulley} = \frac{s_E}{s_R}$$

Working Equation:

$$s_E = s_R(MA_{pulley})$$

Substitution:

$$s_E = (7.00 \text{ ft})(4)$$
$$= 28.0 \text{ ft}$$

. . . .

EXAMPLE 4

The pulley system in Fig. 10.16 is used to raise a 650-lb object 25 ft. What is the mechanical advantage? What force is exerted?

$$MA_{pulley} = \text{number of strands holding the resistance}$$
$$= 5$$

To find the force exerted:

Data:

$$MA_{pulley} = 5$$
$$F_R = 650 \text{ lb}$$
$$F_E = \text{?}$$

Basic Equation:

$$\text{MA}_{\text{pulley}} = \frac{F_R}{F_E}$$

Working Equation:

$$F_E = \frac{F_R}{\text{MA}_{\text{pulley}}}$$

Substitution:

$$F_E = \frac{650 \text{ lb}}{5}$$
$$= 130 \text{ lb}$$

. . . .

PROBLEMS 10.4

Find the mechanical advantage of each pulley system.

1.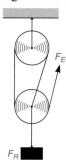

2.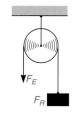

3.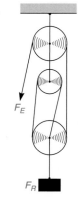

4.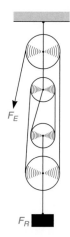

5.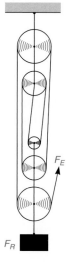

6.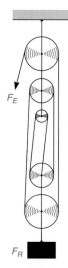

7.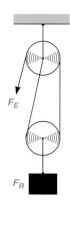

8.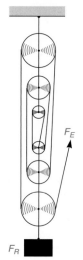

Draw each pulley system for Problems 9–14.

9. One fixed and two movable. Find the system's MA.
10. Two fixed and two movable with an MA of 5.
11. Three fixed and three movable with an MA of 6.
12. Four fixed and three movable. Find the system's MA.

Figure 10.16

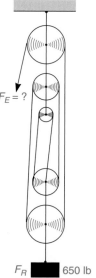

$F_E = ?$

F_R 650 lb

Three fixed
Two movable
MA = ?

SKETCH

12 cm^2 w

4.0 cm

DATA

$A = 12 \text{ cm}^2$, $l = 4.0$ cm, $w = ?$

BASIC EQUATION

$A = lw$

WORKING EQUATION

$w = \frac{A}{l}$

SUBSTITUTION

$w = \frac{12 \text{ cm}^2}{4.0 \text{ cm}} = 3.0$ cm

13. Four fixed and four movable with an MA of 8.
14. Three fixed and four movable with an MA of 8.
15. What is the MA of a single movable pulley?
16. (a) What effort will lift a 250-lb weight by using a single movable pulley? (b) If the weight is moved 15.0 ft, how many feet of rope are pulled by the person exerting the effort?
17. A system consisting of two fixed pulleys and two movable pulleys has a mechanical advantage of 4. (a) If a force of 97.0 N is exerted, what weight is raised? (b) If the weight is raised 20.5 m, what length of rope is pulled?
18. A 400-lb weight is lifted 30.0 ft. (a) Using a system of one fixed and two movable pulleys, find the effort force and effort distance. (b) If an effort force of 65.0 N is applied through an effort distance of 13.0 m, find the weight of the resistance and the distance it is moved.
19. Can an effort force of 75.0 N lift a 275-N weight using the pulley system in Problem 3?
20. (a) What effort will lift a 1950-N weight using the pulley system in Problem 5? (b) If the weight is moved 3.00 m, how much rope must be pulled through the pulley system by the person exerting the force?
21. Complete the following pulley system mechanical advantage chart, which lists two possible arrangements of fixed and movable pulleys for each given mechanical advantage.

	Mechanical Advantage (MA)							
Pulleys	**1**	**2**	**3**	**4**	**5**	**6**	**7**	**8**
Fixed	1	1	2					
Movable	0	1	1					
Fixed		0	1					
Movable		1	1					

22. Can you arrange a pulley system containing 10 pulleys and obtain a mechanical advantage of 12? Why or why not?

10.5 The Inclined Plane

An **inclined plane** is a plane surface set at an angle from the horizontal used to raise objects that are too heavy to lift vertically. Gangplanks, chutes, and ramps are all examples of the inclined plane (Fig. 10.17). The work done in raising a resistance using the inclined plane equals the resistance times the height. This must also equal the work input, which can be found by multiplying the effort times the length of the plane.

$$F_R \cdot s_R = F_E \cdot s_E \qquad \text{(law of machines)}$$

$$\boxed{F_R \cdot \text{height of plane} = F_E \cdot \text{length of plane}}$$

Figure 10.17   Inclined plane

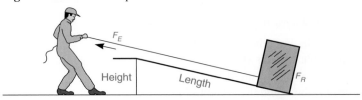

From the preceding equation,

$$\boxed{\frac{F_R}{F_E} = \frac{\text{length of plane}}{\text{height of plane}} = MA_{\text{inclined plane}}}$$

EXAMPLE 1

A worker is pushing a box weighing $15\overline{0}0$ N up a ramp 6.00 m long onto a platform 1.50 m above the ground. What is the mechanical advantage? What effort is applied?

Sketch:

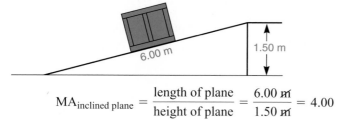

$$MA_{\text{inclined plane}} = \frac{\text{length of plane}}{\text{height of plane}} = \frac{6.00 \ \cancel{m}}{1.50 \ \cancel{m}} = 4.00$$

To find the effort force:

Data:

$$F_R = 15\overline{0}0 \text{ N}$$
$$MA_{\text{inclined plane}} = 4.00$$
$$F_E = \ ?$$

Basic Equation:

$$MA_{\text{inclined plane}} = \frac{F_R}{F_E}$$

Working Equation:

$$F_E = \frac{F_R}{MA_{\text{inclined plane}}}$$

Substitution:

$$F_E = \frac{15\overline{0}0 \text{ N}}{4.00}$$
$$= 375 \text{ N}$$

· · · · · · · · · · · · · · · · ·

EXAMPLE 2

Find the length of the shortest ramp that can be used to push a $60\overline{0}$-lb resistance onto a platform 3.50 ft high by exerting a force of 72.0 lb.

Data:

$$F_R = 60\overline{0} \text{ lb}$$
$$F_E = 72.0 \text{ lb}$$
$$\text{height} = 3.50 \text{ ft}$$
$$\text{length} = \ ?$$

Basic Equation:

$$F_R \cdot \text{height} = F_E \cdot \text{length}$$

Working Equation:

$$\text{length} = \frac{F_R \cdot \text{height}}{F_E}$$

Substitution:

$$length = \frac{(60\bar{0} \text{ lb})(3.50 \text{ ft})}{72.0 \text{ lb}}$$
$$= 29.2 \text{ ft}$$

· · · · · · · · · · · · · · · · ·

EXAMPLE 3

An inclined plane is 13.0 m long and 5.00 m high. What is its mechanical advantage and what weight can be raised by exerting a force of 375 N?

$$MA_{\text{inclined plane}} = \frac{\text{length of plane}}{\text{height of plane}} = \frac{13.0 \text{ m}}{5.00 \text{ m}} = 2.60$$

To find the weight of the resistance:

Data:

$$MA_{\text{inclined plane}} = 2.60$$
$$F_E = 375 \text{ N}$$
$$F_R = ?$$

Basic Equation:

$$MA_{\text{inclined plane}} = \frac{F_R}{F_E}$$

Working Equation:

$$F_R = (F_E)(MA_{\text{inclined plane}})$$

Substitution:

$$F_R = (375 \text{ N})(2.60)$$
$$= 975 \text{ N}$$

· · · · · · · · · · · · · · · · ·

PHYSICS CONNECTION

The Physics of Handicap Ramps

Handicap ramps are inclined planes. They make locations that are at different elevations accessible to people with physical disabilities. There are many factors related to physics that play a part in the design and construction of a wheelchair ramp.

The most important factor in designing a wheelchair ramp is to make sure the ideal mechanical advantage of the incline is at least 12. The general guideline is that for each 1 in. of height, there should be a 12-in. "run" or horizontal component to the incline. However, this does not mean that if someone needs to go up 5 feet to a door, there should be a 60-ft-long incline. Imagine someone unable to continue upward along the incline and rolling back down a 60-ft inclined plane. That would be a very scary and dangerous situation for a person in a wheelchair. As a result, if the length is more than 30 ft, then a 5-ft-long landing must be placed somewhere in the incline.

A feature that is often overlooked is the landing at the top of the incline. A landing must be placed at the top of any wheelchair ramp to allow the wheelchair rider room to open a door without being on the incline.

Finally, frictional forces must be taken into consideration. Most manufacturers of wheelchair ramps use concrete with a brushed finish or aluminum with adhesive pads or ridges in the metal so the coefficient of friction between the ramp and the wheels prevents the wheels from losing traction as the wheelchair makes its way up the incline.

Figure 10.18 A school with appropriately sloped inclines and landings

PROBLEMS 10.5

Given $F_R \cdot \text{height} = F_E \cdot \text{length}$, find each missing quantity.

	F_R	F_E	Height of Plane	Length of Plane
1.	20.0 N	5.30 N	3.40 cm	____ cm
2.	9800 N	2340 N	____ m	3.79 m
3.	119 lb	____ lb	13.2 in.	74.0 in.
4.	____ N	1760 N	82.1 cm	3.79 m
5.	3700 N	1200 N	____ cm	112 cm

Given $\text{MA}_{\text{inclined plane}} = \dfrac{\text{length of plane}}{\text{height of plane}}$, find each missing quantity.

	MA	Length of Plane	Height of Plane
6.	9.00	3.40 ft	____ ft
7.	____	3.79 m	0.821 m
8.	1.30	____ ft	9.72 ft
9.	____	74.0 cm	13.2 cm
10.	17.4	____ in.	13.4 in.

11. An inclined plane is 10.0 m long and 2.50 m high. (a) Find its mechanical advantage. (b) A resistance of 727 N is pushed up the plane. What effort is needed? (c) An effort of 200 N is applied to push an 815-N resistance up the inclined plane. Is the effort enough?

12. A safe is loaded onto a truck whose bed is 5.50 ft above the ground. The safe weighs 538 lb. (a) If the effort applied is 140 lb, what length of ramp is needed? (b) What is the MA of the inclined plane? (c) Another safe weighing 257 lb is loaded onto the same truck. If the ramp is 21.1 ft long, what effort is needed?

13. A 3.00-m-long plank is used to raise a cooling unit 1.00 m. What is the MA of the ramp made by the plank?

14. A 2.75-m-long board is used to slide a compressor a vertical distance of 0.750 m. What is the MA of the ramp made by the board?

15. A resistance of 325 N is raised by using a ramp 5.76 m long and by applying a force of 75.0 N. (a) How high can it be raised? (b) Find the MA of the ramp.

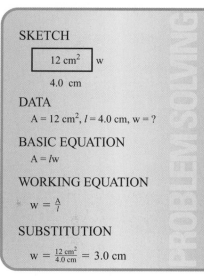

SKETCH

12 cm² | w

4.0 cm

DATA

$A = 12 \text{ cm}^2$, $l = 4.0$ cm, $w = ?$

BASIC EQUATION

$A = lw$

WORKING EQUATION

$w = \dfrac{A}{l}$

SUBSTITUTION

$w = \dfrac{12 \text{ cm}^2}{4.0 \text{ cm}} = 3.0$ cm

PROBLEM SOLVING

Figure 10.19 The screw is an inclined plane wound around a cylinder. The hypotenuse of the triangular section of paper corresponds to the inclined plane (threads) of a screw as it is wound around the pencil.

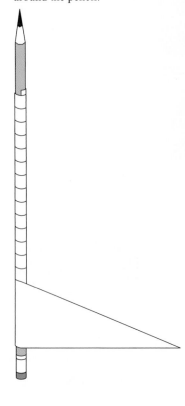

16. A plank 12 ft long is used as an inclined plane to a platform 3.0 ft high. (a) What force must be used to push a load weighing 480 lb up the plank? (b) Find the MA of the inclined plane.
17. A pallet stacked with bags of cement weighing a total of $55\overline{0}0$ N must be pushed up a 2.30-m incline to a 75.0-cm-high platform. What force must be applied to get the job done?
18. A nursery loading dock is 1.20 m above the ground. What force must be used to push a 255-N pallet of fertilizer up a 3.80-m incline to the platform?

10.6 The Screw

A **screw** is an inclined plane wrapped around a cylinder. To illustrate, cut a sheet of paper in the shape of a right triangle and wind it around a pencil as shown in Fig. 10.19. The jackscrew, wood screw, and auger are examples of this simple machine (Fig. 10.20). The distance a beam rises or the distance the wood screw advances into a piece of wood in one revolution is called the **pitch** of the screw. Therefore, the pitch of a screw is also the distance between two successive threads.

From the law of machines,

$$F_R \cdot s_R = F_E \cdot s_E$$

However, for advancing a screw with a screwdriver

$$s_R = \text{pitch of screw}$$
$$s_E = \text{circumference of the handle of the screwdriver}$$

or

$$s_E = 2\pi r$$

where r is the radius of the handle of the screwdriver. Therefore,

$$\boxed{F_R \cdot \text{pitch} = F_E \cdot 2\pi r}$$

so

$$\boxed{\frac{F_R}{F_E} = \frac{2\pi r}{\text{pitch}} = \text{MA}_{\text{screw}}}$$

In the case of a jackscrew, r is the length of the handle turning the screw and not the radius of the screw.

Figure 10.20

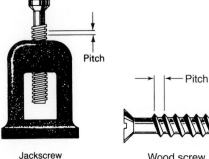

Jackscrew

(a)

Pitch

Wood screw

(b)

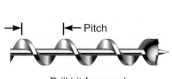

Pitch

Drill bit for wood

(c)

Snow blower/auger system

(d)

Find the mechanical advantage of a jackscrew having a pitch of 25.0 mm and a handle radius of 35.0 cm.

EXAMPLE 1

Data:

$$\text{pitch} = 25.0 \text{ mm} = 2.50 \text{ cm}$$
$$r = 35.0 \text{ cm}$$
$$\text{MA}_{\text{screw}} = ?$$

Basic Equation:

$$\text{MA}_{\text{screw}} = \frac{2\pi r}{\text{pitch}}$$

Working Equation: Same

Substitution:

$$\text{MA}_{\text{screw}} = \frac{2\pi(35.0 \text{ cm})}{2.50 \text{ cm}}$$
$$= 88.0$$

. . . .

What resistance can be lifted using the jackscrew in Example 1 if an effort of 203 N is exerted?

EXAMPLE 2

Data:

$$\text{MA}_{\text{screw}} = 88.0$$
$$F_E = 203 \text{ N}$$
$$F_R = ?$$

Basic Equation:

$$\text{MA}_{\text{screw}} = \frac{F_R}{F_E}$$

Working Equation:

$$F_R = (F_E)(\text{MA}_{\text{screw}})$$

Substitution:

$$F_R = (203 \text{ N})(88.0)$$
$$= 17,900 \text{ N}$$

. . . .

A 19,400-N weight is raised using a jackscrew having a pitch of 5.00 mm and a handle length of 255 mm. What force must be applied?

EXAMPLE 3

Data:

$$\text{pitch} = 5.00 \text{ mm}$$
$$r = 255 \text{ mm}$$
$$F_R = 19,400 \text{ N}$$
$$F_E = ?$$

Basic Equation:

$$F_R \cdot \text{pitch} = F_E \cdot 2\pi r$$

Working Equation:

$$F_E = \frac{F_R \, (\text{pitch})}{2\pi r}$$

Substitution:

$$F_E = \frac{(19{,}400 \text{ N})(5.00 \text{ mm})}{2\pi \, (255 \text{ mm})}$$

$$= 60.5 \text{ N}$$

. . . .

PROBLEMS 10.6

Given $F_R \cdot \text{pitch} = F_E \cdot 2\pi r$, find each missing quantity.

	F_R	F_E	Pitch	r
1.	20.7 N	5.30 N	3.70 mm	_____ mm
2.	_____ lb	17.6 lb	0.130 in.	24.5 in.
3.	234 N	9.80 N	_____ mm	53.9 mm
4.	1190 N	_____ N	2.97 mm	67.4 mm
5.	370 lb	12.0 lb	_____ in.	11.2 in.

Given $MA_{\text{screw}} = \dfrac{2\pi r}{\text{pitch}}$, find each missing quantity.

	MA	r	Pitch
6.	7.00	34.0 mm	_____ mm
7.	_____	3.79 in.	0.812 in.
8.	9.00	_____ in.	0.970 in.
9.	_____	7.40 mm	1.32 mm
10.	13.0	_____ mm	2.10 mm

11. A 3650-lb car is raised using a jackscrew having eight threads to the inch and a handle 15.0 in. long. (a) What effort must be applied? (b) What is the MA?

12. The mechanical advantage of a jackscrew is 97.0. (a) If the handle is 34.5 cm long, what is the pitch? (b) How much weight can be raised by applying an effort of 405 N to the jackscrew?

13. A wood screw with pitch 0.125 in. is advanced into wood using a screwdriver whose handle is 1.50 in. in diameter. (a) What is the mechanical advantage of the screw? (b) What is the resistance of the wood if 15.0 lb of effort is applied on the wood screw? (c) What is the resistance of the wood if 15.0 lb of effort is applied to the wood screw using a screwdriver whose handle is 0.500 in. in diameter?

14. The handle of a jackscrew is 60.0 cm long. (a) If the mechanical advantage is 78.0, what is the pitch? (b) How much weight can be raised by applying a force of $43\overline{0}$ N to the jackscrew handle?

10.7 The Wedge

A **wedge** is an inclined plane in which the plane is moved instead of the resistance. Examples are shown in Fig. 10.21.

    Finding the mechanical advantage of a wedge is not practical because of the large amount of friction. A narrow wedge is easier to drive than a thick wedge. Therefore, the mechanical advantage depends on the ratio of its length to its thickness.

Figure 10.21 Inclined planes where the plane moves instead of the resistance

Nail

Wood chisel

Hatchet

10.8 Compound Machines

A **compound machine** is a combination of simple machines. Examples are shown in Fig. 10.22. In most compound machines, *the total mechanical advantage is the product of the mechanical advantage of each simple machine.*

$$MA_{\text{compound machine}} = (MA_1)(MA_2)(MA_3) \cdots$$

Figure 10.22 Compound machines multiply mechanical advantage. (Reprinted courtesy of Caterpillar Inc.)

(a)

(b)

A crate weighing $95\overline{0}0$ N is pulled up the inclined plane using the pulley system shown in Fig. 10.23.

(a) Find the mechanical advantage of the total system.
(b) What effort force (F_E) is needed?

Figure 10.23

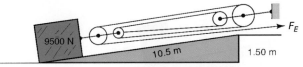

9500 N

10.5 m   1.50 m

F_E

(a) First, find the MA of the inclined plane.

$$MA_{\text{inclined plane}} = \frac{\text{length of plane}}{\text{height of plane}} = \frac{10.5 \text{ m}}{1.50 \text{ m}} = 7.00$$

The MA of the pulley system = 5 (the number of supporting strands).
The MA of the total system (compound machine) is

$$(MA_{\text{inclined plane}})(MA_{\text{pulley system}}) = (7.00)(5) = 35.0$$

(b) Data:

$$MA_{\text{compound machine}} = 35.0$$
$$F_R = 95\overline{0}0 \text{ N}$$
$$F_E = ?$$

Basic Equation:

$$MA_{\text{compound machine}} = \frac{F_R}{F_E}$$

Working Equation:

$$F_E = \frac{F_R}{MA_{\text{compound machine}}}$$

Substitution:

$$F_E = \frac{95\overline{0}0 \text{ N}}{35.0}$$
$$= 271 \text{ N}$$

· · · · · · · · · · · · · · · ·

SKETCH

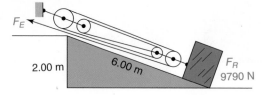

12 cm^2 w

4.0 cm

DATA

$A = 12 \text{ cm}^2, l = 4.0 \text{ cm}, w = ?$

BASIC EQUATION

$A = lw$

WORKING EQUATION

$w = \frac{A}{l}$

SUBSTITUTION

$w = \frac{12 \text{ cm}^2}{4.0 \text{ cm}} = 3.0 \text{ cm}$

PROBLEMS 10.8

1. The box shown in Fig. 10.24 being pulled up an inclined plane using the indicated pulley system (called a block and tackle) weighs 9790 N. If the inclined plane is 6.00 m long and the height of the platform is 2.00 m, find the mechanical advantage of this compound machine.

Figure 10.24

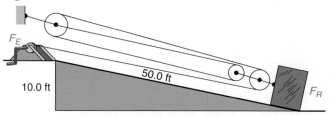

2. What effort force must be exerted to move the box to the platform in Problem 1?
3. Find the mechanical advantage of the compound machine shown in Fig. 10.25. The radius of the crank is 1.00 ft and the radius of the axle is 0.500 ft.

Figure 10.25

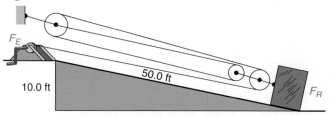

4. If an effort of $30\overline{0}$ lb is exerted, what weight can be moved up the inclined plane using the compound machine in Problem 3?
5. What effort is required to move a load of 1.50 tons up the inclined plane using the compound machine in Problem 3? (1 ton $= 200\overline{0}$ lb)
6. Find the mechanical advantage of the compound machine in Problem 1 if the inclined plane is 8.00 m long and 2.00 m high.
7. What effort force is needed to move a box of weight $250\overline{0}$ N to the platform in Problem 6?

8. Find the mechanical advantage of the compound machine in Problem 3 if the radius of the crank is 40.0 cm, the radius of the axle is 12.0 cm, the length of the inclined plane is 12.0 m, and the height of the inclined plane is 50.0 cm.

9. If an effort of $45\overline{0}$ N is exerted in Problem 8, what weight can be moved up the inclined plane?

10. What effort force (in N) is needed to move 2.50 metric tons up the inclined plane in Problem 8?

10.9 The Effect of Friction on Simple Machines

Figure 10.26 Friction has been ignored in our study of pulleys.

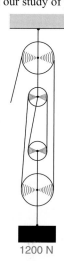

1200 N

The *law of simple machines* has been stated for a particular machine and in the general case in the previous sections. Each has been stated in terms of what is called *ideal mechanical advantage* (IMA), in which we have 100% efficiency. Actually, in every machine energy is lost through heat to overcome friction. This lost energy decreases the efficiency of the machine; that is, more work must be put into a machine than is gotten out of the machine. This lost energy is heat energy, which results in machine wear or even burning out of certain parts of the machine.

Throughout this chapter we have been discussing simple machines, mechanical advantage, resistance force, effort force, resistance distance, and effort distance in the ideal case while ignoring friction. For example, in the pulley system in Fig. 10.26, we find the IMA is 4 to 1. Ideally, it takes 300 N of effort force to lift the resistant force of 1200 N; that is, it ideally takes 1 N of force to raise 4 N of weight. However, it actually takes 400 N of effort to lift the 1200-N weight; the *actual mechanical advantage* (AMA) is then 3 to 1; that is, it actually takes 1 N of force to raise 3 N of weight.

In general, the actual mechanical advantage is found by the following formula:

$$\text{AMA} = \frac{F_R}{F_E} = \frac{\text{resistance force}}{\text{effort force}}$$

In Section 5.3, we studied the effects of sliding friction. The actual effects of sliding friction are substantial in inclined plane problems. In Example 1 of Section 10.5, the inclined plane (repeated in Fig. 10.27) has an IMA of 4 to 1. Actually, it takes 545 N of effort to move the $150\overline{0}$-N box up the ramp. Therefore, the AMA is

$$\text{AMA} = \frac{F_R}{F_E} = \frac{150\overline{0} \text{ N}}{545 \text{ N}} = 2.75$$

That is, it actually takes 1.00 N of force to push 2.75 N up the ramp.

Figure 10.27

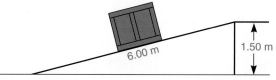

6.00 m

1.50 m

TRY THIS ACTIVITY

Reducing Friction

Observe the amount of effort force required to drag a heavy book up an inclined plane. Before repeating this process, place several small wooden dowels or marbles under the book. Drag the book up the incline again and observe the amount of effort force required. How do the wooden dowels or marbles reduce the effort force required to move the book up the incline? The ancient Egyptians may have used large dowels to reduce the effort force to drag massive stone blocks to the tops of pyramids.

Glossary

Compound Machine A combination of simple machines. Its total mechanical advantage is the product of the mechanical advantage of each simple machine. (p. 287)

Efficiency The ratio of the work output to the work input of a machine. (p. 269)

Effort The force applied to a machine. (p. 268)

Effort Arm The distance from the effort force to the fulcrum of a lever. (p. 269)

Fixed Pulley A pulley that is fastened to a fixed object. (p. 276)

Fulcrum A pivot about which a lever is free to turn. (p. 269)

Inclined Plane A plane surface set at an angle from the horizontal used to raise objects that are too heavy to lift vertically. (p. 280)

Law of Simple Machines Resistance force × resistance distance = effort force × effort distance. (p. 268)

Lever A rigid bar free to turn on a pivot called a fulcrum. (p. 269)

Machine An object or system that is used to transfer energy from one place to another and allows work to be done that could not otherwise be done or could not be done as easily. (p. 267)

Mechanical Advantage The ratio of the resistance force to the effort force. (p. 269)

Movable Pulley A pulley that is fastened to the object to be moved. (p. 276)

Pitch The distance a screw advances in one revolution of the screw. Also the distance between two successive threads. (p. 284)

Pulley A grooved wheel that turns readily on an axle and is supported in a frame. (p. 276)

Resistance The force overcome by a machine. (p. 268)

Resistance Arm The distance from the resistance force to the fulcrum of a lever. (p. 269)

Screw An inclined plane wrapped around a cylinder. (p. 284)

Simple Machine Any one of six mechanical devices in which an applied force results in useful work. The six simple machines are the lever, the wheel and axle, the pulley, the inclined plane, the screw, and the wedge. (p. 268)

Wedge An inclined plane in which the plane is moved instead of the resistance. (p. 286)

Wheel-and-Axle A large wheel attached to an axle so that both turn together. (p. 274)

Formulas

10.1   resistance force × resistance distance = effort force × effort distance

$$MA = \frac{\text{resistance force}}{\text{effort force}}$$

$$\text{efficiency} = \frac{\text{work output}}{\text{work input}} \times 100\% = \frac{F_{\text{output}} \times s_{\text{output}}}{F_{\text{input}} \times s_{\text{input}}} \times 100\%$$

10.2 $MA_{\text{lever}} = \dfrac{\text{effort arm}}{\text{resistance arm}} = \dfrac{s_E}{s_R}$

$$F_R \cdot s_R = F_E \cdot s_E$$

10.3 $MA_{\text{wheel-and-axle}} = \dfrac{\text{radius of effort force}}{\text{radius of resistance force}} = \dfrac{r_E}{r_R}$

$$F_R \cdot r_R = F_E \cdot r_E$$

10.4 MA_{pulley} = number of strands holding the resistance

$$MA_{\text{pulley}} = \frac{s_E}{s_R}$$

10.5 $MA_{\text{inclined plane}} = \dfrac{\text{length of plane}}{\text{height of plane}}$

$F_R \cdot \text{height} = F_E \cdot \text{length}$

10.6 $MA_{\text{screw}} = \dfrac{2\pi r}{\text{pitch}}$

$F_R \cdot \text{pitch} = F_E \cdot 2\pi r$

10.8 $MA_{\text{compound machine}} = (MA_1)(MA_2)(MA_3) \cdots$

10.9 $AMA = \dfrac{F_R}{F_E} = \dfrac{\text{resistance force}}{\text{effort force}}$

Review Questions

1. Which of the following is not a simple machine?
   - (a) Pulley
   - (b) Lever
   - (c) Wedge
   - (d) Automobile
2. The force applied to the machine is the
   - (a) effort.
   - (b) frictional.
   - (c) horizontal.
   - (d) resistance.
3. Efficiency is
   - (a) the same as mechanical advantage.
   - (b) a percentage.
   - (c) impossible to determine.
4. A second-class lever has
   - (a) two fulcrums.
   - (b) two effort arms.
   - (c) two resistance arms.
   - (d) a resistance arm shorter than the effort arm.
5. A pulley has eight strands holding the resistance. The mechanical advantage is
   - (a) 4.   (b) 8.   (c) 16.   (d) 64.
6. The mechanical advantage of a compound machine
   - (a) is the sum of the MA of each simple machine.
   - (b) is the product of the MA of each simple machine.
   - (c) cannot be found.
   - (d) is none of the above.
7. Cite three examples of machines used to multiply speed.
8. What name is given to the force overcome by the machine?
9. State the law of simple machines in your own words.
10. What is the term used for the ratio of the resistance force to the effort force?
11. What is the term used for the ratio of the amount of work obtained from a machine to the amount of work put into the machine?
12. Does a friction-free machine exist?
13. What is the pivot point of a lever called?
14. In your own words, state how to find the MA of a lever.
15. Which type of lever do you think would be most efficient?
16. State the law of simple machines as it is applied to levers.

PROBLEM SOLVING

SKETCH

12 cm^2 w

4.0 cm

DATA

$A = 12 \text{ cm}^2, \ l = 4.0 \text{ cm}, \ w = ?$

BASIC EQUATION

$A = lw$

WORKING EQUATION

$w = \dfrac{A}{l}$

SUBSTITUTION

$w = \dfrac{12 \text{ cm}^2}{4.0 \text{ cm}} = 3.0 \text{ cm}$

17.   Where is the fulcrum located in a third-class lever?
18.   In your own words, explain the law of simple machines as applied to the wheel-and-axle.
19.   Does the MA of a wheel-and-axle depend on the force applied?
20.   Describe the difference between a fixed pulley and a movable pulley.
21.   Does the MA of a pulley depend on the radius of the pulley?
22.   How can you find the MA of an inclined plane?
23.   In your own words, describe the pitch of a screw.
24.   How does the MA of a jackscrew differ from the MA of a screwdriver?

Review Problems

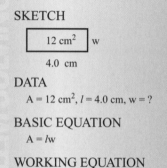

SKETCH

12 cm² | w

4.0 cm

DATA

$A = 12$ cm², $l = 4.0$ cm, $w = ?$

BASIC EQUATION

$A = lw$

WORKING EQUATION

$w = \frac{A}{l}$

SUBSTITUTION

$w = \frac{12 \text{ cm}^2}{4.0 \text{ cm}} = 3.0$ cm

1.   A girl uses a lever to lift a box. The box has a resistance force of $25\overline{0}$ N while she exerts an effort force of 125 N. What is the mechanical advantage of the lever?
2.   A bicycle requires 1575 N m of input but only puts out 1150 N m of work. What is the bicycle's efficiency?
3.   A lever uses an effort arm of 2.75 m and has a resistance arm of 72.0 cm. What is the lever's mechanical advantage?
4.   Two people are on a teeter-totter. One person exerts a force of 540 N and is 2.00 m from the fulcrum. If they are to remain balanced, how much force does the other person exert if she is (a) also 2.00 m from the fulcrum? (b) 3.00 m from the fulcrum?
5.   A wheel-and-axle has an effort force of 125 N and an effort radius of 17.0 cm. (a) If the resistance force is 325 N, what is the resistance radius? (b) Find the mechanical advantage.
6.   What is the mechanical advantage of a pulley system having 12 strands holding the resistance?
7.   A pulley system has a mechanical advantage of 5. What is the resistance force if an effort of 135 N is exerted?
8.   An inclined plane has a height of 1.50 m and a length of 4.50 m. (a) What effort must be exerted to pull up an 875-N box? (b) What is the mechanical advantage?
9.   What height must a 10.0-ft-long inclined plane be to lift a 1000-lb crate with 230 lb of effort?
10.   A screw has a pitch of 0.0200 cm. An effort force of 29.0 N is used to turn a screwdriver whose handle diameter is 36.0 mm. What is the maximum resistance force?
11.   A 945-N resistance force is overcome with a 13.5-N effort using a screwdriver whose handle is 24.0 mm in diameter. What is the pitch of the screw?
12.   Find the mechanical advantage of a jackscrew with a 1.50-cm pitch and a handle 36.0 cm long.
13.   A courier uses a bicycle with rear wheel radius 35.6 cm and gear radius 4.00 cm. If a force of 155 N is applied to the chain, the wheel rim moves 14.0 cm. (a) If the efficiency is 95.0%, what is the ideal mechanical advantage of the wheel and gear? (b) What is the actual mechanical advantage of the wheel and gear? (c) What is the force on the pavement applied by the wheel?
14.   (a) If the gear radius is doubled on the courier's bicycle in Problem 13, how does the mechanical advantage change? (b) How far did the courier move the chain to produce the 14.0-cm linear movement of the rim?
15.   A farmer uses a pulley system to raise a 225-N bale 16.5 m. A 129-N force is applied by pulling a rope 33.0 m. What is the mechanical advantage of the pulley system?
16.   A laborer uses a lever to raise a 1250-N rock a distance of 13.0 cm by applying a force of 225 N. If the efficiency of the lever is 88.7%, how far does the laborer have to move his end of the lever?

Find the mechanical advantage of each pulley system.

17.

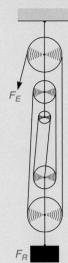

F_E

F_R

18.

F_E

F_R

19. (a) Find the mechanical advantage of the compound machine in Fig. 10.28. The radius of the crank is 32.0 cm and the radius of the axle is 8.00 cm. (b) If an effort force of 75 N is applied to the handle of the crank, what force can be moved up the inclined plane?

Figure 10.28

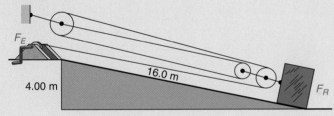

F_E

16.0 m

4.00 m

F_R

20. If an effort force of 45 N is applied to a simple machine and moves a resistance of 270 N, what is the actual mechanical advantage?

A P P L I E D   C O N C E P T S

1. In the third century BC, Archimedes said, "Give me a long enough lever and a firm fulcrum and I will lift the earth." (a) Using the moon as a fixed fulcrum, how long a lever would Archimedes have needed to lift the earth? (b) What would be the mechanical advantage of such a simple machine? (Disregard the mass of the lever. Assume the weight of the earth is 5.85×10^{25} N, Archimedes' weight is 858 N, and the distance from the earth to the moon is 3.84×10^8 m.)

2. (a) What is the mechanical advantage of the fishing pole in Fig. 10.29? (b) If the fisherman's hand moves forward 30.5 cm, how far will the tip of the fishing pole move? (c) How fast will the tip of the fishing pole move if the forward motion is completed in 0.554 s? (d) In general, what is the benefit of using a simple machine that has a mechanical advantage less than 1.0?

3. A snowblower auger has a radius of 7.75 in. and a pitch of 6.80 in. (a) What is the mechanical advantage of this auger system? (b) How much effort force is needed for the auger to throw 23.4 lb of snow? (c) What happens to the mechanical advantage if the pitch is reduced?

Figure 10.29

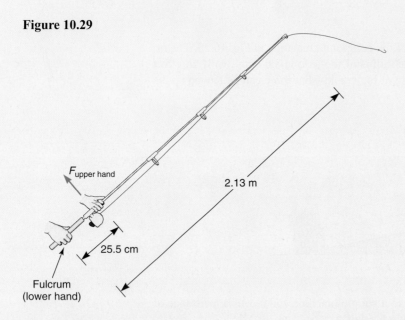

4. Aaron, a bicycle mechanic, is studying the mechanical advantage of the rear wheel. The rear wheel's radius is 14.0 in. and the chain is currently on a gear with radius 1.65 in. (Fig. 10.30). (a) If the chain applies a force of 54.5 lb on the wheel, what is the mechanical advantage of the wheel? (b) What is the resistance force? (c) How many inches of chain must be used to turn the wheel one complete rotation? (d) Finally, under what circumstances is it beneficial for a bicycle to have a mechanical advantage less than 1.0?

Figure 10.30

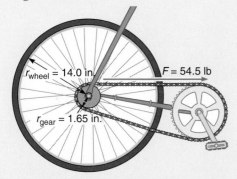

5. Willie is using a wheelbarrow (Fig. 10.31) to move 345 lb of patio blocks. (a) What is the mechanical advantage of the wheelbarrow handles? (b) What is the mechanical advantage of the wheelbarrow's wheel-and-axle? (c) How can the design of the wheelbarrow be altered to increase the mechanical advantage?

Figure 10.31

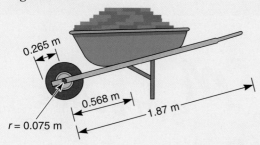

CHAPTER 11

UNIVERSAL GRAVITATION AND SATELLITE MOTION

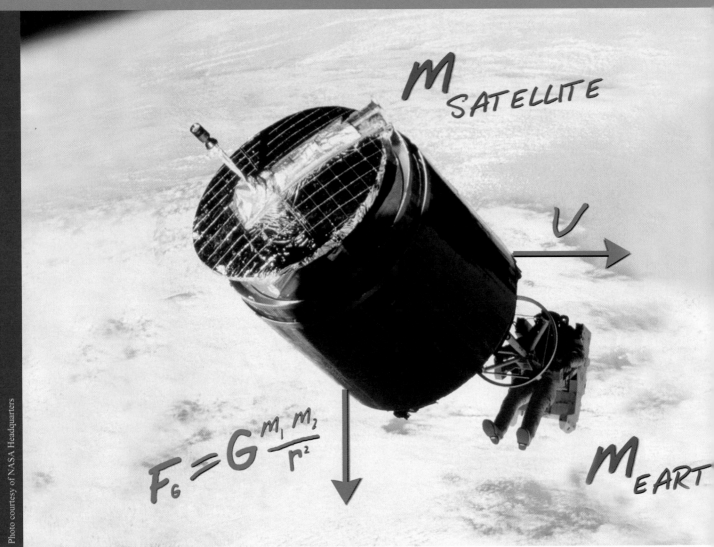

Photo courtesy of NASA Headquarters

What allows thousands of satellites to orbit the earth? Why does vertical motion on the moon appear to take place in slow motion? In this chapter we will discover how we can send massive objects into orbit and why a person weighs less on the moon than on the earth. In this chapter we appreciate the importance of understanding the difference between mass and weight.

MATHEMATICS REVIEW

A.1 Signed Numbers

Signed numbers have many applications in the study of physics. The rules for working with signed numbers follow.

Adding Signed Numbers

To add two positive numbers, add their absolute values.* A positive sign may or may not be placed before the result. It is usually omitted.

Add:

EXAMPLE 1

(a) $\quad +4$
$\quad\quad \underline{+7}$
$\quad\quad +11 \quad$ or $\quad 11$

(b) $(+3) + (+5) = +8 \quad$ or $\quad 8$

To add two negative numbers, add their absolute values and place a negative sign before the result.

Add:

EXAMPLE 2

(a) $\quad -2$
$\quad\quad \underline{-5}$
$\quad\quad -7$

(b) $(-6) + (-7) = -13$
(c) $(-8) + (-4) = -12$

To add a negative number and a positive number, find the difference of their absolute values. Place the sign of the number having the larger absolute value before the result.

Add:

EXAMPLE 3

(a) $\quad +4$
$\quad\quad \underline{-6}$
$\quad\quad -2$

(b) $\quad -2$
$\quad\quad \underline{+8}$
$\quad\quad +6$

(c) $\quad -8$
$\quad\quad \underline{+3}$
$\quad\quad -5$

(d) $\quad +9$
$\quad\quad \underline{-4}$
$\quad\quad +5$

(e) $(+7) + (-2) = +5$
(g) $(-3) + (+10) = +7$

(f) $(-9) + (+6) = -3$
(h) $(+4) + (-12) = -8$

---

*The absolute value of a number is its nonnegative value. For example, the absolute value of -6 is 6; the absolute value of $+10$ is 10; and the absolute value of 0 is 0.

To add three or more signed numbers:

1. Add the positive numbers.
2. Add the negative numbers.
3. Add the sums from steps 1 and 2 according to the rules for addition of signed numbers.

EXAMPLE 4

Add: $(-2) + 4 + (-6) + 10 + (-7)$.

$$
\begin{array}{lll}
\text{Step 1:} & +4 & \\
& +10 & \\
& +14 & \\
\hline
\end{array}
\qquad
\begin{array}{ll}
\text{Step 2:} & -2 \\
& -6 \\
& -7 \\
\hline
& -15
\end{array}
\qquad
\begin{array}{ll}
\text{Step 3:} & -15 \\
& +14 \\
\hline
& -1
\end{array}
$$

Therefore, $(-2) + 4 + (-6) + 10 + (-7) = -1$.

. . . .

Subtracting Signed Numbers

To subtract two signed numbers, change the sign of the *number being subtracted* and *add* according to the rules for addition.

EXAMPLE 5

Subtract:

(a) Subtract: $\begin{array}{r} +3 \\ +7 \\ \hline -4 \end{array}$ $\leftrightarrow$ Add: $\begin{array}{r} +3 \\ -7 \\ \hline -4 \end{array}$ To subtract, change the sign of the number being subtracted, $+7$, and add.

(b) Subtract: $\begin{array}{r} -9 \\ -6 \\ \hline -3 \end{array}$ $\leftrightarrow$ Add: $\begin{array}{r} -9 \\ +6 \\ \hline -3 \end{array}$ To subtract, change the sign of the number being subtracted, -6, and add.

(c) Subtract: $\begin{array}{r} +8 \\ -4 \\ \hline +12 \end{array}$ $\leftrightarrow$ Add: $\begin{array}{r} +8 \\ +4 \\ \hline +12 \end{array}$

(d) Subtract: $\begin{array}{r} -6 \\ +8 \\ \hline -14 \end{array}$ $\leftrightarrow$ Add: $\begin{array}{r} -6 \\ -8 \\ \hline -14 \end{array}$

(e) $(+6) - (+8) = (+6) + (-8) = -2$ To subtract, change the sign of the number being subtracted, $+8$, and add.

(f) $(-3) - (-5) = (-3) + (+5) = +2$

(g) $(+10) - (-3) = (+10) + (+3) = +13$

(h) $(-5) - (+2) = (-5) + (-2) = -7$

. . . .

When more than two signed numbers are involved in subtraction, change the sign of *each* number being subtracted and add the resulting signed numbers.

EXAMPLE 6

Subtract: $(-2) - (+4) - (-1) - (-3) - (+5)$
$= (-2) + (-4) + (+1) + (+3) + (-5)$.

Step 1:	+1	Step 2:	−2	Step 3:	+4
	+3		−4		−11
	+4		−5		−7
			−11		

Therefore, $(-2) - (+4) - (-1) - (-3) - (+5) = -7$.

· · · · · · · · · · · · · · · · ·

When combinations of addition and subtraction of signed numbers occur in the same problem, change *only* the sign of each number being subtracted. Then add the resulting signed numbers.

Find the result:

$$(-2) + (-4) - (-3) - (+6) + (+1) - (+2) + (-7) - (-5)$$
$$= (-2) + (-4) + (+3) + (-6) + (+1) + (-2) + (-7) + (+5)$$

EXAMPLE 7

Step 1:	+3	Step 2:	−2	Step 3:	+9
	+1		−4		−21
	+5		−6		−12
	+9		−2		
			−7		
			−21		

Therefore, $(-2) + (-4) - (-3) - (+6) + (+1) - (+2) + (-7) - (-5) = -12$

· · · · · · · · · · · · · · · · ·

Multiplying Signed Numbers

To multiply two signed numbers:

1. If the signs of the numbers are both positive or both negative, find the product of their absolute values. This product is always positive.
2. If the signs of the numbers are unlike, find the product of their absolute values and place a negative sign before the result.

Multiply:

EXAMPLE 8

(a)	+3	(b)	−5	(c)	−6	(d)	+2
	+4		−8		+7		−3
	+12		+40		−42		−6

(e) $(+3)(+5) = +15$ (f) $(-7)(-8) = +56$
(g) $(-1)(+6) = -6$ (h) $(+4)(-2) = -8$

· · · · · · · · · · · · · · · · ·

To multiply more than two signed numbers, first multiply the absolute values of the numbers. If there is an odd number of negative factors, place a negative sign before the result. If there is an even number of negative factors, the product is positive. *Note:* An *even* number is a number divisible by 2.

Multiply:

EXAMPLE 9

(a) $(+5)(-6)(+2)(-1) = +60$
(b) $(-3)(-3)(+4)(-5) = -180$

· · · · · · · · · · · · · · · · ·

Dividing Signed Numbers

The rules for dividing signed numbers are similar to those for multiplying signed numbers.
To divide two signed numbers:

1. If the signs of the numbers are both positive or both negative, divide their absolute values. This quotient is always positive.
2. If the two numbers have different signs, divide their absolute values and place a negative sign before the quotient.

Note: Division by 0 is undefined.

EXAMPLE 10

Divide:

(a) $\dfrac{+10}{+2} = +5$　　(b) $\dfrac{-18}{-3} = +6$　　(c) $\dfrac{+20}{-4} = -5$　　(d) $\dfrac{-24}{+2} = -12$

Problems A.1

Perform the indicated operations.

1. $(-5) + (-6)$　　2. $(+1) + (-10)$　　3. $(-3) + (+8)$　　4. $(+5) + (+7)$
5. $(-5) + (+3)$　　6. $0 + (-3)$　　7. $(-7) - (-3)$　　8. $(+2) - (-9)$
9. $(-4) - (+2)$　　10. $(+4) - (+7)$　　11. $0 - (+3)$　　12. $0 - (-2)$
13. $(-9)(-2)$　　14. $(+4)(+6)$　　15. $(-7)(+3)$　　16. $(+5)(-8)$
17. $(+6)(0)$　　18. $(0)(-4)$　　19. $\dfrac{+36}{+12}$　　20. $\dfrac{-9}{-3}$
21. $\dfrac{+16}{-2}$　　22. $\dfrac{-15}{+3}$　　23. $\dfrac{0}{+6}$　　24. $\dfrac{4}{0}$
25. $(+2) + (-1) + (+10)$　　26. $(-7) + (+2) + (+9) + (-8)$
27. $(-9) + (-3) + (+3) + (-8) + (+4)$
28. $(+8) + (-2) + (-6) + (+7) + (-6) + (+9)$
29. $(-4) - (+5) - (-4)$　　30. $(+3) - (-5) - (-6) - (+5)$
31. $(-7) - (-4) - (+6) - (+4) - (-5)$
32. $(-8) - (+7) - (+3) - (-7) - (-8) - (-2)$
33. $(+5) + (-2) - (+7)$　　34. $(-3) - (-8) - (+3) + (-9)$
35. $(-2) - (+1) - (-10) + (+12) + (-9)$
36. $(-1) - (-11) + (+2) - (-10) + (+8)$
37. $(+3)(-5)(+3)$　　38. $(-1)(+2)(+2)(-1)$
39. $(+2)(-4)(-6)(-3)(+2)$　　40. $(-1)(+3)(-2)(-4)(+5)(-1)$

A.2 Powers of 10

The ability to work quickly and accurately with powers of 10 is important in scientific and technical fields.

> When multiplying two powers of 10, add the exponents. That is,
> $$10^a \times 10^b = 10^{a+b}$$

EXAMPLE 1

Multiply:
(a) $(10^6)(10^3) = 10^{6+3} = 10^9$　　(b) $(10^4)(10^2) = 10^{4+2} = 10^6$
(c) $(10^1)(10^{-3}) = 10^{1+(-3)} = 10^{-2}$　　(d) $(10^{-2})(10^{-5}) = 10^{[-2+(-5)]} = 10^{-7}$

When dividing two powers of 10, subtract the exponents as follows:
$$10^a \div 10^b = 10^{a-b}$$

Divide: ◄

EXAMPLE 2

(a) $\dfrac{10^7}{10^4} = 10^{7-4} = 10^3$

(b) $\dfrac{10^3}{10^5} = 10^{3-5} = 10^{-2}$

(c) $\dfrac{10^{-2}}{10^{+3}} = 10^{(-2)-(+3)} = 10^{-5}$

(d) $\dfrac{10^4}{10^{-2}} = 10^{4-(-2)} = 10^6$

· · · · · · · · · · · · · · · · ·

To raise a power of 10 to a power, multiply the exponents as follows:
$$(10^a)^b = 10^{ab}$$

Find each power: ◄

EXAMPLE 3

(a) $(10^2)^3 = 10^{(2)(3)} = 10^6$
(c) $(10^4)^{-5} = 10^{(4)(-5)} = 10^{-20}$

(b) $(10^{-3})^2 = 10^{(-3)(2)} = 10^{-6}$
(d) $(10^{-3})^{-4} = 10^{(-3)(-4)} = 10^{12}$

· · · · · · · · · · · · · · · · ·

Next, we will show that $10^0 = 1$. To do this, we need to use the substitution principle, which states that

$$\text{if } \quad a = b \quad \text{and} \quad a = c \quad \text{then} \quad b = c$$

First,

$$\dfrac{10^n}{10^n} = 10^{n-n} \qquad \text{To divide powers, subtract the exponents.}$$
$$= 10^0$$

Second,

$$\dfrac{10^n}{10^n} = 1 \qquad \text{Any number other than zero divided by itself equals 1.}$$

That is, since

$$\dfrac{10^n}{10^n} = 10^0 \quad \text{and} \quad \dfrac{10^n}{10^n} = 1$$

then $10^0 = 1$.

We also will use the fact that $\dfrac{1}{10^a} = 10^{-a}$. To show this, we write

$$\dfrac{1}{10^a} = \dfrac{10^0}{10^a} \qquad (1 = 10^0)$$
$$= 10^{0-a} \qquad \text{To divide powers, subtract the exponents.}$$
$$= 10^{-a}$$

We also need to show that $\dfrac{1}{10^{-a}} = 10^a$. We write

$$\frac{1}{10^{-a}} = \frac{10^0}{10^{-a}}$$
$$= 10^{0-(-a)}$$
$$= 10^a$$

In summary,

$$\boxed{\quad 10^0 = 1 \qquad \frac{1}{10^a} = 10^{-a} \qquad \frac{1}{10^{-a}} = 10^a \quad}$$

Actually, any number (except zero) raised to the zero power equals 1.

Problems A.2

Do as indicated. Express the results using positive exponents.

1. $(10^5)(10^3)$
2. $10^6 \div 10^2$
3. $(10^2)^4$
4. $(10^{-2})(10^{-3})$
5. $\dfrac{10^3}{10^6}$
6. $(10^{-3})^3$
7. $10^5 \div 10^{-2}$
8. $(10^{-2})^{-3}$
9. $(10^4)(10^{-1})$
10. $\dfrac{10^0}{10^{-4}}$
11. $(10^0)(10^{-4})$
12. $\dfrac{10^{-4}}{10^{-3}}$
13. $(10^0)^{-2}$
14. 10^{-3}
15. $\dfrac{1}{10^{-5}}$
16. $\dfrac{(10^4)(10^{-2})}{(10^6)(10^3)}$
17. $\dfrac{(10^{-2})(10^{-3})}{(10^3)^2}$
18. $\dfrac{(10^2)^4}{(10^{-3})^2}$
19. $\left(\dfrac{1}{10^3}\right)^2$
20. $\left(\dfrac{10^2}{10^{-3}}\right)^2$
21. $\left(\dfrac{10 \cdot 10^2}{10^{-1}}\right)^2$
22. $\left(\dfrac{1}{10^{-3}}\right)^2$
23. $\dfrac{(10^4)(10^{-2})}{10^{-8}}$
24. $\dfrac{(10^4)(10^6)}{(10^0)(10^{-2})(10^3)}$

A.3 Solving Linear Equations

An equation is a mathematical sentence stating that two quantities are equal. To solve an equation means to find the number or numbers that can replace the variable in the equation to make the equation a true statement. The value we find that makes the equation a true statement is called the *root* or solution of the equation. When the root of an equation is found, we say we have *solved* the equation.

If $a = b$, then $a + c = b + c$ or $a - c = b - c$. (If the same quantity is added to or subtracted from both sides of an equation, the resulting equation is equivalent to the original equation.)

To solve an equation using this rule, think first of undoing what has been done to the variable.

Solve: $x - 5 = -9$. ◀

EXAMPLE 1

$$x - 5 = -9$$
$$x - 5 + 5 = -9 + 5 \qquad \text{Undo the subtraction by adding 5 to both sides.}$$
$$x = -4$$

Solve: $x + 4 = 29$. ◀

EXAMPLE 2

$$x + 4 = 29$$
$$x + 4 - 4 = 29 - 4 \qquad \text{Undo the addition by subtracting 4 from both sides.}$$
$$x = 25$$

If $a = b$, then $ac = bc$ or $a/c = b/c$ with $c \neq 0$. (If both sides of an equation are multiplied or divided by the same nonzero quantity, the resulting equation is equivalent to the original equation.)

Solve: $3x = 18$. ◀

EXAMPLE 3

$$3x = 18$$
$$\frac{3x}{3} = \frac{18}{3} \qquad \text{Undo the multiplication by dividing both sides by 3.}$$
$$x = 6$$

Solve: $x/4 = 9$. ◀

EXAMPLE 4

$$\frac{x}{4} = 9$$
$$4\left(\frac{x}{4}\right) = 4 \cdot 9 \qquad \text{Undo the division by multiplying both sides by 4.}$$
$$x = 36$$

When more than one operation is indicated on the variable in an equation, undo the additions and subtractions first, then undo the multiplications and divisions.

Solve: $3x + 5 = 17$. ◀

EXAMPLE 5

$$3x + 5 = 17$$
$$3x + 5 - 5 = 17 - 5 \qquad \text{Subtract 5 from both sides.}$$
$$3x = 12$$
$$\frac{3x}{3} = \frac{12}{3} \qquad \text{Divide both sides by 3.}$$
$$x = 4$$

EXAMPLE 6

Solve: $2x - 7 = 10$.

$$2x - 7 = 10$$
$$2x - 7 + 7 = 10 + 7 \qquad \text{Add 7 to both sides.}$$
$$2x = 17$$
$$\frac{2x}{2} = \frac{17}{2} \qquad \text{Divide both sides by 2.}$$
$$x = \frac{17}{2} = 8.5$$

· · · · · · · · · · · · · · · · · · ·

EXAMPLE 7

Solve: $(x/5) - 10 = 22$.

$$\frac{x}{5} - 10 = 22$$
$$\frac{x}{5} - 10 + 10 = 22 + 10 \qquad \text{Add 10 to both sides.}$$
$$\frac{x}{5} = 32$$
$$5\left(\frac{x}{5}\right) = 5(32) \qquad \text{Multiply both sides by 5.}$$
$$x = 160$$

· · · · · · · · · · · · · · · · · · ·

To solve an equation with variables on both sides:

1. Add or subtract either variable term from both sides of the equation.
2. Add or subtract from both sides of the equation the constant term that now appears on the same side of the equation with the variable. Then solve.

EXAMPLE 8

Solve: $3x + 6 = 7x - 2$.

$$3x + 6 = 7x - 2$$
$$3x + 6 - 3x = 7x - 2 - 3x \qquad \text{Subtract } 3x \text{ from both sides.}$$
$$6 = 4x - 2$$
$$6 + 2 = 4x - 2 + 2 \qquad \text{Add 2 to both sides.}$$
$$8 = 4x$$
$$\frac{8}{4} = \frac{4x}{4} \qquad \text{Divide both sides by 4.}$$
$$2 = x$$

· · · · · · · · · · · · · · · · · · ·

EXAMPLE 9

Solve: $4x - 2 = -5x + 10$.

$$4x - 2 = -5x + 10$$
$$4x - 2 + 5x = -5x + 10 + 5x \qquad \text{Add } 5x \text{ to both sides.}$$
$$9x - 2 = 10$$
$$9x - 2 + 2 = 10 + 2 \qquad \text{Add 2 to both sides.}$$
$$9x = 12$$

$$\frac{9x}{9} = \frac{12}{9} \qquad \text{Divide both sides by 9.}$$

$$x = \frac{4}{3}$$

· · · · · · · · · · · · · · · ·

To solve equations containing parentheses, first remove the parentheses and then proceed as before. The rules for removing parentheses follow:

1. If the parentheses are preceded by a plus (+) sign, they may be removed without changing any signs.

    Examples:
    $$2 + (3 - 5) = 2 + 3 - 5$$
    $$3 + (x + 4) = 3 + x + 4$$
    $$5x + (-6x + 9) = 5x - 6x + 9$$

2. If the parentheses are preceded by a minus (−) sign, the parentheses may be removed if *all* the signs of the numbers (or letters) within the parentheses are changed.

    Examples:
    $$2 - (3 - 5) = 2 - 3 + 5$$
    $$5 - (x - 7) = 5 - x + 7$$
    $$7x - (-4x - 11) = 7x + 4x + 11$$

3. If the parentheses are preceded by a number, the parentheses may be removed if each of the terms inside the parentheses is multiplied by that (signed) number.

    Examples:
    $$2(x + 4) = 2x + 8$$
    $$-3(x - 5) = -3x + 15$$
    $$2 - 4(3x - 5) = 2 - 12x + 20$$

EXAMPLE 10

Solve: $3(x - 4) = 15$.

$$3(x - 4) = 15$$
$$3x - 12 = 15 \qquad \text{Remove parentheses.}$$
$$3x - 12 + 12 = 15 + 12 \qquad \text{Add 12 to both sides.}$$
$$3x = 27$$
$$\frac{3x}{3} = \frac{27}{3} \qquad \text{Divide both sides by 3.}$$
$$x = 9$$

· · · · · · · · · · · · · · · ·

EXAMPLE 11

Solve: $2x - (3x + 15) = 4x - 1$.

$$2x - (3x + 15) = 4x - 1$$
$$2x - 3x - 15 = 4x - 1 \qquad \text{Remove parentheses.}$$
$$-x - 15 = 4x - 1 \qquad \text{Combine like terms.}$$
$$-x - 15 + x = 4x - 1 + x \qquad \text{Add } x \text{ to both sides.}$$
$$-15 = 5x - 1$$

$$-15 + 1 = 5x - 1 + 1 \qquad \text{Add 1 to both sides.}$$
$$-14 = 5x$$
$$\frac{-14}{5} = \frac{5x}{5} \qquad \text{Divide both sides by 5.}$$
$$-2.8 = x$$

....

Problems A.3

Solve each equation.

1. $3x = 4$
2. $\dfrac{y}{2} = 10$
3. $x - 5 = 12$

4. $x + 1 = 9$
5. $2x + 10 = 10$
6. $4x = 28$

7. $2x - 2 = 33$
8. $4 = \dfrac{x}{10}$
9. $172 - 43x = 43$

10. $9x + 7 = 4$
11. $6y - 24 = 0$
12. $3y + 15 = 75$

13. $15 = \dfrac{105}{y}$
14. $6x = x - 15$
15. $2 = \dfrac{50}{2y}$

16. $9y = 67.5$
17. $8x - 4 = 36$
18. $10 = \dfrac{136}{4x}$

19. $2x + 22 = 75$
20. $9x + 10 = x - 26$
21. $4x + 9 = 7x - 18$
22. $2x - 4 = 3x + 7$
23. $-2x + 5 = 3x - 10$
24. $5x + 3 = 2x - 18$
25. $3x + 5 = 5x - 11$
26. $-5x + 12 = 12x - 5$
27. $13x + 2 = 20x - 5$
28. $5x + 3 = -9x - 39$
29. $-4x + 2 = -10x - 20$
30. $9x + 3 = 6x + 8$
31. $3x + (2x - 7) = 8$
32. $11 - (x + 12) = 100$
33. $7x - (13 - 2x) = 5$
34. $20(7x - 2) = 240$
35. $-3x + 5(x - 6) = 12$
36. $3(x + 117) = 201$
37. $5(2x - 1) = 8(x + 3)$
38. $3(x + 4) = 8 - 3(x - 2)$
39. $-2(3x - 2) = 3x - 2(5x + 1)$
40. $\dfrac{x}{5} - 2\left(\dfrac{2x}{5} + 1\right) = 28$

A.4 Solving Quadratic Equations

A quadratic equation in one variable is an equation that can be written in the form

$$ax^2 + bx + c = 0 \qquad \text{(where } a \neq 0\text{)}$$

EXAMPLE 1

Solve: $x^2 = 16$.

To solve a quadratic equation of this type, take the square root of both sides of the equation.

$$x^2 = 16$$
$$x = \pm 4 \qquad \text{Take the square root of both sides.}$$

....

In general, solve equations of the form $ax^2 = b$, where $a \neq 0$, as follows:

$$ax^2 = b$$
$$x^2 = \frac{b}{a} \qquad \text{Divide both sides by } a.$$
$$x = \pm \sqrt{\frac{b}{a}} \qquad \text{Take the square root of both sides.}$$

Solve: $2x^2 - 18 = 0$.

EXAMPLE 2

$$2x^2 - 18 = 0$$
$$2x^2 = 18 \qquad \text{Add 18 to both sides.}$$
$$x^2 = 9 \qquad \text{Divide both sides by 2.}$$
$$x = \pm 3 \qquad \text{Take the square root of both sides.}$$

Solve: $5y^2 = 100$.

EXAMPLE 3

$$5y^2 = 100$$
$$y^2 = 20 \qquad \text{Divide both sides by 5.}$$
$$y = \pm\sqrt{20} \qquad \text{Take the square root of both sides.}$$
$$y = \pm 4.47$$

The solutions of the general quadratic equation

$$ax^2 + bx + c = 0 \qquad \text{(where } a \neq 0\text{)}$$

are given by the formula (called the *quadratic formula*)

$$x = \frac{-b \pm \sqrt{b^2 - 4ac}}{2a}$$

where a = coefficient of the x^2 term
         b = coefficient of the x term
         c = constant term

The symbol ($\pm$) is used to combine two expressions or equations into one. For example, $a \pm 2$ means $a + 2$ or $a - 2$. Similarly,

$$x = \frac{-b \pm \sqrt{b^2 - 4ac}}{2a}$$

means

$$x = \frac{-b + \sqrt{b^2 - 4ac}}{2a} \quad \text{or} \quad x = \frac{-b - \sqrt{b^2 - 4ac}}{2a}$$

In the equation, $4x^2 - 3x - 7 = 0$, identify a, b, and c.

EXAMPLE 4

$$a = 4, \quad b = -3, \quad \text{and} \quad c = -7$$

Solve $x^2 + 2x - 8 = 0$ using the quadratic formula.

EXAMPLE 5

First, $a = 1$, $b = 2$, and $c = -8$. Then

$$x = \frac{-b \pm \sqrt{b^2 - 4ac}}{2a}$$

$$x = \frac{-2 \pm \sqrt{(2)^2 - 4(1)(-8)}}{2(1)}$$

$$= \frac{-2 \pm \sqrt{4 - (-32)}}{2}$$

$$= \frac{-2 \pm \sqrt{36}}{2}$$

$$= \frac{-2 \pm 6}{2}$$

$$= \frac{-2 + 6}{2} \quad \text{or} \quad \frac{-2 - 6}{2}$$

$$= \frac{4}{2} \quad \text{or} \quad \frac{-8}{2}$$

$$= 2 \quad \text{or} \quad -4 \qquad \text{The solutions are 2 and } -4.$$

If the number under the radical sign is not a perfect square, find the square root of the number by using a calculator and proceed as before.

EXAMPLE 6

Solve $4x^2 - 7x = 32$ using the quadratic formula.
Before identifying a, b, and c, the equation must be set equal to zero. That is,

$$4x^2 - 7x - 32 = 0$$

First, $a = 4$, $b = -7$, and $c = -32$. Then

$$x = \frac{-b \pm \sqrt{b^2 - 4ac}}{2a}$$

$$= \frac{-(-7) \pm \sqrt{(-7)^2 - 4(4)(-32)}}{2(4)}$$

$$= \frac{7 \pm \sqrt{49 - (-512)}}{8}$$

$$= \frac{7 \pm \sqrt{561}}{8}$$

$$= \frac{7 \pm 23.7}{8} \qquad (\sqrt{561} = 23.7)$$

$$= \frac{7 + 23.7}{8} \quad \text{or} \quad \frac{7 - 23.7}{8}$$

$$= 3.84 \quad \text{or} \quad -2.09$$

The approximate solutions are 3.84 and -2.09.

Problems A.4
Solve each equation.

1. $x^2 = 36$
2. $y^2 = 100$
3. $2x^2 = 98$
4. $5x^2 = 0.05$
5. $3x^2 - 27 = 0$
6. $2y^2 - 15 = 17$
7. $10x^2 + 4.9 = 11.3$
8. $2(32)(48 - 15) = v^2 - 27^2$
9. $2(107) = 9.8t^2$
10. $65 = \pi r^2$
11. $2.50 = \pi r^2$
12. $24^2 = a^2 + 16^2$

Find the values of a, b, and c, in each quadratic equation.

13. $3x^2 + x - 5 = 0$
14. $-2x^2 + 7x + 4 = 0$
15. $6x^2 + 8x + 2 = 0$
16. $5x^2 - 2x - 15 = 0$
17. $9x^2 + 6x = 4$
18. $6x^2 = x + 9$

19. $5x^2 + 6x = 0$ 20. $7x^2 - 45 = 0$ 21. $9x^2 = 64$

22. $16x^2 = 49$

Solve each quadratic equation using the quadratic formula.

23. $x^2 - 10x + 21 = 0$ 24. $2x^2 + 13x + 15 = 0$ 25. $6x^2 + 7x = 20$

26. $15x^2 = 4x + 4$ 27. $6x^2 - 2x = 19$ 28. $4x^2 = 28x - 49$

29. $18x^2 - 15x = 26$ 30. $48x^2 + 9 = 50x$

31. $16.5x^2 + 8.3x - 14.7 = 0$ 32. $125x^2 - 167x + 36 = 0$

A.5   Right-Triangle Trigonometry

A **right triangle** is a triangle with one right angle (90°), two acute angles (less than 90°), two legs, and a hypotenuse (the side opposite the right angle) (Fig. A.1).

When it is necessary to label a triangle, the vertices are often labeled using capital letters and the sides opposite the vertices are labeled using the corresponding lowercase letters (Fig. A.2).

The side opposite angle A is a.
The side adjacent to angle A is b.
The side opposite angle B is b.
The side adjacent to angle B is a.
The side opposite angle C is c and is called the *hypotenuse*.

If we consider a certain acute angle of a right triangle, the two legs can be identified as the side opposite or the side adjacent to the acute angle.

The side opposite angle A is the same as the side adjacent to angle B.
The side adjacent to angle A is the same as the side opposite angle B.
The side opposite angle B is the same as the side adjacent to angle A.
The side adjacent to angle B is the same as the side opposite angle A.

A **ratio** is a comparison of two quantities by division. In a right triangle (Fig. A.3), there are three very important ratios:

$$\frac{\text{side opposite angle } A}{\text{hypotenuse}}$$ is called **sine** A (abbreviated sin A)

$$\frac{\text{side adjacent to angle } A}{\text{hypotenuse}}$$ is called **cosine** A (abbreviated cos A)

$$\frac{\text{side opposite angle } A}{\text{side adjacent to angle } A}$$ is called **tangent** A (abbreviated tan A)

$$\sin A = \frac{\text{side opposite angle } A}{\text{hypotenuse}}$$

$$\cos A = \frac{\text{side adjacent to angle } A}{\text{hypotenuse}}$$

$$\tan A = \frac{\text{side opposite angle } A}{\text{side adjacent to angle } A}$$

The ratios are defined similarly for angle B:

$$\sin B = \frac{\text{side opposite angle } B}{\text{hypotenuse}}$$

$$\cos B = \frac{\text{side adjacent to angle } B}{\text{hypotenuse}}$$

$$\tan B = \frac{\text{side opposite angle } B}{\text{side adjacent to angle } B}$$

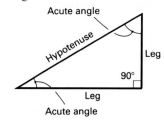

Figure A.1   Parts of a right triangle.

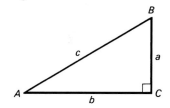

Figure A.2   Labeling a right triangle.

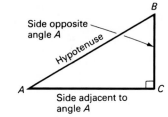

Figure A.3

EXAMPLE 1

Find the three trigonometric ratios of angle A in Fig. A.4.

$$\sin A = \frac{\text{side opposite angle } A}{\text{hypotenuse}} = \frac{3}{5} = 0.60$$

$$\cos A = \frac{\text{side adjacent to angle } A}{\text{hypotenuse}} = \frac{4}{5} = 0.80$$

$$\tan A = \frac{\text{side opposite angle } A}{\text{side adjacent to angle } A} = \frac{3}{4} = 0.75$$

Figure A.4

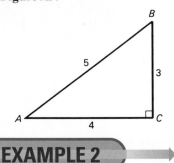

EXAMPLE 2

Find the three trigonometric ratios of angle B in Fig. A.4.

$$\sin B = \frac{\text{side opposite angle } B}{\text{hypotenuse}} = \frac{4}{5} = 0.80$$

$$\cos B = \frac{\text{side adjacent to angle } B}{\text{hypotenuse}} = \frac{3}{5} = 0.60$$

$$\tan B = \frac{\text{side opposite angle } B}{\text{side adjacent to angle } B} = \frac{4}{3} = 1.33$$

Note: Every acute angle has three trigonometric ratios associated with it.

In this book we assume that you will be using a calculator. When calculations involve a trigonometric ratio, we will use the following generally accepted practice for significant digits:

Angle Expressed to Nearest:	Length of Side Contains:
1°	Two significant digits
0.1°	Three significant digits
0.01°	Four significant digits

A useful and time-saving fact about right triangles is that *the sum of the two acute angles of any right triangle is always* 90°. That is,

$$A + B = 90°$$

Why is this true? We know that the sum of the three interior angles of any triangle is 180°. A right triangle must contain a right angle, whose measure is 90°. This leaves 90° to be divided between the two acute angles. Therefore, if one acute angle is known, the other acute angle may be found by subtracting the known angle from 90°. That is,

$$A = 90° - B$$
$$B = 90° - A$$

EXAMPLE 3

Find angle B and side a in the right triangle in Fig. A.5.
To find angle B, we use

$$B = 90° - A = 90° - 30.0° = 60.0°$$

To find side a, we use a trigonometric ratio. Note that we are looking for the *side opposite* angle A and that the *hypotenuse* is given. The trigonometric ratio having these two quantities is sine.

Figure A.5

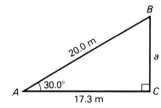

$$\sin A = \frac{\text{side opposite angle } A}{\text{hypotenuse}}$$

$$\sin 30.0° = \frac{a}{20.0 \text{ m}}$$

$$(\sin 30.0°)(20.0 \text{ m}) = \left(\frac{a}{20.0 \text{ m}}\right)(20.0 \text{ m}) \qquad \text{Multiply both sides by 20.0 m.}$$

$$10.0 \text{ m} = a$$

. . . .

EXAMPLE 4

Find angle A, angle B, and side a in the right triangle in Fig. A.6.

First, find angle A. The *side adjacent* to angle A and the *hypotenuse* are given. Therefore, we use cos A to find angle A because cos A uses these two quantities:

Figure A.6

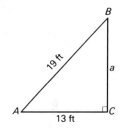

$$\cos A = \frac{\text{side adjacent to } A}{\text{hypotenuse}}$$

$$\cos A = \frac{13 \text{ ft}}{19 \text{ ft}} = 0.684$$

Using a calculator as in Section B.3 of Appendix B, we find that $A = 47°$.

To find angle B, we use

$$B = 90° - A = 90° - 47° = 43°$$

To find side a, we use sin A because the *hypotenuse* is given and side a is the *side opposite* angle A:

$$\sin A = \frac{\text{side opposite angle } A}{\text{hypotenuse}}$$

$$\sin 47° = \frac{a}{19 \text{ ft}}$$

$$(\sin 47°)(19 \text{ ft}) = \left(\frac{a}{19 \text{ ft}}\right)(19 \text{ ft}) \qquad \text{Multiply both sides by 19 ft.}$$

$$14 \text{ ft} = a$$

. . . .

EXAMPLE 5

Find angle A, angle B, and the hypotenuse in the right triangle in Fig. A.7.

To find angle A, use tan A:

Figure A.7

$$\tan A = \frac{\text{side opposite angle } A}{\text{side adjacent to angle } A}$$

$$\tan A = \frac{12.00 \text{ km}}{19.00 \text{ km}} = 0.6316$$

$$A = 32.28°$$

To find angle B,

$$B = 90° - A = 90° - 32.28° = 57.72°$$

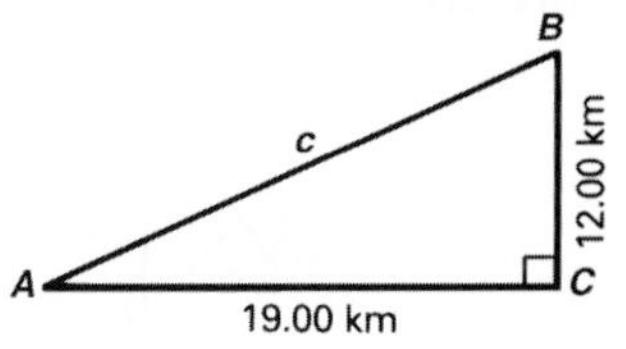

To find the hypotenuse, use $\sin A$:

$$\sin A = \frac{\text{side opposite angle } A}{\text{hypotenuse}}$$

$$\sin 32.28° = \frac{12.00 \text{ km}}{c}$$

$$(\sin 32.28°)(c) = \left(\frac{12.00 \text{ km}}{c}\right)(c) \qquad \text{Multiply both sides by } c.$$

$$(\sin 32.28°)(c) = 12.00 \text{ km}$$

$$\frac{c(\sin 32.28°)}{\sin 32.28°} = \frac{12.00 \text{ km}}{\sin 32.28°} \qquad \text{Divide both sides by } \sin 32.28°.$$

$$c = \frac{12.00 \text{ km}}{\sin 32.28°}$$

$$= 22.47 \text{ km}$$

Figure A.8

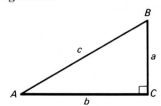

When the two legs of a right triangle are given, the hypotenuse can be found without using trigonometric ratios. From geometry, *the sum of the squares of the legs of a right triangle is equal to the square of the hypotenuse* (**Pythagorean theorem**; see Fig. A.8):

$$a^2 + b^2 = c^2$$

or, taking the square root of each side of the equation,

$$\boxed{c = \sqrt{a^2 + b^2}}$$

Also, if one leg and the hypotenuse are given, the other leg can be found by using

$$\boxed{\begin{aligned} a &= \sqrt{c^2 - b^2} \\ b &= \sqrt{c^2 - a^2} \end{aligned}}$$

EXAMPLE 6

Figure A.9

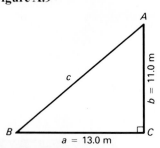

Find the hypotenuse of the right triangle in Fig. A.9.

$$c = \sqrt{a^2 + b^2}$$

$$c = \sqrt{(13.0 \text{ m})^2 + (11.0 \text{ m})^2}$$

$$= \sqrt{169 \text{ m}^2 + 121 \text{ m}^2}$$

$$= \sqrt{290 \text{ m}^2}$$

$$= 17.0 \text{ m}$$

EXAMPLE 7

Figure A.10

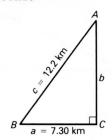

Find side b in the right triangle in Fig. A.10.

$$b = \sqrt{c^2 - a^2}$$

$$b = \sqrt{(12.2 \text{ km})^2 - (7.30 \text{ km})^2}$$

$$= 9.77 \text{ km}$$

Problems A.5

Use right triangle ABC in Fig. A.11 to fill in each blank.

Figure A.11

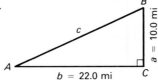

1. The side opposite angle A is _____.
2. The side opposite angle B is _____.
3. The hypotenuse is _____.
4. The side adjacent to angle A is _____.
5. The side adjacent to angle B is _____.
6. The angle opposite side a is _____.
7. The angle opposite side b is _____.
8. The angle opposite side c is _____.
9. The angle adjacent to side a is _____.
10. The angle adjacent to side b is _____.

Use a calculator to find each trigonometric ratio rounded to four significant digits.

11. $\sin 71°$
12. $\cos 40°$
13. $\tan 61°$
14. $\tan 41.2°$
15. $\cos 11.5°$
16. $\sin 79.4°$
17. $\cos 49.63°$
18. $\tan 53.45°$
19. $\tan 17.04°$
20. $\cos 34°$
21. $\sin 27.5°$
22. $\cos 58.72°$

Find each angle rounded to the nearest whole degree.

23. $\sin A = 0.2678$
24. $\cos B = 0.1046$
25. $\tan A = 0.9237$
26. $\sin B = 0.9253$
27. $\cos B = 0.6742$
28. $\tan A = 1.351$

Find each angle rounded to the nearest tenth of a degree.

29. $\sin B = 0.5963$
30. $\cos A = 0.9406$
31. $\tan B = 1.053$
32. $\sin A = 0.9083$
33. $\cos A = 0.8660$
34. $\tan B = 0.9433$

Find each angle rounded to the nearest hundredth of a degree.

35. $\sin A = 0.3792$
36. $\cos B = 0.06341$
37. $\tan B = 0.3010$
38. $\sin A = 0.4540$
39. $\cos B = 0.8141$
40. $\tan A = 2.369$

Solve each triangle (find the missing angles and sides) using trigonometric ratios.

41.

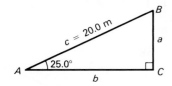

42.

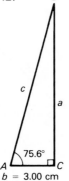

$b = 3.00$ cm

43.

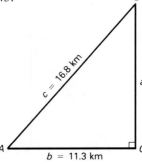

$b = 11.3$ km

44.

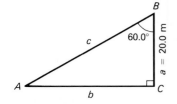

45.

$b = 22.0$ mi

46.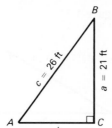

47.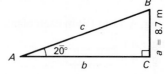

48.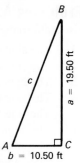

49.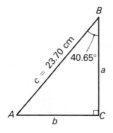

50.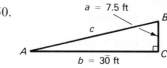

Find the missing side in each right triangle using the Pythagorean theorem.

51.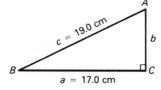

52.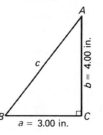

53.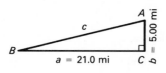

54.

55.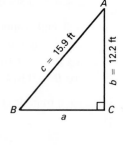

56.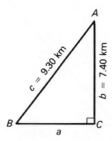

57.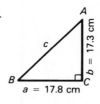

58.

59.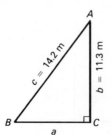

60.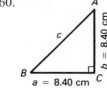

61.　A round taper is shown in Fig. A.12.
　　(a)　Find $\angle BAC$.　　　　　　(b)　Find the length BC.
　　(c)　Find the diameter of end x.
62.　The distance between two parallel flat surfaces, a, of a hexagonal nut is $\frac{3}{4}$ in. Find the distance between any two farthest corners, b (Fig. A.13).
63.　Find distances c and d between the holes of the plate shown in Fig. A.14.

Figure A.12　　　　　　　　　　**Figure A.13**　　　**Figure A.14**

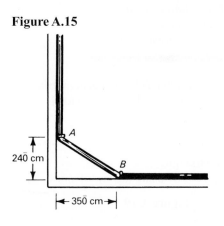
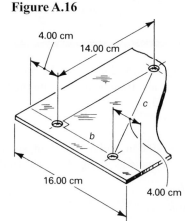
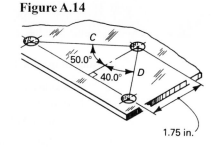

64.　A piece of electric conduit cuts across a corner of a room $24\overline{0}$ cm from the corner. It meets the adjoining wall $35\overline{0}$ cm from the corner. Find length AB of the conduit (Fig. A.15).
65.　Find the distances between holes on the plate shown in Fig. A.16.
66.　Find length x in Fig. A.17. (*Note: $AB = BC$.*)

Figure A.15　　　　　　　　　**Figure A.16**　　　　　**Figure A.17**

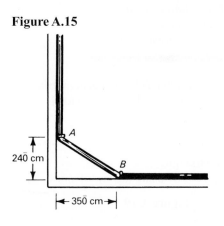
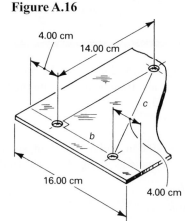
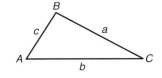

A.6　Law of Sines and Law of Cosines

For those classes and individuals with general triangle trigonometry skills, this section is written as a review. This text is written so that no more than right triangle trigonometry needs to be used, but those with the prerequisite skills may prefer to use the more advanced trigonometry techniques.

An **oblique**, or **general**, triangle is a triangle that contains no right angles. We shall use the standard notation of labeling the vertices of a triangle by the capital letters A, B, and C and using the small letters a, b, and c as the labels for the sides opposite angles A, B, and C, respectively (see Fig. A.18).

Figure A.18　Oblique, or general, triangle ABC.

Solving a triangle means finding all those sides and angles that are not given or known. To solve a triangle, we need three parts (including at least one side). Solving any oblique triangle falls into one of four cases where the following parts of a triangle are known:

1.　Two sides and an angle opposite one of them (SSA).
2.　Two angles and a side opposite one of them (AAS).
3.　Two sides and the included angle (SAS).
4.　Three sides (SSS).

One law that we use to solve triangles is called the **law of sines**. In words, for any triangle the ratio of any side to the sine of the opposite angle is a constant. The formula for the law of sines is as follows:

LAW OF SINES

$$\frac{a}{\sin A} = \frac{b}{\sin B} = \frac{c}{\sin C}$$

In order to use the law of sines, we must know either of the following:

1. Two sides and an angle opposite one of them (SSA).
2. Two angles and a side opposite one of them (AAS). *Note:* Knowing two angles and any side is sufficient because knowing two angles, we can easily find the third.

You must select the proportion that contains three parts that are known and the unknown part.

When calculations with measurements involve a trigonometric function, we shall use the following rule for significant digits:

Angle Expressed to Nearest	Length of Side Contains
1°	Two significant digits
0.1°	Three significant digits
0.01°	Four significant digits

The following relationship is very helpful as a check when solving a general triangle: The longest side of any triangle is opposite the largest angle and the shortest side is opposite the smallest angle.

EXAMPLE 1

If $A = 65.0°$, $a = 20.0$ m, and $b = 15.0$ m, solve the triangle.

First, draw a triangle as in Fig. A.19 and find angle B by using the law of sines:

$$\frac{a}{\sin A} = \frac{b}{\sin B}$$

$$\frac{20.0 \text{ m}}{\sin 65.0°} = \frac{15.0 \text{ m}}{\sin B}$$

$$\sin B = \frac{(15.0 \text{ m})(\sin 65.0°)}{20.0 \text{ m}} = 0.6797$$

$$B = 42.8°$$

Figure A.19

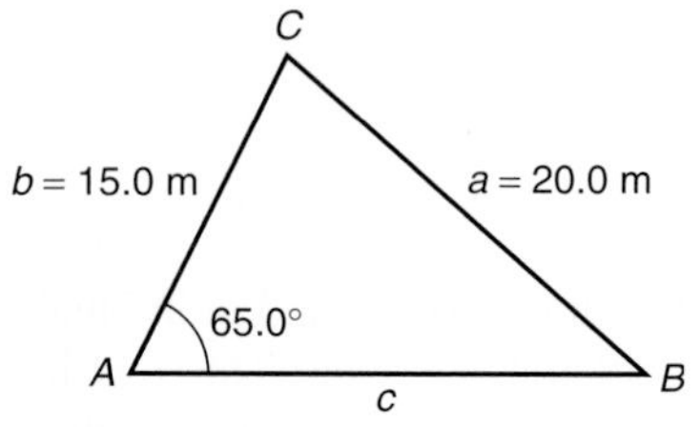

This angle may be found using a calculator as follows:

15 ⊗ sin 65) ÷ 20 = sin⁻¹ ANS =

```
42.82261353
```

So $B = 42.8°$ rounded to the nearest tenth of a degree.

To find C, use the fact that the sum of the angles of any triangle is 180°. Therefore,

$$C = 180° - 65.0° - 42.8°$$

$$= 72.2°$$

Finally, find c using the law of sines.

$$\frac{a}{\sin A} = \frac{c}{\sin C}$$

$$\frac{20.0 \text{ m}}{\sin 65.0°} = \frac{c}{\sin 72.2°}$$

$$c = \frac{(20.0 \text{ m})(\sin 72.2°)}{\sin 65.0°} = 21.0 \text{ m} \qquad \text{(Rounded to three significant digits)}$$

This side may be found using a calculator as follows:

That is, side $c = 21.0$ m rounded to three significant digits.
The solution is $B = 42.8°$, $C = 72.2°$, and $c = 21.0$ m.

・・・・・・・・・・・・・・・・・・

If $C = 25°$, $c = 59$ ft, and $B = 108°$, solve the triangle.   **EXAMPLE 2**
First, draw a triangle as in Fig. A.20 and find b:

Figure A.20

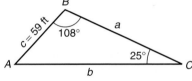

$$\frac{c}{\sin C} = \frac{b}{\sin B}$$

$$\frac{59 \text{ ft}}{\sin 25°} = \frac{b}{\sin 108°}$$

$$b = \frac{(59 \text{ ft})(\sin 108°)}{\sin 25°} = 130 \text{ ft} \qquad \text{(Rounded to two significant digits)}$$

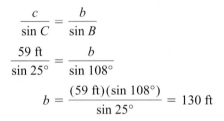

$$A = 180° - 25° - 108° = 47°$$

Find a:

$$\frac{a}{\sin A} = \frac{c}{\sin C}$$

$$\frac{a}{\sin 47°} = \frac{59 \text{ ft}}{\sin 25°}$$

$$a = \frac{(59 \text{ ft})(\sin 47°)}{\sin 25°} = 1\overline{0}0 \text{ ft}$$

The solution is $A = 47°$, $a = 1\overline{0}0$ ft, and $b = 130$ ft.

・・・・・・・・・・・・・・・・・・

The Ambiguous Case

The solution of a triangle when two sides and an angle opposite one of the sides (SSA) are given requires special care. There may be one, two, or no triangles formed from the given data. By construction and discussion, let's study the possibilities.

EXAMPLE 3

Construct a triangle given that $A = 35°$, $b = 10$, and $a = 7$.

As you can see from Fig. A.21, two triangles that satisfy the given information can be drawn: triangles ACB and ACB'. Note that in one triangle angle B is acute and in the other triangle angle B is obtuse.

Figure A.21

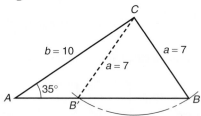

EXAMPLE 4

Construct a triangle given that $A = 45°$, $b = 10$, and $a = 5$.

As you can see from Fig. A.22, no triangle can be drawn that satisfies the given information. Side a is simply not long enough to reach the side opposite angle C.

Figure A.22

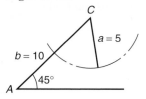

EXAMPLE 5

Construct a triangle given that $A = 60°$, $b = 6$, and $a = 10$.

As you can see from Fig. A.23, only one triangle that satisfies the given information can be drawn. Side a is too long for two solutions.

Figure A.23

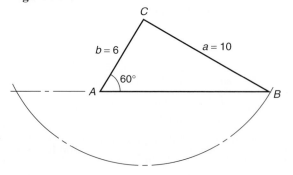

In summary, let's list the possible cases when two sides and an angle opposite one of the sides are given. Assume that *acute* angle A and adjacent side b are given. As a result of $h = b \sin A$, h is also determined. Depending on the length of the opposite side, a, we have the four cases shown in Fig. A.24.

Figure A.24 Possible triangles when two sides and an acute angle opposite one of the sides are given.

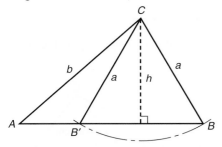

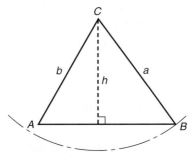

(a) When $h < a < b$, there are two possible triangles. In words, when the side opposite the given *acute* angle is less than the known adjacent side but greater than the altitude, there are two possible triangles.

(b) When $h < b < a$, there is only one possible triangle. In words, when the side opposite the given *acute* angle is greater than the known adjacent side, there is only one possible triangle.

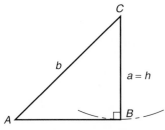

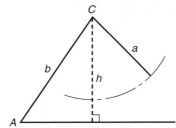

(c) When $a = h$, there is one possible (right) triangle. In words, when the side opposite the given *acute* angle equals the length of the altitude, there is only one possible (right) triangle.

(d) When $a < h$, there is no possible triangle. In words, when the side opposite the given *acute* angle is less than the length of the altitude, there is no possible triangle.

If angle A is *obtuse*, we have two possible cases (Fig. A.25).

Figure A.25 Possible triangles when two sides and an obtuse angle opposite one of the sides are given.

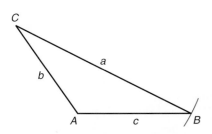

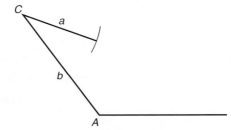

(a) When $a > b$, there is one possible triangle. In words, when the side opposite the given *obtuse* angle is greater than the known adjacent side, there is only one possible triangle.

(b) When $a \le b$, there is no possible triangle. In words, when the side opposite the given *obtuse* angle is less than or equal to the known adjacent side, there is no possible triangle.

Note: If the given parts are not angle A, side opposite a, and side adjacent b as in our preceding discussions, then you must substitute the given angle and sides accordingly. This is why it is so important to understand the general word description corresponding to each case.

EXAMPLE 6

If $A = 26°$, $a = 25$ cm, and $b = 41$ cm, solve the triangle.
First, find h:

$$h = b \sin A = (41 \text{ cm})(\sin 26°) = 18 \text{ cm}$$

Since $h < a < b$, there are two solutions. First, let's find B in triangle ACB in Fig. A.26:

$$\frac{a}{\sin A} = \frac{b}{\sin B}$$

$$\frac{25 \text{ cm}}{\sin 26°} = \frac{41 \text{ cm}}{\sin B}$$

$$\sin B = \frac{(41 \text{ cm})(\sin 26°)}{25 \text{ cm}} = 0.7189$$

$$B = 46°$$

Figure A.26

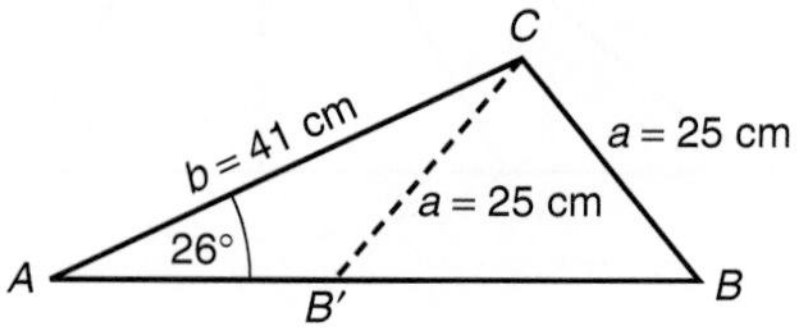

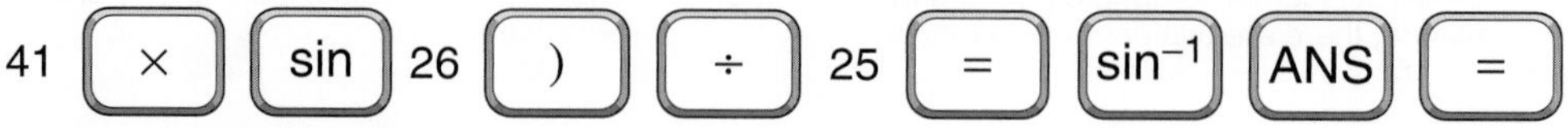

$$41 \quad \boxed{\times} \quad \boxed{\sin} \quad 26 \quad \boxed{)} \quad \boxed{\div} \quad 25 \quad \boxed{=} \quad \boxed{\sin^{-1}} \quad \boxed{\text{ANS}} \quad \boxed{=}$$

$$\boxed{45.96610103}$$

$$C = 180° - 26° - 46° = 108°$$

Find c:

$$\frac{c}{\sin C} = \frac{a}{\sin A}$$

$$\frac{c}{\sin 108°} = \frac{25 \text{ cm}}{\sin 26°}$$

$$c = \frac{(25 \text{ cm})(\sin 108°)}{\sin 26°} = 54 \text{ cm}$$

Therefore, the first solution is $B = 46°$, $C = 108°$, and $c = 54$ cm.

The second solution occurs when B is obtuse, as in triangle ACB'. That is, find the obtuse angle whose sine is 0.7189.

$$B' = 180° - 46° = 134°$$

Then $C = 180° - 26° - 134° = 20°$.
For c,

$$\frac{c}{\sin C} = \frac{a}{\sin A}$$

$$\frac{c}{\sin 20°} = \frac{25 \text{ cm}}{\sin 26°}$$

$$c = \frac{(25 \text{ cm})(\sin 20°)}{\sin 26°} = 20 \text{ cm}$$

The second solution is $B' = 134°$, $C = 20°$, and $c = 20$ cm.

· · · · · · · · · · · · · · · · ·

EXAMPLE 7

If $A = 62.0°$, $a = 415$ m, and $b = 855$ m, solve the triangle.
First, find h:

$$h = b \sin A$$
$$h = (855 \text{ m})(\sin 62.0°)$$
$$= 755 \text{ m}$$

Since $a < h$, there is no possible solution. What would happen if you applied the law of sines anyway? You would obtain

$$\frac{a}{\sin A} = \frac{b}{\sin B}$$

$$\frac{415 \text{ m}}{\sin 62.0°} = \frac{855 \text{ m}}{\sin B}$$

$$\sin B = \frac{(855 \text{ m})(\sin 62.0°)}{415 \text{ m}} = 1.819 \qquad \text{(Tilt!)}$$

Note: $\sin B = 1.819$ is impossible because $-1 \le \sin B \le 1$.

·················

In summary:

1. ***Given two angles and one side (AAS):*** There is only one possible triangle.
2. ***Given two sides and an angle opposite one of them (SSA):*** There are three possibilities. If the side opposite the given angle is:
   (a) greater than the known adjacent side, there is only one possible triangle.
   (b) less than the known adjacent side but greater than the altitude, there are two possible triangles.
   (c) less than the altitude, there is no possible triangle.

Since solving a general triangle requires several operations, errors are often introduced. The following points may be helpful in avoiding some of these errors:

1. Always choose a given value over a calculated value when doing calculations.
2. Always check your results to see that the largest angle is opposite the largest side and the smallest angle is opposite the smallest side.
3. Avoid finding the largest angle by the law of sines whenever possible because it is often not clear whether the resulting angle is acute or obtuse.

Law of Cosines

When the law of sines cannot be used, we use the **law of cosines**. In words, the square of any side of a triangle is equal to the sum of the squares of the other two sides minus twice the product of these two sides and the cosine of their included angle (see Fig. A.27). By formula, the law is stated as follows.

LAW OF COSINES
$a^2 = b^2 + c^2 - 2bc \cos A$
$b^2 = a^2 + c^2 - 2ac \cos B$
$c^2 = a^2 + b^2 - 2ab \cos C$

Figure A.27

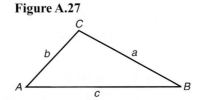

There are two cases when the law of sines does not apply and we use the law of cosines to solve triangles:

1. Two sides and the included angle are known (SAS).
2. All three sides are known (SSS).

Do you see that when the law of cosines is used, there is no possibility of an ambiguous case? If not, draw a few triangles for each of these two cases (SAS and SSS) to convince yourself intuitively.

EXAMPLE 8

Figure A.28

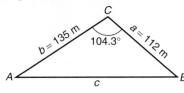

If $a = 112$ m, $b = 135$ m, and $C = 104.3°$, solve the triangle.

First, draw a triangle as in Fig. A.28 and find c by using the law of cosines:

$$c^2 = a^2 + b^2 - 2ab \cos C$$
$$c^2 = (112 \text{ m})^2 + (135 \text{ m})^2 - 2(112 \text{ m})(135 \text{ m})(\cos 104.3°)$$
$$c = 196 \text{ m}$$

This side may be found using a calculator as follows:

112 x^2 + 135 x^2 − 2 × 112 × 135 ×

COS 104.3 = $\sqrt{}$ ANS =

195.5460308

So $c = 196$ m rounded to three significant digits.

To find A, use the law of sines since it requires less computation:

$$\frac{a}{\sin A} = \frac{c}{\sin C}$$
$$\frac{112 \text{ m}}{\sin A} = \frac{196 \text{ m}}{\sin 104.3°}$$
$$\sin A = \frac{(112 \text{ m})(\sin 104.3°)}{196 \text{ m}} = 0.5537$$
$$A = 33.6°$$
$$B = 180° - 104.3° - 33.6° = 42.1°$$

The solution is $A = 33.6°$, $B = 42.1°$, and $c = 196$ m.

· · · · · · · · · · · · · · · · ·

EXAMPLE 9

If $a = 375.0$ ft, $b = 282.0$ ft, and $c = 114.0$ ft, solve the triangle.

First, draw a triangle as in Fig. A.29 and find A by using the law of cosines:

Figure A.29

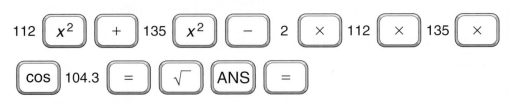

$$a^2 = b^2 + c^2 - 2bc \cos A$$
$$(375.0 \text{ ft})^2 = (282.0 \text{ ft})^2 + (114.0 \text{ ft})^2 - 2(282.0 \text{ ft})(114.0 \text{ ft}) \cos A$$
$$\cos A = \frac{(375.0 \text{ ft})^2 - (282.0 \text{ ft})^2 - (114.0 \text{ ft})^2}{-2(282.0 \text{ ft})(114.0 \text{ ft})}$$
$$\cos A = -0.7482$$
$$A = 138.43° \quad \text{(Rounded to the nearest hundredth of a degree)}$$

375 x^2 − 282 x^2 − 114 x^2 = ANS ÷

(−) 2 ÷ 282 ÷ 114 = $\cos^{-1}$ ANS =

138.432994

Next, to find B, use the law of sines:

$$\frac{a}{\sin A} = \frac{b}{\sin B}$$

$$\frac{375.0 \text{ ft}}{\sin 138.43°} = \frac{282.0 \text{ ft}}{\sin B}$$

$$\sin B = \frac{(282.0 \text{ ft})(\sin 138.43°)}{375.0 \text{ ft}} = 0.4990$$

$$B = 29.93°$$

$$C = 180° - 138.43° - 29.93° = 11.64°$$

The solution is $A = 138.43°$, $B = 29.93°$, and $C = 11.64°$.

· · · · · · · · · · · · · · · ·

Problems A.6

Solve each triangle using the labels as shown in Fig. A.30.*

Figure A.30

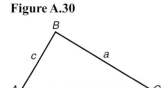

Express the lengths of sides to three significant digits and the angles to the nearest tenth of a degree.

1. $A = 69.0°$, $a = 25.0$ m, $b = 16.5$ m
2. $C = 57.5°$, $c = 166$ mi, $b = 151$ mi
3. $B = 61.4°$, $b = 124$ cm, $c = 112$ cm
4. $A = 19.5°$, $a = 487$ km, $c = 365$ km
5. $B = 75.3°$, $A = 57.1°$, $b = 257$ ft
6. $C = 59.6°$, $B = 43.9°$, $b = 4760$ m
7. $A = 115.0°$, $a = 5870$ m, $b = 4850$ m
8. $A = 16.4°$, $a = 205$ ft, $b = 187$ ft

Express the lengths of sides to four significant digits and the angles to the nearest hundredth of a degree.

9. $C = 72.58°$, $b = 28.63$ cm, $c = 42.19$ cm
10. $A = 58.95°$, $a = 3874$ m, $c = 2644$ m
11. $B = 28.76°$, $C = 19.30°$, $c = 39,750$ mi
12. $A = 35.09°$, $B = 48.64°$, $a = 8.362$ km

Express the lengths of sides to two significant digits and the angles to the nearest degree.

13. $A = 25°$, $a = 50$ cm, $b = 40$ cm
14. $B = 42°$, $b = 5.3$ km, $c = 4.6$ km
15. $C = 8°$, $c = 16$ m, $a = 12$ m
16. $A = 105°$, $a = 460$ mi, $c = 380$ mi

For each general triangle, (a) determine the number of solutions and (b) solve the triangle, if possible. Express the lengths of sides to three significant digits and the angles to the nearest tenth of a degree.

17. $A = 37.0°$, $a = 21.5$ cm, $b = 16.4$ cm
18. $B = 55.0°$, $b = 182$ m, $c = 203$ m
19. $C = 26.5°$, $c = 42.7$ km, $a = 47.2$ km
20. $B = 40.4°$, $b = 81.4$ m, $c = 144$ m
21. $A = 71.5°$, $a = 3.45$ m, $c = 3.50$ m
22. $C = 17.2°$, $c = 2.20$ m, $b = 2.00$ m
23. $B = 105.0°$, $b = 16.5$ mi, $a = 12.0$ mi
24. $A = 98.8°$, $a = 707$ ft, $b = 585$ ft

Express the lengths of sides to two significant digits and the angles to the nearest degree.

25. $C = 18°$, $c = 24$ mi, $a = 45$ mi
26. $B = 36°$, $b = 75$ cm, $a = 95$ cm
27. $C = 60°$, $c = 150$ m, $b = 180$ m
28. $A = 30°$, $a = 4800$ ft, $c = 3600$ ft
29. $B = 8°$, $b = 450$ m, $c = 850$ m
30. $B = 45°$, $c = 2.5$ m, $b = 3.2$ m

Express the lengths of sides to four significant digits and the angles to the nearest hundredth of a degree.

31. $B = 41.50°$, $b = 14.25$ km, $a = 18.50$ km
32. $A = 15.75°$, $a = 642.5$ m, $c = 592.7$ m
33. $C = 63.85°$, $c = 29.50$ cm, $b = 38.75$ cm
34. $B = 50.00°$, $b = 41,250$ km, $c = 45,650$ km

---

*Because of differences in rounding, your answers may differ slightly from the answers in the text if you choose to solve for the parts of a triangle in an order different from that chosen by the authors.

35. $C = 8.75°, c = 89.30$ m, $a = 61.93$ m
36. $A = 31.50°, a = 375.0$ mm, $b = 405.5$ mm

Express the lengths of sides to three significant digits and the angles to the nearest tenth of a degree.

37. $A = 60.0°, b = 19.5$ m, $c = 25.0$ m   38. $B = 19.5°, a = 21.5$ ft, $c = 12.5$ ft
39. $C = 109.0°, a = 14\overline{0}$ km, $b = 215$ km   40. $A = 94.7°, c = 875$ yd, $b = 185$ yd
41. $a = 19.2$ m, $b = 21.3$ m, $c = 27.2$ m
42. $a = 125$ km, $b = 195$ km, $c = 145$ km
43. $a = 4.25$ ft, $b = 7.75$ ft, $c = 5.50$ ft
44. $a = 3590$ m, $b = 7950$ m, $c = 4650$ m

Express the lengths of sides to two significant digits and the angles to the nearest degree.

45. $A = 45°, b = 51$ m, $c = 39$ m   46. $B = 6\overline{0}°, a = 160$ cm, $c = 230$ cm
47. $a = 7\overline{0}00$ m, $b = 5600$ m, $c = 4800$ m
48. $a = 5.8$ cm, $b = 5.8$ cm, $c = 9.6$ cm
49. $C = 135°, a = 36$ ft, $b = 48$ ft   50. $A = 5°, b = 19$ m, $c = 25$ m

Express the lengths of sides to four significant digits and the angles to the nearest hundredth of a degree.

51. $B = 19.25°, a = 4815$ m, $c = 1925$ m
52. $C = 75.00°, a = 37,550$ mi, $b = 45,250$ mi
53. $C = 108.75°, a = 405.0$ mm, $b = 325.0$ mm
54. $A = 111.05°, b = 1976$ ft, $c = 325\overline{0}$ ft
55. $a = 207.5$ km, $b = 105.6$ km, $c = 141.5$ km
56. $a = 19.45$ m, $b = 36.50$ m, $c = 25.60$ m

SCIENTIFIC CALCULATOR

There are several kinds and brands of calculators. Some are very simple to use; others do more difficult calculations. We demonstrate various operations on common basic scientific calculators that use algebraic logic, which follows the steps commonly used in mathematics. Yours may differ. If so, consult your manual.

To demonstrate how to use a calculator, we show what buttons are pushed and the order in which they are pushed. We assume that you know how to add, subtract, multiply, and divide on the calculator.

B.1 Scientific Notation

Numbers expressed in scientific notation can be entered into many calculators. The results may then also be given in scientific notation.

Multiply $(6.5 \times 10^8)(1.4 \times 10^{-15})$ and write the result in scientific notation. ◀ — **EXAMPLE 1**

6.5 [EE] 8 [×] 1.4 [EE] [(−)] 15 [=]

$$9.1 \times 10^{-7}$$

The result is 9.1×10^{-7}.

· · · · · · · · · · · · · · · ·

Divide $\dfrac{3.24 \times 10^{-5}}{7.2 \times 10^{-12}}$ and write the result in scientific notation. ◀ — **EXAMPLE 2**

3.24 [EE] [(−)] 5 [÷] 7.2 [EE] [(−)] 12 [=]

$$4.5 \times 10^{6}$$

The result is 4.5×10^6.

· · · · · · · · · · · · · · · ·

Find the value of $\dfrac{(-6.3 \times 10^4)(-5.07 \times 10^{-9})(8.11 \times 10^{-6})}{(5.63 \times 10^{12})(-1.84 \times 10^7)}$ and write the result in ◀ — **EXAMPLE 3**

scientific notation rounded to three significant digits.

EE (−) 6 ÷ 5.63 EE 12 ÷ (−) 1.84 EE 7 =

-2.500593772 10⁻²⁹

The result rounded to three significant digits is -2.50×10^{-29}.

·····················

B.2 Squares and Square Roots

EXAMPLE 1

Find the value of $(46.8)^2$.

46.8 x^2 =

2190.24

The result is 2190.24.

·····················

EXAMPLE 2

Find the value of $(6.3 \times 10^{-18})^2$.

6.3 EE (−) 18 x^2 =

3.969 x 10⁻³⁵

The result is 3.969×10^{-35}.

·····················

EXAMPLE 3

Find the value of $\sqrt{158.65}$ and round to four significant digits.

$\sqrt{}$ 158.65 =

12.59563416

The result rounded to four significant digits is 12.60.

·····················

EXAMPLE 4

Find the value of $\sqrt{6.95 \times 10^{-15}}$ and round to three significant digits.

$\sqrt{}$ 6.95 EE (−) 15 =

8.336666 x 10⁻⁸

The result rounded to three significant digits is 8.34×10^{-8}.

·····················

Find the value of $\sqrt{15.7^2 + 27.6^2}$ and round to three significant digits. ◄

EXAMPLE 5

$\boxed{\sqrt{}}$ 15.7 $\boxed{x^2}$ $\boxed{+}$ 27.6 $\boxed{x^2}$ $\boxed{=}$

$\boxed{31.75295262}$

The result is 31.8 rounded to three significant digits.

Note: You may need to use parentheses with some calculators.

. . . .

Find the value of $\dfrac{14}{\sqrt{5}} - \sqrt{\dfrac{15}{8}}$ and round the result to three significant digits. ◄

EXAMPLE 6

14 $\boxed{\div}$ $\boxed{\sqrt{}}$ 5 $\boxed{)}$* $\boxed{-}$ $\boxed{\sqrt{}}$ 15 $\boxed{\div}$ 8 $\boxed{)}$* $\boxed{=}$

$\boxed{4.891683943}$

The result is 4.89 rounded to three significant digits.

. . . .

Find the value of $\sqrt{\left(\dfrac{16}{1.3}\right)^2 + \left[\dfrac{1}{2\pi(60)(6 \times 10^{-5})}\right]^2}$ rounded to three significant digits. ◄

EXAMPLE 7

$\boxed{\sqrt{}}$ $\boxed{(}$ 16 $\boxed{\div}$ 1.3 $\boxed{)}$ $\boxed{x^2}$ $\boxed{+}$ $\boxed{(}$ $\boxed{(}$ 2

$\boxed{\times}$ $\boxed{\pi}$ $\boxed{\times}$ 60 $\boxed{\times}$ 6 $\boxed{EE}$ $\boxed{(-)}$ 5 $\boxed{)}$ $\boxed{x^{-1}}$

$\boxed{)}$ $\boxed{x^2}$ $\boxed{)}$ $\boxed{=}$

$\boxed{45.89092973}$

The result is 45.9 rounded to three significant digits.

Note: You will need to insert parentheses to clarify the order of operations. You may need to supply other parentheses.

. . . .

B.3 Trigonometric Operations

Calculators must have sine, cosine, and tangent buttons for use in this book.

Note: Make certain that your calculator is in the degree mode (not in the radian mode) for this section and when working problems in degrees.

_____

Note: You may need to insert a right parenthesis to clarify the order of operations. The square root key sometimes includes the left parenthesis. If not, you may need to supply it.

EXAMPLE 1

Find sin 26° rounded to four significant digits.

| sin | 26 | = |

$$0.438371147$$

That is, sin 26° = 0.4384 rounded to four significant digits.

. . . .

EXAMPLE 2

Find cos 36.75° rounded to four significant digits.

| cos | 36.75 | = |

$$0.801253813$$

That is, cos 36.75° = 0.8013 rounded to four significant digits.

. . . .

EXAMPLE 3

Find tan 70.6° rounded to four significant digits.

| tan | 70.6 | = |

$$2.839653913$$

That is, tan 70.6° = 2.840 rounded to four significant digits.

. . . .

Since we use right triangles almost exclusively, we show how to find the angle of a right triangle when the value of a given trigonometric ratio is known. That is, we will find angle A when $0° \leq A \leq 90°$.

EXAMPLE 4

Given sin A = 0.4321, find angle A to the nearest tenth of a degree.

| sin⁻¹ | .4321 | = |

$$25.60090542$$

Note: Make certain your calculator is in the degree mode.
Thus, A = 25.6° to the nearest tenth of a degree.

. . . .

EXAMPLE 5

Given cos B = 0.6046, find angle B to the nearest tenth of a degree.

| cos⁻¹ | .6046 | = |

$$52.79993633$$

Thus, B = 52.8° to the nearest tenth of a degree.

. . . .

Given $\tan A = 2.584$, find angle A to the nearest tenth of a degree. ◄

EXAMPLE 6

| tan⁻¹ | 2.584 | = |

$$68.8437168$$

Thus, $A = 68.8°$ to the nearest tenth of a degree.

....

Trigonometric functions often occur in expressions that must be evaluated.

Given $a = (\tan 54°)(25.6 \text{ m})$, find a rounded to three significant digits. ◄

EXAMPLE 7

| tan | 54 |) | × | 25.6 | = |

$$35.23537716$$

Thus, $a = 35.2$ m rounded to three significant digits.

....

Given $b = \dfrac{452 \text{ m}}{\cos 37.5°}$, find b rounded to three significant digits. ◄

EXAMPLE 8

| 452 | ÷ | cos | 37.5 | = |

$$569.7335311$$

Thus, $b = 57\overline{0}$ m rounded to three significant digits.

....

B.4 Finding a Power

To raise a number to a power, use the ⌃ button as follows.

Find the value of 4^5. ◄

EXAMPLE 1

| 4 | ∧ | or | y^x | 5 | = |

$$1024$$

That is, $4^5 = 1024$.

....

EXAMPLE 2

Find the value of 1.5^{-4} rounded to three significant digits.

1.5 $\boxed{\wedge}$ or $\boxed{y^x}$ $\boxed{(-)}$ 4 $\boxed{=}$

$$\boxed{0.197530864}$$

That is, $1.5^{-4} = 0.198$ rounded to three significant digits.

. . . .

Problems B.4

Do as indicated and round each result to three significant digits.

1. $(6.43 \times 10^8)(5.16 \times 10^{10})$
2. $(4.16 \times 10^{-5})(3.45 \times 10^{-7})$
3. $(1.456 \times 10^{12})(-4.69 \times 10^{-18})$
4. $(-5.93 \times 10^9)(7.055 \times 10^{-12})$
5. $(7.45 \times 10^8) \div (8.92 \times 10^{18})$
6. $(1.38 \times 10^{-6}) \div (4.324 \times 10^6)$
7. $\dfrac{-6.19 \times 10^{12}}{7.755 \times 10^{-8}}$
8. $\dfrac{1.685 \times 10^{10}}{1.42 \times 10^{24}}$
9. $\dfrac{(5.26 \times 10^{-8})(8.45 \times 10^6)}{(-6.142 \times 10^9)(1.056 \times 10^{-12})}$
10. $\dfrac{(-2.35 \times 10^{-9})(1.25 \times 10^{11})(4.65 \times 10^{17})}{(8.75 \times 10^{23})(-5.95 \times 10^{-6})}$
11. $(68.4)^2$
12. $(3180)^2$
13. $\sqrt{46,500}$
14. $\sqrt{0.000634}$
15. $(1.45 \times 10^5)^2$
16. $(1.095 \times 10^{-18})^2$
17. $\sqrt{4.63 \times 10^{18}}$
18. $\sqrt{9.49 \times 10^{-15}}$
19. $\sqrt{(4.68)^2 + (9.63)^2}$
20. $\sqrt{(18.4)^2 - (6.5)^2}$
21. $18\sqrt{3} + \left(\dfrac{28.1}{19}\right)^2$
22. $\dfrac{8}{\sqrt{2}} + \sqrt{\dfrac{58}{14.5}}$
23. $25^2 - \sqrt{\dfrac{29.8}{0.0256}}$
24. $\dfrac{18.3}{6\sqrt{5}} - \left(\dfrac{225}{147}\right)^2$
25. $(12.6^2 + 21.5^2)^2 + (34.2^2 - 26.4^2)^2$
26. $\sqrt{21.4^2 + 18.7^2} + \sqrt{31.5^2 - 16.3^2}$
27. $\dfrac{91.4 - 48.6}{91.4 - 15.9}$
28. $\dfrac{14.7 + 9.6}{45.7 + 68.2}$
29. $\sqrt{\left(\dfrac{80.5}{25.6}\right)^2 + \left[\dfrac{1}{2\pi(60)(1.5 \times 10^{-7})}\right]^2}$
30. $\sqrt{\left(\dfrac{175}{36.5}\right)^2 + \left[\dfrac{1}{2\pi(60)(8.5 \times 10^{-10})}\right]^2}$
31. $\dfrac{(17.2)(11.6) + (8)(17.6) - (6)(16)}{(5)(15) + (8.5)(15) + (10)(26.5)}$
32. $\dfrac{(18.8)(5.5) + (7.75)(16.5) - (9.25)(13.85)}{(6.25)(12.5) + (4.75)(16.5) + (11.5)(14.1)}$
33. $\sin 13°$
34. $\cos 22°$
35. $\tan 52.3°$
36. $\tan 31.25°$
37. $\cos 59.36°$
38. $\sin 84.55°$
39. $\sin 48°$
40. $\cos 48°$
41. $\tan 75°$
42. $\sin 8°$
43. $\sin 8.7°$
44. $\cos 35°$

Find each angle rounded to the nearest tenth of a degree.

45. $\sin A = 0.6527$
46. $\cos B = 0.2577$
47. $\tan A = 0.4568$
48. $\sin B = 0.4658$
49. $\cos A = 0.5563$
50. $\tan B = 1.496$

51. $\sin B = 0.1465$ 52. $\cos A = 0.4968$ 53. $\tan B = 1.987$
54. $\sin A = 0.2965$ 55. $\cos B = 0.3974$ 56. $\tan A = 0.8885$

Find each angle to the nearest tenth of a degree between $0°$ and $90°$ and each side to three significant digits.

57. $b = (\sin 58.2°)(296 \text{ m})$
58. $a = (\cos 25.2°)(54.5 \text{ m})$

59. $c = \dfrac{37.5 \text{ m}}{\cos 65.2°}$
60. $b = \dfrac{59.7 \text{ m}}{\tan 41.2°}$

61. $\tan A = \dfrac{512 \text{ km}}{376 \text{ km}}$
62. $\cos B = \dfrac{75.2 \text{ m}}{89.5 \text{ m}}$

63. $a = (\cos 19.5°)(15.7 \text{ cm})$
64. $c = \dfrac{235 \text{ km}}{\sin 65.2°}$

65. $b = \dfrac{36.7 \text{ m}}{\tan 59.2°}$
66. $a = (\tan 5.7°)(135 \text{ m})$

Find the value of each power and round each result to three significant digits.

67. 12^4
68. 1.8^3
69. 0.46^5
70. 9^{-3}
71. 14^{-5}
72. 0.65^{-4}

TABLES

Table 1   U.S. Weights and Measures

Units of Length	Units of Volume	Units of Weight
Standard unit—inch (in. or ″)	*Liquid*	Standard unit—pound (lb)
12 inches = 1 foot (ft or ′)	16 ounces (fl oz) = 1 pint (pt)	16 ounces (oz) = 1 pound
3 feet = 1 yard (yd)	2 pints = 1 quart (qt)	2000 pounds = 1 ton (T)
$5\frac{1}{2}$ yards or $16\frac{1}{2}$ feet = 1 rod (rd)	4 quarts = 1 gallon (gal)	
5280 feet = 1 mile (mi)	*Dry*	
	2 pints (pt) = 1 quart (qt)	
	8 quarts = 1 peck (pk)	
	4 pecks = 1 bushel (bu)	

Table 2   Conversion Table for Length

	cm	m	km	in.	ft	mi
1 centimetre =	1	10^{-2}	10^{-5}	0.394	3.28×10^{-2}	6.21×10^{-6}
1 metre =	100	1	10^{-3}	39.4	3.28	6.21×10^{-4}
1 kilometre =	10^{5}	1000	1	3.94×10^{4}	3280	0.621
1 inch =	2.54	2.54×10^{-2}	2.54×10^{-5}	1	8.33×10^{-2}	1.58×10^{-5}
1 foot =	30.5	0.305	3.05×10^{-4}	12	1	1.89×10^{-4}
1 mile =	1.61×10^{5}	1610	1.61	6.34×10^{4}	5280	1

Table 3   Conversion Table for Area

Metric	U.S.
$1 \text{ m}^2 = 10{,}000 \text{ cm}^2$	$1 \text{ ft}^2 = 144 \text{ in}^2$
$= 1{,}000{,}000 \text{ mm}^2$	$1 \text{ yd}^2 = 9 \text{ ft}^2$
$1 \text{ cm}^2 = 100 \text{ mm}^2$	$1 \text{ rd}^2 = 30.25 \text{ yd}^2$
$= 0.0001 \text{ m}^2$	$1 \text{ acre} = 160 \text{ rd}^2$
$1 \text{ km}^2 = 1{,}000{,}000 \text{ m}^2$	$= 4840 \text{ yd}^2$
	$= 43{,}560 \text{ ft}^2$
	$1 \text{ mi}^2 = 640 \text{ acres}$

	m^2	cm^2	ft^2	in^2
1 square metre =	1	10^{4}	10.8	1550
1 square centimetre =	10^{-4}	1	1.08×10^{-3}	0.155
1 square foot =	9.29×10^{-2}	929	1	144
1 square inch =	6.45×10^{-4}	6.45	6.94×10^{-3}	1

$1 \text{ circular mil} = 5.07 \times 10^{-6} \text{ cm}^2 = 7.85 \times 10^{-7} \text{ in}^2$
$1 \text{ hectare} = 10{,}000 \text{ m}^2 = 2.47 \text{ acres}$

	Metric	U.S.
	$1\ m^3 = 10^6\ cm^3$ $1\ cm^3 = 10^{-6}\ m^3$ $= 10^3\ mm^3$	$1\ ft^3 = 1728\ in^3$ $1\ yd^3 = 27\ ft^3$

	m^3	cm^3	L	ft^3	in^3
$1\ m^3 =$	1	10^6	1000	35.3	6.10×10^4
$1\ cm^3 =$	10^{-6}	1	1.00×10^{-3}	3.53×10^{-5}	6.10×10^{-2}
$1\ litre =$	1.00×10^{-3}	1000	1	3.53×10^{-2}	61.0
$1\ ft^3 =$	2.83×10^{-2}	2.83×10^4	28.3	1	1728
$1\ in^3 =$	1.64×10^{-5}	16.4	1.64×10^{-2}	5.79×10^{-4}	1

1 U.S. fluid gallon = 4 U.S. fluid quarts = 8 U.S. pints = 128 U.S. fluid ounces = 231 in^3 = 0.134 ft^3
1 L = 1000 cm^3 = 1.06 qt 1 fl oz = 29.5 cm^3 1 ft^3 = 7.47 gal = 28.3 L

Table 5 Conversion Table for Mass

	g	kg	slug	oz	lb	ton
1 gram =	1	0.001	6.85×10^{-5}	3.53×10^{-2}	2.21×10^{-3}	1.10×10^{-6}
1 kilogram =	1000	1	6.85×10^{-2}	35.3	2.21	1.10×10^{-3}
1 slug =	1.46×10^4	14.6	1	515	32.2	1.61×10^{-2}
1 ounce =	28.4	2.84×10^{-2}	1.94×10^{-3}	1	6.25×10^{-2}	3.13×10^{-5}
1 pound =	454	0.454	3.11×10^{-2}	16	1	5.00×10^{-4}
1 ton =	9.07×10^5	907	62.2	3.2×10^4	2000	1

1 metric ton = 1000 kg = 2205 lb

Quantities in the shaded areas are not mass units. When we write, for example, 1 kg "=" 2.21 lb, this means that a kilogram is a mass that weighs 2.21 pounds under standard conditions of gravity ($g = 9.80\ m/s^2 = 32.2\ ft/s^2$).

Table 6 Conversion Table for Density

	$slug/ft^3$	kg/m^3	g/cm^3	lb/ft^3	lb/in^3
1 slug per ft^3 =	1	515	0.515	32.2	1.86×10^{-2}
1 kilogram per m^3 =	1.94×10^{-3}	1	0.001	6.24×10^{-2}	3.61×10^{-5}
1 gram per cm^3 =	1.94	1000	1	62.4	3.61×10^{-2}
1 pound per ft^3 =	3.11×10^{-2}	16.0	1.60×10^{-2}	1	5.79×10^{-4}
1 pound per in^3 =	53.7	2.77×10^4	27.7	1728	1

Quantities in the shaded areas are weight densities and, as such, are dimensionally different from mass densities.
Note that

$$D_w = D_m g$$

where D_w = weight density
  D_m = mass density
  $g = 9.80\ m/s^2 = 32.2\ ft/s^2$

Table 7   Conversion Table for Time

	yr	day	h	min	s
1 year =	1	365	8.77×10^3	5.26×10^5	3.16×10^7
1 day =	2.74×10^{-3}	1	24	1440	8.64×10^4
1 hour =	1.14×10^{-4}	4.17×10^{-2}	1	60	3600
1 minute =	1.90×10^{-6}	6.94×10^{-4}	1.67×10^{-2}	1	60
1 second =	3.17×10^{-8}	1.16×10^{-5}	2.78×10^{-4}	1.67×10^{-2}	1

Table 8   Conversion Table for Speed

	ft/s	km/h	m/s	mi/h	cm/s
1 foot per second =	1	1.10	0.305	0.682	30.5
1 kilometre per hour =	0.911	1	0.278	0.621	27.8
1 metre per second =	3.28	3.60	1	2.24	100
1 mile per hour =	1.47	1.61	0.447	1	44.7
1 centimetre per second =	3.28×10^{-2}	3.60×10^{-2}	0.01	2.24×10^{-2}	1
1 mi/min = 88.0 ft/s = 60.0 mi/h					

Table 9   Conversion Table for Force

	N	lb	oz
1 newton =	1	0.225	3.60
1 pound =	4.45	1	16
1 ounce =	0.278	0.0625	1

Table 10   Conversion Table for Power

	Btu/h	ft lb/s	hp	kW	W
1 British thermal unit per hour =	1	0.216	3.93×10^{-4}	2.93×10^{-4}	0.293
1 foot pound per second =	4.63	1	1.82×10^{-3}	1.36×10^{-3}	1.36
1 horsepower =	2550	550	1	0.746	746
1 kilowatt =	3410	738	1.34	1	1000
1 watt =	3.41	0.738	1.34×10^{-3}	0.001	1

Table 11   Conversion Table for Pressure

	atm	Inches of Water	mm Hg	N/m² (Pa)	lb/in²	lb/ft²
1 atmosphere =	1	407	$76\overline{0}$	1.01×10^5	14.7	2120
1 inch of water[a] at 4°C =	2.46×10^{-3}	1	1.87	249	3.61×10^{-2}	5.20
1 millimetre of mercury[a] at 0°C =	1.32×10^{-3}	0.535	1	133	1.93×10^{-2}	2.79
1 newton per metre² (pascal) =	9.87×10^{-6}	4.02×10^{-3}	7.50×10^{-3}	1	1.45×10^{-4}	2.09×10^{-2}
1 pound per in² =	6.81×10^{-2}	27.7	51.7	6.90×10^3	1	144
1 pound per ft² =	4.73×10^{-4}	0.192	0.359	47.9	6.94×10^{-3}	1

[a]Where the acceleration of gravity has the standard value, $g = 9.80$ m/s² $= 32.2$ ft/s².

Table 12   Mass and Weight Density

Substance	Mass Density (kg/m³)	Weight Density (lb/ft³)
Solids		
Copper	8,890	555
Iron	7,800	490
Lead	11,300	708
Aluminum	2,700	169
Brass	8,700	540
Ice	917	57
Wood, white pine	420	26
Concrete	2,300	140
Cork	240	15
Liquids		
Water	$1,0\overline{0}0$[a]	62.4
Seawater	1,025	64.0
Oil	870	54.2
Mercury	13,600	846
Alcohol	790	49.4
Gasoline	680	42.0
	At 0°C and 1 atm Pressure	At 32°F and 1 atm Pressure
Gases[b]		
Air	1.29	0.081
Carbon dioxide	1.96	0.123
Carbon monoxide	1.25	0.078
Helium	0.178	0.011
Hydrogen	0.0899	0.0056
Oxygen	1.43	0.089
Nitrogen	1.25	0.078
Ammonia	0.760	0.047
Propane	2.02	0.126

[a]Metric weight density of water $= 98\overline{0}0$ N/m³.
[b]The density of a gas is found by pumping the gas into a container, measuring its volume and mass or weight, and then using the appropriate density formula.

Table 13   Specific Gravity of Certain Liquids[a]

Liquid	Specific Gravity
Benzene	0.90
Ethyl alcohol	0.79
Gasoline	0.68
Kerosene	0.82
Mercury	13.6
Seawater	1.025
Sulfuric acid	1.84
Turpentine	0.87
Water	1.000

[a]At room temperature (20°C or 68°F)

Table 14   Conversion Table for Energy, Work, and Heat

	Btu	ft lb	J	cal	kWh
1 British thermal unit =	1	778	1060	252	2.93×10^{-4}
1 foot pound =	1.29×10^{-3}	1	1.36	0.324	3.77×10^{-7}
1 joule =	9.48×10^{-4}	0.738	1	0.239	2.78×10^{-7}
1 calorie =	3.97×10^{-3}	3.09	4.19	1	1.16×10^{-6}
1 kilowatt-hour =	3410	2.66×10^{6}	3.60×10^{6}	8.60×10^{5}	1

Table 15   Heat Constants

	Melting Point (°C)	Boiling Point (°C)	Specific Heat cal/g °C or kcal/kg °C or Btu/lb °F	J/kg °C	Heat of Fusion cal/g or kcal/kg	J/kg	Vaporization cal/g or kcal/kg	J/kg
Alcohol, ethyl	−117	78.5	0.58	2400	24.9	1.04×10^{5}	204	8.54×10^{5}
Aluminum	660	2057	0.22	920	76.8	3.21×10^{5}		
Brass	840		0.092	390				
Copper	1083	2330	0.092	390	49.0	2.05×10^{5}		
Glass			0.21	880				
Ice	0		0.51	2100	$8\overline{0}$	3.35×10^{5}		
Iron (steel)	1540	3000	0.115	481	7.89	3.30×10^{4}		
Lead	327	1620	0.031	130	5.86	2.45×10^{4}		
Mercury	−38.9	357	0.033	140	2.82	1.18×10^{4}	65.0	2.72×10^{5}
Silver	961	1950	0.056	230	26.0	1.09×10^{5}		
Steam			0.48	$200\overline{0}$				
Water (liquid)	0	$10\overline{0}$	1.00	4190	$8\overline{0}$	3.35×10^{5}	$54\overline{0}$	2.26×10^{6}
Zinc	419	907	0.092	390	23.0	9.63×10^{4}		

Table 16   Coefficient of Linear Expansion

Material	α (metric)	α (U.S.)
Aluminum	$2.3 \times 10^{-5}/C°$	$1.3 \times 10^{-5}/F°$
Brass	$1.9 \times 10^{-5}/C°$	$1.0 \times 10^{-5}/F°$
Concrete	$1.1 \times 10^{-5}/C°$	$6.0 \times 10^{-6}/F°$
Copper	$1.7 \times 10^{-5}/C°$	$9.5 \times 10^{-6}/F°$
Glass	$9.0 \times 10^{-6}/C°$	$5.1 \times 10^{-6}/F°$
Pyrex	$3.0 \times 10^{-6}/C°$	$1.7 \times 10^{-6}/F°$
Steel	$1.3 \times 10^{-5}/C°$	$6.5 \times 10^{-6}/F°$
Zinc	$2.6 \times 10^{-5}/C°$	$1.5 \times 10^{-5}/F°$

Table 17   Coefficient of Volume Expansion

Liquid	β (metric)	β (U.S.)
Acetone	$1.49 \times 10^{-3}/C°$	$8.28 \times 10^{-4}/F°$
Alcohol, ethyl	$1.12 \times 10^{-3}/C°$	$6.62 \times 10^{-4}/F°$
Carbon tetrachloride	$1.24 \times 10^{-3}/C°$	$6.89 \times 10^{-4}/F°$
Mercury	$1.8 \times 10^{-4}/C°$	$1.0 \times 10^{-4}/F°$
Petroleum	$9.6 \times 10^{-4}/C°$	$5.33 \times 10^{-4}/F°$
Turpentine	$9.7 \times 10^{-4}/C°$	$5.39 \times 10^{-4}/F°$
Water	$2.1 \times 10^{-4}/C°$	$1.17 \times 10^{-4}/F°$

Table 18   Charge

Charge on one electron = 1.60×10^{-19} coulomb

1 coulomb = 6.25×10^{18} electrons of charge

1 ampere-hour = 3600 C

Table 19   Relationships of Metric SI Base and Derived Units

This chart shows graphically how the 17 SI-derived units with special names are derived from the base and supplementary units. It was provided by the National Institute of Standards and Technology.

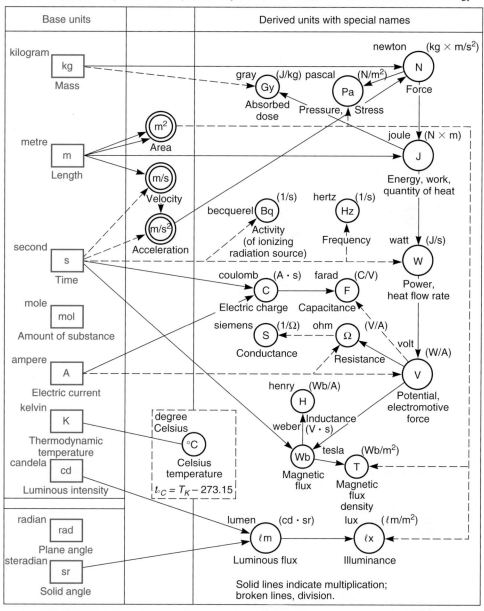

Solid lines indicate multiplication; broken lines, division.

Table 20   Electric Symbols

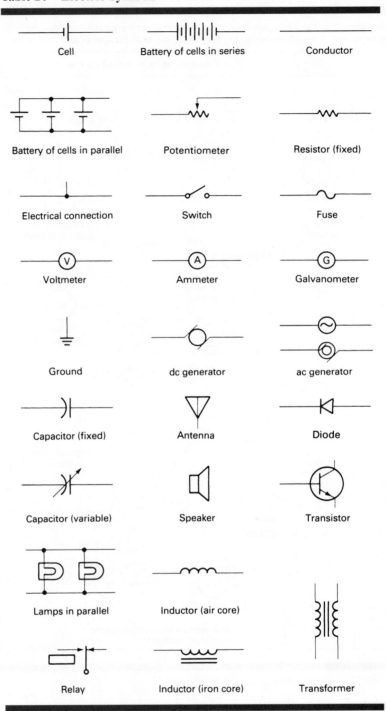

Table 21   Periodic Table

Key:
- Symbol — Cl   17 — Atomic number
- Atomic mass* — 35.453
- $3p^5$ — Electron configuration

Group I	Group II	Transition Elements										Group III	Group IV	Group V	Group VI	Group VII	Group 0
H 1 1.0079 $1s^1$																	He 2 4.00260 $1s^2$
Li 3 6.94 $2s^1$	Be 4 9.01218 $2s^2$											B 5 10.81 $2p^1$	C 6 12.011 $2p^2$	N 7 14.0067 $2p^3$	O 8 15.9994 $2p^4$	F 9 18.9984 $2p^5$	Ne 10 20.18 $2p^6$
Na 11 22.9898 $3s^1$	Mg 12 24.305 $3s^2$											Al 13 26.9815 $3p^1$	Si 14 28.0855 $3p^2$	P 15 30.974 $3p^3$	S 16 32.06 $3p^4$	Cl 17 35.453 $3p^5$	Ar 18 39.948 $3p^6$

Transition elements (periods 4–7):

		Sc 21 44.9559 $3d^14s^2$	Ti 22 47.9 $3d^24s^2$	V 23 50.9415 $3d^34s^2$	Cr 24 51.996 $3d^54s^1$	Mn 25 54.938 $3d^54s^2$	Fe 26 55.847 $3d^64s^2$	Co 27 58.9332 $3d^74s^2$	Ni 28 58.7 $3d^84s^2$	Cu 29 63.546 $3d^{10}4s^1$	Zn 30 65.39 $3d^{10}4s^2$
K 19 39.0983 $4s^1$	Ca 20 40.08 $4s^2$	↑	↑	↑	↑	↑	↑	↑	↑	↑	↑
Rb 37 85.47 $5s^1$	Sr 38 87.62 $5s^2$	Y 39 88.9059 $4d^15s^2$	Zr 40 91.22 $4d^25s^2$	Nb 41 92.9064 $4d^45s^1$	Mo 42 95.94 $4d^55s^1$	Tc 43 (98) $4d^55s^2$	Ru 44 101.07 $4d^75s^1$	Rh 45 102.906 $4d^85s^1$	Pd 46 106.4 $4d^{10}5s^0$	Ag 47 107.868 $4d^{10}5s^1$	Cd 48 112.41 $4d^{10}5s^2$
Cs 55 132.905 $6s^1$	Ba 56 137.33 $6s^2$	57–71†	Hf 72 178.49 $5d^26s^2$	Ta 73 180.95 $5d^36s^2$	W 74 183.85 $5d^46s^2$	Re 75 186.207 $5d^56s^2$	Os 76 190.2 $5d^66s^2$	Ir 77 192.22 $5d^76s^2$	Pt 78 195.08 $5d^96s^1$	Au 79 196.97 $5d^{10}6s^1$	Hg 80 200.59 $5d^{10}6s^2$
Fr 87 (223) $7s^1$	Ra 88 226.025 $7s^2$	89–103‡	Rf 104 (261) $6d^27s^2$	Ha 105 (262) $6d^37s^2$	106 (263)	107 (262)	108 (265)	109 (266)			

Period 4 p-block: Ga 31 69.73 $4p^1$ | Ge 32 72.6 $4p^2$ | As 33 74.9216 $4p^3$ | Se 34 78.96 $4p^4$ | Br 35 79.904 $4p^5$ | Kr 36 83.80 $4p^6$

Period 5 p-block: In 49 114.82 $5p^1$ | Sn 50 118.7 $5p^2$ | Sb 51 121.75 $5p^3$ | Te 52 127.60 $5p^4$ | I 53 126.90 $5p^5$ | Xe 54 131.3 $5p^6$

Period 6 p-block: Tl 81 204.38 $6p^1$ | Pb 82 207.2 $6p^2$ | Bi 83 208.980 $6p^3$ | Po 84 (209) $6p^4$ | At 85 (210) $6p^5$ | Rn 86 (222) $6p^6$

†Lanthanide series

La 57 138.906 $5d^16s^2$	Ce 58 140.12 $5d^14f^16s^2$	Pr 59 140.908 $4f^36s^2$	Nd 60 144.24 $4f^46s^2$	Pm 61 (145) $4f^56s^2$	Sm 62 150.4 $4f^66s^2$	Eu 63 151.96 $4f^76s^2$	Gd 64 157.25 $5d^14f^76s^2$	Tb 65 158.925 $5d^14f^86s^2$	Dy 66 162.50 $4f^{10}6s^2$	Ho 67 164.930 $4f^{11}6s^2$	Er 68 167.26 $4f^{12}6s^2$	Tm 69 168.934 $4f^{13}6s^2$	Yb 70 173.04 $4f^{14}6s^2$	Lu 71 174.967 $5d^14f^{14}6s^2$

‡Actinide series

Ac 89 (227) $6d^17s^2$	Th 90 232.038 $6d^27s^2$	Pa 91 231.036 $5f^26d^17s^2$	U 92 238.029 $5f^36d^17s^2$	Np 93 237.048 $5f^46d^17s^2$	Pu 94 (244) $5f^66d^07s^2$	Am 95 (243) $5f^76d^07s^2$	Cm 96 (247) $5f^76d^17s^2$	Bk 97 (247) $5f^96d^07s^2$	Cf 98 (251) $5f^{10}6d^07s^2$	Es 99 (252) $5f^{11}6d^07s^2$	Fm 100 (257) $5f^{12}6d^07s^2$	Md 101 (258) $5f^{13}6d^07s^2$	No 102 (259) $6d^07s^2$	Lr 103 (260) $6d^17s^2$

*Atomic mass values averaged over isotopes in percentages in which they occur on the earth's surface. For many unstable elements, mass number of the most stable known isotope is given in parentheses.

Table 22 The Greek Alphabet

Capital	Lowercase	Name
A	α	alpha
B	β	beta
Γ	γ	gamma
Δ	δ	delta
E	ε	epsilon
Z	ζ	zeta
H	η	eta
Θ	θ	theta
I	ι	iota
K	κ	kappa
Λ	λ	lambda
M	μ	mu
N	ν	nu
Ξ	ξ	xi
O	o	omicron
Π	π	pi
P	ρ	rho
Σ	σ	sigma
T	τ	tau
Υ	υ	upsilon
Φ	ϕ	phi
X	χ	chi
Ψ	ψ	psi
Ω	ω	omega

GLOSSARY

A

Absolute Pressure   The actual air pressure given by the gauge reading plus the normal atmospheric pressure.

Absolute Zero   The lowest possible temperature.

Acceleration   Change in velocity per unit time.

Acceleration Due to Gravity   The acceleration of a freely falling object. On the earth's surface the acceleration due to gravity is 9.80 m/s^2 (metric) or 32.2 ft/s^2 (U.S.).

Accuracy   The number of digits, called significant digits, in a measurement, which indicates the number of units that we are reasonably sure of having counted. The greater the number of significant digits, the better is the accuracy.

Actual Power   A measure of the actual power available to be converted into other forms of energy.

Adhesion   The force of attraction between different or unlike molecules.

Alpha Ray   A ray consisting of alpha particles, each having two protons and two neutrons, and positively charged, that is, it curves in the direction that known positive charges curve in a magnetic field.

Alternating Current   A current that flows in one direction in a conductor, changes direction, and then flows in the other direction.

Ammeter   An instrument that measures the current flowing in a circuit.

Ampère's Rule   To find the direction of a magnetic field near a current and a straight wire, hold the wire in your right hand with your thumb extended in the direction of the current. Your fingers circle the wire in the direction of the flux lines.

Amplification   The process of increasing the strength of an electronic signal.

Amplitude   The maximum displacement of any part of a wave or a vibration from its equilibrium, or rest, position.

Angular Acceleration   The rate of change of angular velocity (change in angular velocity/time).

Angular Displacement   The angle through which any point on a rotating body moves.

Angular Momentum   For a rotating body about a fixed axis, the angular momentum is the product of the moment of inertia and the angular velocity of the body.

Angular Velocity   The rate of angular displacement (angular displacement/time).

Apparent Power   The product of the effective values of alternating current and voltage.

Approximate Number   A number that has been determined by some measurement or estimation process.

Archimedes' Principle   Any object placed in a fluid apparently loses weight equal to the weight of the displaced fluid.

Area   The number of square units contained in a figure.

Armature   The rotating coil or electromagnet in a generator.

Astronomy   The branch of science that studies everything that takes place outside of the earth's atmosphere.

Atmospheric Pressure   The pressure caused by the weight of the air in the atmosphere.

Atom   The smallest particle of an element that can exist in a stable or independent state.

Atomic Mass   The mass of a single atom, usually expressed in atomic mass units, u.

Atomic Mass Number   The total number of nucleons (protons and neutrons) in a nucleus, A.

Atomic Mass Unit (u)   A unit of measure of atomic mass based on the mass of the common carbon atom, which has six protons and six neutrons, so the mass of the carbon 12 atom has been given the exact value of 12 u. Thus, the approximate mass of a single proton or a single neutron is 1 u, and the mass of an atom in atomic mass units is simply the sum of the number of its protons and its neutrons.

Atomic Number   The number of protons in a nucleus, Z.

Average Binding Energy per Nucleon   The total binding energy of the nucleus divided by the total number of nucleons.

B

Becquerel   (Bq) Unit of source activity; 1 Bq = 1 disintegration/s.

Bending   Consists of both tension and compression stresses. It occurs when a force is placed on a beam causing it to sag.

Bernoulli's Principle   For the horizontal flow of a fluid through a tube, the sum of the pressure and energy of motion (kinetic energy) per unit volume of the fluid is constant.

Beta Ray   A ray consisting of a stream of beta particles (electrons), which are emitted from neutrons in a nucleus as they decay into protons and electrons. This ray is negatively charged and curves in the opposite direction of an alpha ray in a magnetic field.

Binding Energy of the Nucleus   The total energy required to break a nucleus apart into separate nucleons.

Biology   The branch of science that studies living organisms.

Bohr Model   An early model of atomic structure in which electrons travel around the nucleus in a number of discrete stable energy levels determined by quantum conditions.

Boyle's Law   If the temperature of a gas is constant, the volume is inversely proportional to the absolute pressure, $V/V' = P'/P$.

Brinell Method   Common industrial method used to measure the hardness of a metal.

Btu (British thermal unit) The amount of heat (energy) necessary to raise the temperature of 1 lb of water 1°F.

Buoyant Force The upward force exerted on a submerged or partially submerged object.

C

Calorie The amount of heat necessary to raise the temperature of 1 g of water 1°C.

Capacitance The ratio of the charge on either plate of a capacitor to the potential difference between the plates.

Capacitive Reactance A measure of the opposition to ac current flow by a capacitor.

Capacitor A circuit component consisting of two parallel plates separated by a thin insulator used to build up and store charge.

Capillary Action The behavior of liquids that causes the liquid level in very small-diameter tubes to be different than in larger-diameter tubes. This behavior is due both to adhesion of the liquid molecules with the tube and to the surface tension of the liquid.

Celsius Scale The metric temperature scale on which ice melts at 0° and water boils at 100°.

Center of Gravity The point of any body at which all of its weight can be considered to be concentrated.

Centripetal Force The force acting on a body in circular motion that causes it to move in a circular path. This force is exerted toward the center of the circle.

Chain Reaction The process of using the neutrons released in each nuclear fission reaction to create further reactions.

Change of Phase (sometimes called *change of state*) A change in a substance from one form of matter (solid, liquid, or gas) to another.

Charles' Law If the pressure on a gas is constant, the volume is directly proportional to its Kelvin or Rankine temperature, $V/T = V'/T'$.

Chemistry The branch of science that studies the composition, structure, properties, and reactions of matter.

Coefficient of Friction The ratio between the frictional force and the normal force of an object. The number represents how rough or smooth two surfaces are when moving across one another.

Coefficient of Linear Expansion A constant that indicates the amount by which a solid expands or contracts when its temperature is changed 1 degree.

Cohesion The force of attraction between like molecules that holds the closely packed molecules of a solid together.

Color A property of the light that reaches our eyes and is determined by its wavelength or its frequency.

Commutator A device in an ac generator that produces a direct current. Composed of a split ring that replaces the slip rings in an ac generator and produces a direct current in the circuit connected to the split ring of the generator.

Compass A small magnetic needle that is free to rotate on a bearing.

Complementary Colors Two colors that, when combined, form white; for example, cyan and red, magenta and green, and yellow and blue.

Component Vector When two or more vectors are added, each of the vectors is called a component of the resultant, or sum, vector.

Compound A substance containing two or more elements.

Compound Machine A combination of simple machines. Its total mechanical advantage is the product of the mechanical advantage of each simple machine.

Compression A stress caused by two forces acting directly toward each other. This stress tends to cause objects to become shorter and thicker.

Concave Mirror A mirror with a surface that curves away from an observer.

Concurrent Forces Two or more forces applied to, or acting at, the same point.

Condensation The change of phase from gas or vapor to a liquid.

Conduction A form of heat transfer from a warmer part of a substance to a cooler part as a result of molecular collisions, which cause the slower-moving molecules to move faster. A transfer of charge from one place to another.

Conductor A material through which an electron charge is readily transferred.

Constructive Interference The superposition of waves to form a larger disturbance (wave) in a medium. Occurs when two crests or troughs of superimposed waves meet.

Convection A form of heat transfer by the movement of warm molecules from one region of a gas or a liquid to another.

Converging Lens A lens that bends the light passing through it to some point beyond the lens. Converging lenses are thicker in the center.

Conversion Factor An expression used to convert from one set of units to another. Often expressed as a fraction whose numerator and denominator are equal to each other although in different units.

Convex Mirror A mirror with a surface that curves inward toward an observer.

Coulomb Force An electric, repulsive force between protons.

Coulomb's Law The force between two point charges is directly proportional to the product of their magnitudes and inversely proportional to the square of the distance between them.

Critical Angle The smallest angle of incidence at which all light striking a surface is totally internally reflected.

Curie (Ci) Unit of source activity; 1 Ci = 3.70×10^{10} disintegrations/s.

Current The flow of charge that passes through a conductor.

Curvilinear Motion Motion along a curved path.

D

Decay Rate The probability per unit time that a decay of radioactive isotopes will occur.

Deceleration An acceleration that indicates an object is slowing down.

Degree An angular unit of measure. Defined as 1/360 of one complete revolution.

Destructive Interference The superposition of waves to form a smaller disturbance (wave) in a medium.

Dew Point The temperature at which air becomes saturated with water vapor and condensation occurs.

Diffraction The property of a wave that describes its ability to bend around obstacles in its path.

Diffusion   The process by which molecules of a gas mix with the molecules of a solid, a liquid, or another gas. Scattering of light by an uneven surface.

Diode   A device that allows current to flow through it in only one direction.

Direct Current   Current that flows in one direction.

Disintegration Energy   The total energy released in radioactive decay in the form of kinetic energy.

Dispersion   The spreading of white light into the full spectrum.

Displacement   The net change in position of an object, or the direct distance and direction it moves; a vector.

Displacement   The distance of an object is simple harmonic motion from its equilibrium or rest, position.

Diverging Lens   A lens that bends the light passing through it so as to spread the light. Diverging lenses are thicker at the edges than at the center.

Doppler Effect   The variation of the frequency heard when a source of sound and the ear are moving relative to each other.

Dry Cell   A voltage-generating cell that consists of a chemical paste and two electrodes of unlike materials, one of which reacts chemically with the electrolyte.

Ductility   A property of a metal that enables it to be drawn through a die to produce a wire.

E

Effective Value   The number of amperes of alternating current that produce the same amount of heat in a resistance as an equal number of amperes of a steady direct current.

Efficiency   The ratio of the work output to the work input of a machine.

Effort   The force applied to a machine.

Effort Arm   The distance from the effort force to the fulcrum of a lever.

Elastic Collision   A collision in which two objects return to their original shape without being permanently deformed.

Elastic Limit   The point beyond which a deformed object cannot return to its original shape.

Elasticity   A measure of a deformed object's ability to return to its original size and shape once the deforming force is removed.

Electric Circuit   A conducting loop in which electrons carrying electric energy may be transferred from a suitable source to do useful work and returned to the source.

Electric Field   An electric field exists where an electric force acts on a charge brought into the area.

Electrolyte   An acid solution that produces large numbers of free electrons at the negative pole of a cell.

Electromagnet   A combination of a solenoid and a magnetic material, such as iron, in the core of the solenoid. When a current is passed through the solenoid, the magnetic fields of the atoms in the magnetic material line up to produce a strong magnetic field.

Electromagnetic Spectrum   The entire range of electromagnetic waves classified according to frequency.

Electromagnetic Theory   Describes the interrelationship between electric fields, magnetic fields, electric charge, and electric current.

Electromagnetic Wave   A wave consisting of two perpendicular transverse waves with one component of the wave being a vibrating electric field and the other component being a corresponding vibrating magnetic field; the electromagnetic wave moves in a direction perpendicular to both electric and magnetic field components.

Electron   A fundamental particle of an atom; negatively charged.

Element   A substance that cannot be separated into simpler substances.

emf   The potential difference across a source.

Energy   The ability to do work. There are many forms of energy, such as mechanical, electrical, thermal, fluid, chemical, atomic, and sound. Work delivered to an electric component or appliance (power $\times$ time).

Equilibrant Force   The force that, when applied at the same point as the resultant force, produces equilibrium.

Equilibrium   An object is in equilibrium when the net force acting on it is zero. A body that is in equilibrium is either at rest or moving at a constant velocity.

Equivalent Resistance   The single resistance that can replace a series and/or parallel combination of resistances in a circuit and provide the same current flow and voltage drop.

Evaporation   The process by which high-energy molecules of a liquid continually leave its surface.

Exact Number   A number that has been determined as a result of counting or by some definition, such as 1 h = 60 min.

Excited State   A high-energy level for an electron in an atom.

Expansion   Property of a gas in which the rapid random movement of its molecules causes the gas to completely occupy the volume of its container.

Experimental Physicist   A physicist who performs experiments to develop and confirm physical theories.

$E = mc^2$ The equation that illustrates and defines the equivalence between mass and energy forms of matter.

F

Fahrenheit Scale   The U.S. temperature scale on which ice melts at 32° and water boils at 212°.

First Condition of Equilibrium   The sum of all parallel forces on a body in equilibrium must be zero.

First Law of Reflection   The angle of incidence equals the angle of reflection.

First Postulate of Special Relativity   The laws of physics are the same for both moving and nonmoving frames of reference.

Fixed Pulley   A pulley that is fastened to a fixed object.

Flow Rate   The volume of fluid flowing past a given point in a pipe per unit time.

Fluid   A substance that takes the shape of its container. Either a liquid or a gas.

Fluorescence   A property of certain substances in which radiation is absorbed at one frequency and then reemitted at a lower frequency.

Flux Lines   Lines indicating the direction of the magnetic field near a magnetic pole.

Focal Length   The distance between the principal focus of a mirror or lens and its vertex.

Force A push or a pull that tends to change the motion of an object or prevent an object from changing motion. Force is a vector quantity with both magnitude and direction.

Formula An equation, usually expressed in letters (called *variables*) and numbers.

Freezing The change of phase from liquid to solid. Also called *solidification*.

Frequency The number of complete vibrations or cycles per second of a wave.

Friction A force that resists the relative motion of two objects in contact caused by the irregularities of two surfaces sliding or rolling across each other.

Fulcrum A pivot about which a lever is free to turn.

Fusion The change of phase from solid to liquid. Also called *melting*.

G

Gamma Ray A ray composed of photons of electromagnetic radiation, which have no mass.

Gas A substance that takes the shape of its container and has the same volume as its container.

Gauge Pressure The amount of air pressure excluding the normal atmospheric pressure.

Gear Train A series of gears that transfers rotational motion from one gear to another.

General Theory of Relativity Extends the special theory of relativity to accelerated frames of reference with the assumption that gravity and acceleration are equivalent and that light has mass and its path can be warped by gravity.

Generator An apparatus consisting of a coil of wire rotating in a magnetic field. A current is induced in the coil, converting mechanical energy into electric energy.

Geology The branch of science that studies the origin, history, and structure of the earth.

Grand Unified Theory A theory linking the five fundamental forces: gravitational, electric, magnetic, strong, and weak forces.

Gravitational Field The area around a massive body in which an object experiences a gravitational force. The more massive and closer an object is to that body, the stronger is the gravitational field.

Gravitational Potential Energy The energy determined by the position of an object relative to a particular reference level.

Ground State The lowest energy level for an electron in an atom.

H

Half-Life The length of time required for one-half of the original amount of the radioactive atoms in a sample to decay.

Hardness A measure of the internal resistance of the molecules of a solid being forced farther apart or closer together.

Heat A form of internal kinetic and potential energy contained in an object associated with the motion of its atoms or molecules and which may be transferred from an object at a higher temperature to one at a lower temperature.

Heat of Fusion The heat required to melt 1 g or 1 kg or 1 lb of a liquid.

Heat of Vaporization The amount of heat required to vaporize 1 g or 1 kg or 1 lb of a liquid.

Heat Pump A device that warms or cools by transferring heat. It contains a vapor (refrigerant) that is easily condensed to a liquid when under pressure. It produces heat during compression and cooling during vaporization.

Hooke's Law A principle of elasticity in solids: The ratio of the force applied to an object to its change in length (resulting in its being stretched or compressed by the applied force) is constant as long as the elastic limit has not been exceeded.

Huygen's Principle Each point on a wave front can be regarded as a new source of small wavelets, which form succeeding waves that spread out uniformly in the forward direction at the same speed.

Hydraulic Principle (Pascal's Principle) The pressure applied to a confined liquid is transmitted without measurable loss throughout the entire liquid to all inner surfaces of the container.

Hydrometer A sealed glass tube weighted at one end so that it floats vertically in a liquid.

Hydrostatic Pressure The pressure a liquid at rest exerts on a submerged object.

Hypothesis A scientifically based prediction that needs testing to verify its validity.

I

Illumination The luminous intensity per unit area.

Impedance A measure of the total opposition to current flow in an ac circuit resulting from the effect of both the resistance and the inductive reactance on the circuit.

Impulse The product of the force exerted and the time interval during which the force acts on the object. Impulse equals the change in momentum of an object in response to the exerted force.

Impulse–Momentum Theorem If the mass of an object is constant, then a change in its velocity results in a change of its momentum. That is, $F\Delta t = \Delta p = m\Delta v = mv_f - mv_i$.

Inclined Plane A plane surface set at an angle from the horizontal used to raise objects that are too heavy to lift vertically.

Index of Refraction A measure of the optical density of a material. Equal to the ratio of the speed of light in vacuum to the speed of light in the material.

Induced Current A current produced in a circuit by motion of the circuit through the flux lines of a magnetic field.

Induced Magnetism Magnetism produced in a magnetic material such as iron when the material is placed in a magnetic field, such as that produced in the core of a current-carrying solenoid.

Inductance A measure of the tendency of a coil of wire to resist a change in the current because the magnetism produced by one part of the coil acts to oppose the change of current in other parts of the coil.

Induction A method of charging one object by bringing a charged object near to, but not touching, it.

Induction Motor An ac motor with an electromagnetic current induced by the moving magnetic field of the ac current.

Inductive Reactance A measure of the opposition to ac current flow in an inductor.

Inductor A circuit component, such as a coil, in which an induced emf opposes any current change in the circuit.

Inelastic Collision   A collision in which two objects couple together.

Inertia   The property of a body that causes it to remain at rest if it is at rest or to continue moving with a constant velocity unless an unbalanced force acts upon it.

Instantaneous Current   The current at any instant of time.

Instantaneous Voltage   The voltage at any instant of time.

Insulator   A substance that does not allow electric current to flow readily through it.

Intensity   The energy transferred by sound per unit time through unit area.

Interference   The effect of two intersecting waves resulting in a loss of displacement in certain areas and an increase in displacement in others.

Internal Potential Energy   The energy determined by the nature or condition of a substance.

Internal Resistance   The resistance within a cell that opposes movement of the electrons.

Isotopes   Nuclei that contain the same number of protons but a different number of neutrons.

K

Kelvin Scale   The metric absolute temperature scale on which absolute zero is 0 K and the units are the same as on the Celsius scale.

Kilocalorie   The amount of heat necessary to raise the temperature of 1 kg of water 1°C.

Kilogram   The basic metric unit of mass.

Kinetic Energy   The energy due to the mass and the velocity of a moving object.

L

Laser   A light source that produces a narrow beam with high intensity. An acronym for "light amplification by stimulated emission of radiation."

Lateral Surface Area   The area of all the lateral (side) faces of a geometric solid.

Law   The highest level of certainty for an explanation of physical occurrences. A law is often accompanied by a formula.

Law of Acceleration   The total force acting on a body is equal to the mass of the body times its acceleration (Newton's second law).

Law of Action and Reaction   For every force applied by object *A* to object *B* (action), there is an equal but opposite force exerted by object *B* on object *A* (reaction) (Newton's third law).

Law of Conservation of Angular Momentum   The angular momentum of a system remains unchanged unless an outside torque acts on it.

Law of Conservation of Mechanical Energy   The sum of the kinetic energy and the potential energy in a system is constant if no resistant forces do work.

Law of Conservation of Momentum   When no outside forces are acting on a system of moving objects, the total momentum of the system remains constant.

Law of Inertia   A body that is in motion continues in motion with the same velocity (at constant speed and in a straight line) and a body at rest continues at rest unless an unbalanced (outside) force acts upon it (Newton's first law).

Law of Refraction   When a beam of light passes at an angle from a medium of lower optical density to a denser medium, the light is bent toward the normal. When a beam passes from a medium of greater optical density to one less dense, the light is bent away from the normal.

Law of Simple Machines   Resistance force × resistance distance = effort force × effort distance.

Lever   A rigid bar free to turn on a pivot called a fulcrum.

Light   Radiant energy that can be seen by the human eye.

Light-Year   The distance that light travels in one earth year: 9.45×10^{15} m or 5.87×10^{12} mi.

Liquid   A substance that takes the shape of its container and has a definite volume.

Load   The object in a circuit that converts electric energy into other forms of energy or work.

Longitudinal Wave   A disturbance in a medium in which the motion of the particles is along the direction of the wave travel.

Loudness   The strength of the sensation of sound to an observer.

Luminous Intensity   A measure of the brightness of a light source.

M

Machine   An object or system that is used to transfer energy from one place to another and allows work to be done that could not otherwise be done or could not be done as easily.

Magnetic   Property of metals or other materials that can attract iron or steel.

Magnetic Field   A field of force near a magnetic pole or a current that can be detected using a magnet.

Malleability   A property of a metal that enables it to be hammered and rolled into a sheet.

Mass   A measure of the inertia of a body. A measure of the quantity of material making up an object.

Mass Density   The mass per unit volume of a substance.

Mass–Energy Equivalence   A physical law stating that mass and energy are equivalent forms of matter; $E = \Delta mc^2$; stated by Einstein.

Matter   Anything that occupies space and has mass.

Mechanical Advantage   The ratio of the resistance force to the effort force.

Mechanical Equivalent of Heat   The relationship between heat and mechanical work.

Melting   The change of phase from solid to liquid. Also called *fusion*.

Meniscus   The crescent-shaped surface of a liquid column in a tube.

Method of Mixtures   When two substances at different temperatures are mixed together, heat flows from the warmer body to the cooler body until they reach the same temperature. Part of the heat lost by the warmer body is transferred to the cooler body and to surrounding objects. If the two substances are well insulated from surrounding objects, the heat lost by the warmer body is equal to the heat gained by the cooler body.

Metre   The basic metric unit of length.

Molecule   The smallest particle of a substance that exists in a stable and independent state.

Moment of Inertia   Rotational inertia; the property of a rotating body that causes it to continue to turn until a torque causes it to change its rotational motion.

Momentum   A measure of the amount of inertia and motion an object has or the difficulty in bringing a moving object to rest. Momentum equals the mass times the velocity of an object.

Motion   A change of position.

Motor   A device that is composed of an armature and a stator. When a current is passed through the armature, the armature rotates in the magnetic field of the stator and converts electric energy to mechanical energy.

Movable Pulley   A pulley that is fastened to the object to be moved.

Multimeter   An instrument used to measure current flow, voltage drop, and resistance.

N

Natural Frequency   The frequency at which an object vibrates when struck by another object, such as a rubber hammer.

Neutron   A fundamental particle in the nucleus of an atom; neutrally charged

Neutron Number   The number of neutrons in an atomic nucleus of a particular nuclide, N. Also, $N = A - Z$, the difference between the atomic mass number and the atomic number. N can be different for nuclei with the same atomic number.

Newton's Law of Universal Gravitation   All objects that have mass are attracted to one another by a gravitational force.

Normal Force   Force perpendicular to the contact surface.

Nuclear Fission   A nuclear reaction in which an atomic nucleus splits into fragments with the release of energy.

Nuclear Fusion   A nuclear reaction in which light nuclei interact to form heavier nuclei with the release of energy.

Nucleus   The center part of an atom made up of protons and neutrons.

Nuclide   A specific type of atom characterized by its nuclear properties, such as the number of neutrons and protons and the energy state of its nucleus.

Number Plane   A plane determined by the horizontal line called the x-axis and a vertical line called the y-axis intersecting at right angles at a point called the origin. These two lines divide the number plane into four quadrants. The x-axis contains positive numbers to the right of the origin and negative numbers to the left of the origin. The y-axis contains positive numbers above the origin and negative numbers below the origin.

O

Ohm's Law   When a voltage is applied across a resistance in an electric circuit, the current equals the voltage drop across the resistance divided by the resistance, $I = V/R$.

Ohmmeter   An instrument that measures the resistance of a circuit component.

Opaque   Absorbing or reflecting almost all light.

Optical Density   A property of a transparent material that is a measure of the speed of light through the given material.

Orbit   The path taken by an object during its revolution around another object, such as the path of the moon or a satellite about the earth or of a planet about the sun.

P

Parallel Circuit   An electric circuit with more than one path for the current to flow. The current is divided among the branches of the circuit.

Particle Theory   Theory that light consists of streams of particles.

Pendulum   An object suspended so that it swings freely back and forth about a pivot.

Period   The time required for a single wave to pass a given point or the time required for one complete vibration of an object in simple harmonic motion.

Periodic Table   A table that contains all of the atomic elements arranged according to their atomic numbers and which can be used to predict their chemical properties.

Phase Angle   The angle between the resistance and impedance vectors in a circuit.

Photoelectric Effect   The emission of electrons by a surface when struck by electromagnetic radiation.

Photometry   The study of the measurement of light.

Photons   Wave packets of energy that carry light and other forms of electromagnetic radiation.

Physicist   A person who is an expert in or who studies physics.

Physics   The branch of science that describes the motion and energy of all matter throughout the universe.

Pitch   The distance a screw advances in one revolution of the screw. Also the distance between two successive threads. The effect of the frequency of sound waves on the ear.

Planck's Constant   A fundamental constant of quantum theory (6.626×10^{-34} J s).

Plane Mirror   A mirror with a flat surface.

Platform Balance   An instrument consisting of two platforms connected by a horizontal rod that balances on a knife edge. The pull of gravity on objects placed on the two platforms is compared.

Polarized Light   Light waves restricted to a single plane that is perpendicular to the direction of the wave motion.

Potential Energy   The stored energy of a body due to its internal characteristics or its position.

Power   The rate of doing work (work divided by time). Energy per unit time consumed in a circuit.

Power Factor   The ratio of the actual power to the apparent power.

Precision   Refers to the smallest unit with which a measurement is made, that is, the position of the last significant digit.

Pressure   The force applied per unit area.

Primary Cell   A cell that cannot be recharged.

Primary Coil   The coil of a transformer that carries an alternating current and induces a current in the secondary coil.

Primary Colors   The colors red, green, and blue; an additive mixture of the three colors of light resulting in white.

Primary Pigments   The complements of the three primary colors; namely, cyan (the complement of red), magenta (the complement of green), and yellow (the complement of blue).

Principle   A rule or fundamental assumption that has been proven in the laboratory.

Problem-Solving Method   An orderly procedure that aids in understanding and solving problems.

Projectile   A propelled object that travels through the air but has no capacity to propel itself.

Projectile Motion The motion of a projectile as it travels through the air influenced only by its initial velocity and gravitational acceleration.

Propagation Velocity The velocity of energy transfer of a wave, given by the distance traveled by the wave in one period divided by the period.

Proton A fundamental particle in the nucleus of the atom; positively charged.

Pulley A grooved wheel that turns readily on an axle and is supported in a frame.

Pulse Nonrepeated disturbance that carries energy through a medium or through space.

Q

Quantum Mechanics A theory that unifies the wave–particle dual nature of electromagnetic radiation. The quantum model is based on the idea that matter, just like light, behaves sometimes as a particle and sometimes as a wave.

Quantum Theory Theory initiated by Planck and Einstein that energy, including electromagnetic radiation, is radiated or absorbed in multiples of certain units of energy.

R

Radian An angular unit of measurement. Defined as that angle with its vertex at the center of a circle whose sides cut off an arc on the circle equal to its radius. Equal to approximately 57.3°.

Radiation A form of heat transfer through energy being radiated or transmitted in the forms of rays, waves, or particles.

Radioactive Decay A type of nuclear decay that occurs when an unstable atom is transformed into a new element through the spontaneous disintegration of its nucleus.

Radiocarbon Dating A method used to obtain age estimates of organic materials using carbon 14 decay.

Rainbow A spectrum of light formed when sunlight strikes raindrops, refracts into them, reflects within them, and then refracts out of them.

Range The horizontal distance that a projectile will travel before striking the ground.

Rankine Scale The U.S. absolute temperature scale on which absolute zero is 0° R and the degree units are the same as on the Fahrenheit scale.

Real Image An image formed by rays of light.

Recharging The passing of an electric current through a secondary cell to restore the original chemicals.

Rectification The process of changing ac to dc.

Rectifier A device that changes ac to dc.

Rectilinear Motion Motion in a straight line.

Reflection The turning back of all or part of a beam of light at the boundary between two different media.

Refraction The bending of light as it passes at an angle from one medium to another of different optical density.

Regular Reflection Reflection of light with very little scattering.

Relative Humidity Ratio of the actual amount of vapor in the atmosphere to the amount of vapor required to reach 100% of saturation at the existing temperature.

Relative Motion The concept that motion can be described differently depending upon the observer's perspective.

Resistance The force overcome by a machine. The opposition to current flow.

Resistance Arm The distance from the resistance force to the fulcrum of a lever.

Resistivity The resistance per unit length of a material with uniform cross section.

Resonance A sympathetic vibration of an object caused by the transfer of energy from another object vibrating at the natural frequency of vibration of the first object. A condition in a circuit when the inductive reactance equals the capacitive reactance and they nullify each other. The current that flows in the circuit is then at its maximum value.

Resultant Force The sum of the forces applied at the same point. The single force that has the same effect as the two or more forces acting together.

Resultant Vector The sum of two or more vectors.

Revolution A unit of measurement in rotational motion. One complete rotation of a body.

Rotational Motion Spinning motion of a body.

Rotor The rotating coil in a generator.

S

Scalar A physical quantity that can be completely described by a number (called its magnitude) and a unit.

Science A system of knowledge that is concerned with establishing accurate conclusions about the behavior of everything in the universe.

Scientific Method An orderly procedure used by scientists in collecting, organizing, and analyzing new information which refutes or supports a scientific hypothesis.

Scientific Notation A form in which a number can be written as a product of a number between 1 and 10 and a power of 10. General form is $M \times 10^n$, where M is a number between 1 and 10 and n is the exponent or power of 10.

Screw An inclined plane wrapped around a cylinder.

Second The basic unit of time.

Second Condition of Equilibrium The sum of the clockwise torques on a body in equilibrium must be equal to the sum of the counterclockwise torques about any point.

Second Law of Reflection The incident ray, the reflected ray, and the normal (perpendicular) to the reflecting surface all lie in the same plane.

Second Postulate of Special Relativity The speed of light is constant regardless of the speed of the observer or of the light source.

Secondary Cell A rechargeable type of cell.

Secondary Coil The coil of a transformer in which a current is induced by the current in the primary coil.

Semiconductors A small number of materials that fall between conductors and insulators in their ability to conduct electric current.

Series Circuit An electric circuit with only one path for the current to flow. The current in a series circuit is the same throughout.

Shearing A stress caused by two forces applied in parallel, opposite directions.

SI (Système International d'Unités)　The international modern metric system of units of measurement.

Significant Digits　The number of digits in a measurement, which indicates the number of units we are reasonably sure of having counted.

Simple Harmonic Motion　A type of linear motion of an object in which the acceleration is directly proportional to its displacement from its equilibrium position and the motion is always directed to the equilibrium position.

Simple Machine　Any one of six mechanical devices in which an applied force results in useful work. The six simple machines are the lever, the wheel and axle, the pulley, the inclined plane, the screw, and the wedge.

Snell's Law　The index of refraction equals the sine of the angle of incidence divided by the sine of the angle of refraction.

Solenoid　A coil of tightly wrapped wire. Commonly used to create a strong magnetic field by passing current through the wire.

Solid　A substance that has a definite shape and a definite volume.

Solidification　The change of phase from liquid to solid. Also called *freezing*.

Sound　Those waves transmitted through a medium with frequencies capable of being detected by the human ear.

Source　The object that supplies electric energy for the flow of electric charge (electrons) in a circuit.

Source Activity　The strength of a source of radiation that can be specified at a given time.

Space-Time　An object's position in the universe can be pinpointed using three spatial dimensions and one time dimension.

Special Theory of Relativity　The laws of physics are the same in moving and nonmoving frames of reference and the speed of light is constant no matter what the speed of the observer or the light source.

Specific Gravity　The ratio of the density of any material to the density of water.

Specific Heat　The amount of heat necessary to change the temperature of 1 kg of a substance 1°C in the metric system or 1 lb of a substance 1°F in the U.S. system.

Speed　The distance traveled per unit of time. A scalar described by a number and a unit.

Speed of Light　The speed at which light and other forms of electromagnetic radiation travel: 3.00×10^8 m/s in a vacuum.

Speed of Sound　The speed at which sound waves travel in a medium: 331 m/s in dry air at 1 atm pressure and 0°C.

Spring Balance　An instrument containing a spring, which stretches in proportion to the force applied to it, and a pointer attached to the spring with a calibrated scale read directly in given units.

Standard Position　A vector is in standard position when its initial point is at the origin of the number plane. The vector is expressed in terms of its length and its angle, measured counterclockwise from the positive *x*-axis to the vector.

Standard Temperature and Pressure (STP)　A commonly used reference in gas laws. Standard temperature is the freezing point of water. Standard pressure is equivalent to atmospheric pressure.

Standards of Measure　A set of units of measurement for length, weight, and other quantities defined in such a way as to be useful to a large number of people.

Standing Waves　A special case of superposition of two waves when no energy propagation occurs along the wave. The wave displacements are constant and remain fixed in location.

Statics　The study of objects that are in equilibrium.

Stator　The field magnets in a generator.

Step-Down Transformer　A transformer used to lower voltage; it has more turns in the primary coil.

Step-Up Transformer　A transformer used to increase voltage; it has more turns in the secondary coil.

Strain　The deformation of an object due to an applied force.

Streamline Flow　The smooth flow of a fluid through a tube.

Stress　The ratio of an outside applied distorting force to the area over which the force acts.

Strong Force　An attractive force among all nucleons (neutrons and protons) independent of their charge.

Superconductor　A material that continuously conducts electric current without resistance when cooled to typically very low temperatures, often near absolute zero.

Superposition of Waves　The algebraic sum of the separate displacements of two or more individual waves passing through a medium.

Surface Tension　The ability of the surface of a liquid to act like a thin, flexible film.

Synchronous Motor　An ac motor whose speed of rotation is constant and is directly proportional to the frequency of its ac power supply

T

Technology　The field that uses scientific knowledge to develop material products or processes that satisfy human needs and desires.

Temperature　A measure of the hotness or coldness of an object.

Tensile Strength　A measure of a solid's resistance to being pulled apart.

Tension　A stress caused by two forces acting directly opposite each other. This stress tends to cause objects to become longer and thinner.

Terminal Speed　The speed attained by a freely falling body when the air resistance equals its weight and no further acceleration occurs.

Theoretical Physicist　A physicist who predominantly uses previous theories and mathematical models to form new theories in physics.

Theory　A scientifically accepted principle that attempts to explain natural occurrences.

Thermal Conductivity　The ability of a material to transfer heat by conduction.

Torque　A measure of the tendency to produce change in rotational motion. Equal to the applied force times the length of the torque arm.

Torsion　A stress related to a twisting motion. This type of stress severely compromises the strength of most materials.

Total Internal Reflection　A condition such that light striking a surface does not pass through the surface but is completely reflected inside it.

Total Surface Area　The total area of all the surfaces of a geometric solid; that is, the lateral surface area plus the area of the bases.

Transformer   A device composed of two coils (primary and secondary) and a magnetic core. Used to step up or step down a voltage.

Translucent   Allowing some but not all light to pass through.

Transparent   Allowing almost all light to pass through so that objects or images can be seen clearly.

Transverse Wave   A disturbance in a medium in which the motion of the particles is perpendicular to the direction of the wave motion.

Turbulent Flow   The erratic, unpredictable flow of a fluid resulting from excessive speed of the flow or sudden changes in direction or size of the tube.

U

Universal Motor   A motor that can be run on either ac or dc power.

V

Vaporization   The change of phase from liquid to a gas or vapor.

Variable   A symbol, usually a letter, used to represent some unknown number or quantity.

Vector   A physical quantity that requires both magnitude (size) and direction to be completely described.

Velocity   The rate of motion in a particular direction. The time rate of change of an object's displacement. Velocity is a vector that gives the direction of travel and the distance traveled per unit of time.

Virtual Image   An image that only appears to the eye to be formed by rays of light.

Viscosity   The internal friction of a fluid caused by molecular attraction, which makes it resist a tendency to flow.

Visible Spectrum   The colors resulting from the dispersion of white light through a glass prism: red, orange, yellow, green, blue, and violet.

Volatility   A measure of a liquid's ability to vaporize. The more volatile the liquid, the greater is its rate of evaporation.

Voltage Drop   The potential difference across a load in a circuit.

Voltmeter   An instrument that measures the difference in potential (voltage drop) between two points in a circuit.

Volume   The number of cubic units contained in a figure.

W

Wave   A disturbance that moves through a medium or through space.

Wavelength   The distance between two successive corresponding points on a wave.

Wave Theory   Theory that light consists of waves traveling out from light sources, like water waves traveling out from the point at which a stone is dropped into water.

Wedge   An inclined plane in which the plane is moved instead of the resistance.

Weight   A measure of the gravitational force or pull exerted on an object by the earth or by another large body.

Weight Density   The weight per unit volume of a substance.

Wheel-and-Axle   A large wheel attached to an axle so that both turn together.

Work   The product of the force in the direction of motion and the displacement.

X

x-component   The horizontal component of a vector that lies along the *x*-axis.

Y

y-component   The vertical component of a vector that lies along the *y*-axis.

Appendix E

Appendix E

Chapter 1

1. Convert 244 pounds to Newtons.
    1 lbs = 4.448 N

2. Convert 250 ft^2 to yd^2.
    1 yd = 3 ft

3. Convert 400 in^3 to cm^3.
    1 in = 2.54 cm

4. Convert 12.3 kg to g. kilo means 1000. g stands for grams.

5. Convert 60 mile / hour to feet / second.
    1 mi = 5280 ft   1 hr = 60 minutes   1 minute = 60 seconds

6. Convert 60 miles / hour to meters / second.
    1 meter = 3.281 ft.

7. Convert 60 miles / hour to kilometers / hour.
    1 mile = 1.609 kilometers

8. Convert 100 miles / hour to feet / second.
    Use previous conversion facts.

9. Convert 14.7 psi to N / m^2
    1 psi = 6895 N / m^2 1 Pascal = 1 N / m^2

10. Convert 365 days to seconds.

Chapter 4

1. S = 440 miles
    t = 6 hours
    V = ?

2. S = 500 miles
    V = 55 miles / hour
    t = ?

3. V_I = 0 ft / s
    V_F = 88 ft / s (60 mph)
    t = 6 s
    a = ?

4. $V_I = 0$ m / s
   $V_F = 45$ m / s (100 mph)
   t = 10 s
   a = ?

5. A ball rolls down a straight hill. It has an initial velocity of 0 ft/ s.
   It reaches a velocity of 24 ft/s in a time of 10 seconds.
   A.) What was the acceleration of the ball?
   B.) What distance did it roll in that time?

6. A ball is dropped. It has an initial velocity of 0 m / s. It reaches a final velocity of 44.7 m / s in a time of 4.6 seconds. How far did it fall?

7. A ball is dropped. $a_g = 32$ ft / s^2. After a time of 5 seconds, what will be the final velocity of the ball?

8. A lead ball is dropped from a TALL building. It falls for a time of 3 seconds. What was the final velocity of the ball?

9. A ball is thrown up into the air. It has an initial velocity of 40 ft / s. It velocity at the peak height is 0 ft /s . The $a_g = 32$ ft / s^2. What time is required for the ball to reach its maximum height?

10. A car has a velocity of 30 m / s (over 60 mph). The car's brakes are applied. If the car's acceleration is -9.5 m /s^2, what will be the stopping time?

11. If someone walked 220 meters north, and then 450 meters west;

    A.) What distance would they travel?
    B.) How far away from their starting point would they be?
      Hint: This is their displacement. Drawing a sketch of the movements might help.

12. At one point an object is traveling at 8 m/s, and then it accelerates at a constant rate to a speed of 18 m/s. What was its average speed during this time interval?

13. If a student travels 15,800 meters to college, and it takes 20 minutes;

    A.) What is the average speed in kilometers per hour?
    B.) What is the average speed in meters per second?

14. An object accelerates from rest to 28 meters/second in 9 seconds. What was the acceleration of the object during this event?

15. How much time would it take an object to go from rest to 40 meters per second if it experienced a constant acceleration of 2.5 m/s^2 ?

16.   A car is traveling at 12 m/s when it accelerates at 2.2 m/s^2 while moving a distance of 250 meters. What is the final speed of the motorcycle?

17.   A hunting lion is stalking its prey. It initially is moving at 0.6 m/s and then breaks into a run, accelerating at 1.20 m/s^2 for 4 seconds. What is the lion's speed after this acceleration?

18.   A car on a highway entrance ramp is traveling at 12 m/s when it then accelerates up to 31 m/s with a constant acceleration of 2.55 m/s^2. What distance does the car travel during this event?

19.   If a truck is initially traveling at 9 m/s when it accelerates at 2.1 m/s^2 over a distance of 75 meters, how fast will it be going at the end?

20.   A boat is traveling at 5 m/s when it accelerates to a final speed of 29 m/s over a distance of 80 meters. What was the acceleration of this boat?

21.   If an object falls from a height of 1.5 meters;

        A.) How long will it take to reach the ground?
        B.) How fast will the object be going when it reaches the ground?

22.   During a football game the quarterback drops the ball while attempting a pass. If the ball falls from a height of 1.8 meters, how much time passes before it touches the ground?

23.   It something is thrown straight up at 17 m/s, how much time will it take for it to stop rising?

24.   An object is launched with a speed of 30 m/s at an angle 25° above the horizontal as shown.

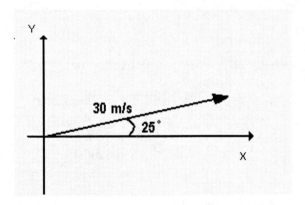

        A.) What is the horizontal speed of the object?
        B.) What is the vertical speed of the object at launch?
        C.) How much time will it take for the object to stop rising?
        D.) How much time will it take for the object to rise and then fall back to its starting height?

Chapter 5

1. m = 22 kg
    F = 550 Newtons
    a = ?

2. a = 5.0 m / s^2
    m = 1500 kilograms
    F = ?

3. F = 225 Newtons
    a = 30 m / s^2
    m = ?

4. A rocket in deep space has an acceleration of 42 m / s^2. If it has a mass of 9000 kg, what force was required to cause this acceleration?

5. What force is required to push an object with a mass of 222 kg with an acceleration of 15 m / s^2 ?

6. A car is pushed with a force of 700 Newtons. The car has a mass of 1500 kilograms. Ignoring friction, what is the acceleration of the car?

7. What is the weight of a package with a mass of 15 kg.?

8. What is the mass of a package with a weight of 90 newtons?

9. What is the weight of a 20 kilogram object?

10. If an object weighs 3675 newtons, what is its mass?

11. If the net force acting on a 5 kilogram object is 28 newtons, what will its acceleration be?

12. If a 10 kilogram object has a force in the x-direction of 8 newtons, what will its acceleration in the x-direction be?

13. If a 1400 kilogram object experiences an acceleration of 0.85 m/s^2 , what net force must be acting on it?

14. Only two forces act on an object. If both act in the x-direction, one being 64 newtons and the other 11 newtons in the opposite direction, what is the net force acting on the object?

15. A 30 kilogram object is acted upon by two forces. One force is 45 newtons in the negative x-direction. The other force is 100 newtons in the positive x-direction, applied at an angle of 42 degrees above the horizontal.

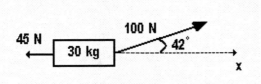

A.) What part of the applied 100 newton force is in the x-direction?
B.) What is the net force acting in the x-direction?
C.) What will the object's acceleration in the x-direction be?

16. If it takes an 84 newton force to stretch a spring 0.06 meters, what must the elastic constant of the spring be?

17. If the frictional force acting on an object is 72 newtons when the normal force is 360 newtons, what is the coefficient of friction between the object and the surface it is resting on?

18. The forces acting on a 5 kilogram object are shown below.

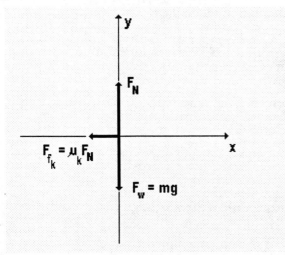

A.) What must the normal force be?

B.) If the coefficient of friction is 0.28, what must the frictional force be?

19. The normal force acting between an object and the surface it rests on is 44 newtons, and the force required to start it sliding is 18 newtons. What must the coefficient of static friction be?

20.   When a 7 kilogram object slides to a stop along a rough horizontal surface, the force acting on it due to friction is 30 newtons as shown in the diagram below.

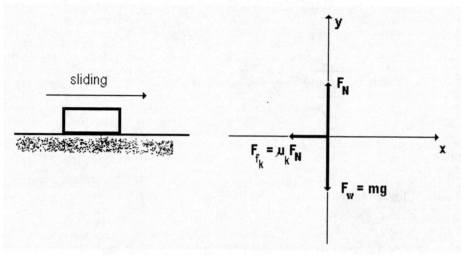

A.) What is the weight of the object?
B.) What is the acceleration of the object in the x-direction?

Chapter 6

1.   A bullet has a mass of 18 grams or 0.018 kilograms. It is traveling with a velocity of 1400 meters / second. What is the momentum of the bullet?

2.   A car is moving with a velocity of 3 m / s (about 7 mph). The car has a mass of 1500 kg (3300 lbs). What is the momentum of the car?

3.   A person pushes a car with a force of 250 Newtons for a time of 5 seconds. What impulse did the person apply to the auto?

4.   A rocket at rest in outer space fires with a force of 32,000 newtons for a time of 6 seconds. What was the Impulse applied?

5.   Using the preceding problem's information, what was the final momentum?

6.   If a 0.2 kilogram baseball is traveling at 40 m/s, what is its momentum?

7.   If a 600 newton force is applied for 1.75 seconds, what is the impulse it supplies?

8.   For how much time must a 70 newton force be applied if it is to cause a 120 kilogram object to have a 14 m/s change in speed?

9.   An 1800 kg car is moving at 34 m/s, when it brakes to a stop. If this takes 4.5 seconds, what average force did the brakes apply in stopping the car?

10. A weapon [the M107 50 caliber sniper rifle] has a mass of 13 kilograms and it fires a 0.045 kilogram bullet at 853 m/s. What is the recoil velocity of this rifle?

Chapter 8

1. A box is lifted 12 meters. It has a weight of 315 Newtons. Calculate the work done.

2. 314 foot pounds of work is performed in a time of 6 seconds. What was the power required to do this?

3. A box with a weight of 400 pounds is lifted a distance of 15 feet in a time of 9 seconds. What was the power required to do this?

4. A piston is pushed with a force of 565 pounds. It moves a distance of 0.3 feet. Calculate the work performed.

5. A piston is pushed with a pressure of 500 pounds per in^2 (psi). It moves through a volume of 22 in^3. What was the work done?

6. An elevator goes up 40 ft in a time of 5 seconds. It has a weight of 2500 lbs. Ignoring friction, what was the minimum power required?

7. A motor has a torque of 212 foot pounds at a angular velocity (speed) of 344 radians per second. Calculate the power of the motor at this speed.

8. A piston is pushed with a pressure of 140 pounds per in^2 (psi). It moves through a volume of 88 in^3. What was the work done?

9. A 60 newton force is applied to an object at an angle of 25 degrees and causes it to move a distance of 40 meters. How much work was done?

10. If it takes 112,000 joules of work to stop a car over a distance of 45 meters, what force must have been applied?

11. If a 4 kilogram object is moving at 25 m/s, what is its kinetic energy?

12. If a 1700 kilogram car is made to go from rest to 26.8 m/s;

   A.) What amount of kinetic energy was it given?
   B.) If the car accelerates to this speed in 4.5 seconds, how much power was delivered?

13.   An 1800 kilogram car is driving along at 22 m/s.

      A.) What is its kinetic energy?
      B.) How much work does it take to stop this car?
      C.) If the car stops over a distance of 60 meters, what average force was applied?
      D.) If the stop takes 3.2 seconds, what power did it take to stop the car?

14.   If a hydraulic lift causes a 1600 kilogram car to rise 2 meters, what is the change in potential energy for the car?

15.   When a weightlifter lifts a 120 kilogram barbell up from the floor to a height of 2.5 meters;

      A.) How much gravitational potential energy was the barbell given?
      B.) How much work did the weightlifter do?
      C.) If the lift took 0.55 seconds, what power did the weightlifter provide?
      D.) If dropped, how fast would the barbell be going when it reached the floor?

16.   If a 15 kilogram object has 440 joules of gravitational energy that is completely turned into kinetic energy, how fast would it be going?

17.   An 80 kilogram object has both gravitational potential energy and kinetic energy. If the total mechanical energy is 60,760 joules when the object is 15 meters above ground, how fast must it be moving?

Chapter 10

A ramp has a length of 40 meters. The height of the ramp is 8 meters.
A weight of 250 newtons is rolled up the ramp with an effort force of
60 newtons. Using this information answer questions number 1-5.

1.   What is the IMA?

2.   What is the AMA?

3.   What is the resistance work?

4.   What is the effort work?

5.   What is the percent efficiency?

Appendix F

Name: _____   **Homework Assignment** _____

Chapter: _____

Problems: _____

_____

_____

_____

_____

_____

_____

_____

_____

_____

_____

_____

_____

_____

_____

_____

_____

_____

Name: _____

Homework Assignment _____

Chapter: _____

Problems: _____

_____

_____

_____

_____

_____

_____

_____

_____

_____

_____

_____

_____

_____

_____

_____

_____

_____

Name: _____

Homework Assignment _____

Chapter: _____

Problems: _____

_____

_____

_____

_____

_____

_____

_____

_____

_____

_____

_____

_____

_____

_____

_____

_____

_____

_____

Name: _____

_____

_____

_____

_____

_____

_____

_____

_____

_____

_____

_____

_____

_____

_____

_____

_____

Name: _____   **Homework Assignment** _____

Chapter: _____

Problems: _____

_____

_____

_____

_____

_____

_____

_____

_____

_____

_____

_____

_____

_____

_____

_____

_____

_____

_____

Name: _____

Homework Assignment _____

Chapter: _____

Problems: _____

_____

_____

_____

_____

_____

_____

_____

_____

_____

_____

_____

_____

_____

_____

_____

_____

Name: _____   **Homework Assignment** _____

                                    Chapter: _____

                                    Problems: _____

_____

_____

_____

_____

_____

_____

_____

_____

_____

_____

_____

_____

_____

_____

_____

_____

_____

Name: _____

Name: _____

Homework Assignment _____

Chapter: _____

Problems: _____

_____

_____

_____

_____

_____

_____

_____

_____

_____

_____

_____

_____

_____

_____

_____

Name: _____

_____

_____

_____

_____

_____

_____

_____

_____

_____

_____

_____

_____

_____

_____

_____

_____